Praise for *Menta* ....
Unlocking the Doors to Triumph

M000276126

Unlocking the Doors to Triumph is an inspirational book from cover to cover. In the self-help literature on mental health and illness, this book is truly a triumph.

—Robert Epstein, Ph.D., West Coast Editor and former Editor-in-Chief of Psychology
Today; *University Research Professor, California School of Professional Psychology at*
Alliant International University

An indispensable resource for all those affected by mental illness. Individuals, their families, and providers alike will benefit greatly from the message of hope and healing and the practical suggestions contained in the book.

—Diane T. Marsh, Ph.D., Professor of Psychology, University of Pittsburgh at Greensburg;
Author of Serious Mental Illness and the Family

Before reading this book, many families would regard the notion of "triumph" to be an oversimplified oxymoronic idea. This book will present a whole new perspective of possibilities to actually achieve such a state. Dr. Gravitz persuasively presents his hypothesis that families can indeed reach for triumph instead of succumbing to defeat when confronting a loved one's mental illness. Using parables and myths to illustrate a point as well as successful strategies used in other disciplines, he leads the reader through what he terms the "family odyssey" or journey to a "life worth living." This family friendly, easily read and understood book has a rightful place on the bookshelf of anyone dealing with serious mental illnesses and other chronic high-family-impact illnesses and conditions.

—Ann Eldridge, President, NAMI Southern Santa Barbara County

Dr. Gravitz' latest book, *Mental Illness and the Family: Unlocking the Doors to Triumph,* offers a clear map for family members under the influence of mental illness. It offers help, hope, and healing for individuals and families to overcome the challenges of a loved one's mental illness and to find the buried treasure—strengths, resilience, celebration, and triumph. This is a must read.

—Jerry Moe, National Director, Betty Ford Center Children's Programs

A brilliant and inspiring book.

—ɯ—

Mental Illness and the Family: Unlocking the Doors to Triumph is an incredibly sensitive and powerful book that helps families learn to cope when a loved one suffers from mental illness. Dr. Gravitz provides a whole host of strategies for helping families move through the stages of healing and recovery and ultimately release themselves from the clutches of mental illness. His artistic use of examples and stories derived from a multitude of sources, including psychology, mythology, spirituality, and his own work with patients, informs, engages, and inspires the reader. Bravo, Dr. Gravitz! Thank you for a most valuable resource for those who are oft forgotten in the struggle with mental illness.

—ɯ—

Dr. Gravitz' new book, *Mental Illness and the Family: Unlocking the Doors to Triumph,* truly is a triumph in itself. This book offers new hope to the millions who are faced with the adversity of mental illness, whether as a sufferer, a family member, or as a professional in the role of helping others. I believe all will find this book immensely useful as it provides great compassion and guidance to the reader in making the shift from feelings of helplessness and hopelessness to the "Triumph" of which Dr. Gravitz so eloquently writes.

—ɯ—

A groundbreaking approach to triumph over mental illness and other major life adversities. . . . By describing how to strengthen each family member, Dr. Gravitz shows that it is never too late for each member to have a full, meaningful life. Drawing from disparate disciplines such as traumatic stress, recovery, spirituality, and modern neuroscience and quantum physics, he again reveals the essential principles of family healing with wit, information, and common sense. The result is an engaging, hopeful, and easy-to-read educational, practical, and spiritual experience.

—ɯ—

Dr. Gravitz has written yet another book that touches the reader's heart so deeply that individuals and families challenged with mental health issues will finally feel the hope that leads to recovery. *Mental Illness and the Family: Unlocking the Doors to Triumph* is a triumph, written with compassion and understanding of life's adversities that hit so many of us. It is more than a self-help book; it is a book that sends the message to a damaged spirit that it will heal. I highly recommend reading how Dr. Gravitz combines sensible approaches to healing and rebuilding broken spirits. His book is both practical and hopeful.

—James Callner, M.A., President of
The Awareness Foundation for OCD and Related Disorders
—◇◇—

As the mythological Phoenix rises from its own ashes, Dr. Gravitz outlines, in multidimensional ways, how family members may experience a rebirth from the traumatic experience of mental illness. This is a book for those who are ready to move beyond coping to surviving and thriving the impact of mental illness on a family member.

—Rex Dickens, Coauthor of How to Cope with Mental Illness in Your Family
—◇◇—

Mental Illness and the Family is an inspiring, well-written manual for exactly how to accomplish the complex task of making lemonade from the lemons that life casts our way. This valuable work offers hope to all those impacted by mental illness and it is a work whose time has come. Through the use of stories, mythology, spirituality, biological research, and more, Dr. Gravitz teaches us how to reshape our relationship with trauma. He paves a path for us to move beyond devastation and chaos to discover more opportunities for positive transformation than we may ever have imagined possible.

—Rebecca Woolis, M.F.T., Author of When Someone You Love Has a Mental Illness:
A Handbook for Family, Friends, and Caregivers
—◇◇—

Following in the steps of *Obsessive Compulsive Disorder: New Help for the Family*, Dr. Gravitz has again addressed the needs of all those families who are feeling frustrated and helpless as they watch their loved ones in their lonely struggle with mental illness. Dr. Gravitz provides hope and inspiration.

—Karron Maidment, R.N., M.A., UCLA OCD Program
—◇◇—

As we enter the 21st century of astonishing discoveries in neuroscience, Dr. Herbert Gravitz does an excellent job of reminding us that human consciousness, contact, and interaction are undeniably the most powerful source of support and healing. In his book *Mental Illness and the Family: Unlocking the Doors to Triumph*, Gravitz shows the professional and patient communities alike that triumph is often closest at hand when our hearts are nearly broken. He brings to our attention over and over the idea that extreme adversity is capable of lifting us to new levels of consciousness. Each chapter leads persuasively to the next and leaves the reader, whether professional or lay, to new understanding and hope. We can almost feel the many years and the treatment style of the author saying, "Although this is a terrible event, WE can prevail." This scholarly presentation coupled with the author's years of clinical experience encourages the reader to believe the words on the page and the suggested directions to triumph. This is a must read for both those challenged by the task of treating families in tragedy and for those to whom tragedy has struck.

—*Paul Michael Remis, M.D., psychiatrist*

—ɯ—

Dr. Gravitz' book offers a fresh and welcome new paradigm of self-understanding and even transformation for families whose lives have been taken over by coping with a mentally ill loved one.

—*Jan Winter, past president of the board of the Mental Health Association in Santa Barbara County*

—ɯ—

Dr. Gravitz shows how families cannot only escape from chaos, but can become triumphant by finding a more purposeful, rewarding life. This book reflects Dr. Gravitz' devotion to helping the entire family not just to survive, but to thrive when under the influence of major mental illness.

—*Bob and Katherine D., parents of sufferer of OCD and bipolar disorder*

—ɯ—

Just as there are people who starve in the midst of plenty, there are others who thrive in the midst of any circumstance! This book shows the way.

—*Len H., spouse of sufferer of schizophrenia*

—ɯ—

MENTAL ILLNESS and the FAMILY

Unlocking the Doors to Triumph

Herbert L. Gravitz, Ph.D.

Healing Visions Press
Santa Barbara, California

Mental Illness and the Family
Unlocking the Doors to Triumph

By Herbert L. Gravitz

Healing Visions Press, Santa Barbara, California
www.HealTheFamily.com

ISBN: 0-96611045-5

Publisher's Cataloging-in-Publications
(Provided by *Quality Books, Inc.*)

Gravitz, Herbert L., 1942-
    Mental illness and the family / Herbert L. Gravitz
    p. cm.
    Includes bibliographical references and index.
LCCN 2003112564
ISBN: 0-96611045-5

    1. Mentally ill—Family relationships. 2. Family—Mental health.
3. Mentally ill—Care.   I. Title

    RC455.4.F3G73 2004616.89
          QBI33-1630

Edited by Gail M. Kearns, To Press and Beyond, Santa Barbara, California.

Cover and book design:
Peri Poloni, Knockout Design, www.knockoutbooks.com

Printed in United States

—⟋⟍—

To the families of those under the influence
of serious mental illness, addiction, and other traumas.

Because injury begets injury,
this triple threat often strikes the same family.

May this book acknowledge your plight,
may it lighten your burden,
and may it provide the meaning, knowledge, and skills
that will lead you to triumph over
life's most painful adversities.

—⟋⟍—

Contents

—w—

—ⱳ—

Acknowledgments

—w—

There are so many people to express gratitude toward who have made this book possible. It is my pleasure to do so.

First and foremost, I want to thank the many families and family members who have trusted me with their heroic stories and the gift of sharing their lives. Just a few of them include the following: Sophie and Phil, the three boys, the grandchildren, and great grandchildren; Ann, Len, Eric, David, and Jason; Mary and Tony, the kids, and grandkids; Alison, Nancy, and John; Katie and Bob; Tim and Sarah; Mark, Kristin, and the children; Ron, Kate, Becky, and Pat; Tom, Kathleen, and the children; Mike and Jody; Roberto and Silvia; Leslie, Rick, the kids, and grandkids; Bill and Diane and the boys; Cynthia and Clark; Paul and Steve; Lynn and Eric; Marianna and Stephon; Deb and Roy; Laura and Dave and the children; Washington and Ginny; and Mary Jo and Stan. You have given so much!

I want to especially thank the first family with whom I had the privilege to know and work. Their courage, their strength, their tenacity, and their love for each other continue to inspire me. Only the stigma of mental illness that continues to exist in our society prevents me from acknowledging them by name, as well as recognizing by name the other families listed above. I look forward to the day when this is no longer true.

I wish to thank the early explorers and pioneers in the field of serious mental illness who influenced my thinking. Fortunately, there are many of them and the absence of their name here in no way implies a lack of contribution to others or to me. They include: Xavier Amador, Ph.D., Joyce Burland, Ph.D., Rosalynn Carter, Marlene Cooper, Ph.D., Rex Dickens, Agnes Hatfield, Ph.D., Kay Redfield Jamison, Ph.D., Harriet Lefley, Ph.D., John March, M.D., Diane Marsh, Ph.D., David Miklowitz, Ph.D., Judith Rapoport, M.D., E. Fuller Torrey, M.D., and Rebecca Woolis, M.F.T.

This work stands on the shoulders not only of the above pioneers but also on the shoulders of pioneers in the fields of traumatic stress, addiction and recovery, altered states of conscious, loss and grief, physical healing, mythology, personal excellence, spirituality, the new physics, and the emerging field of energy. Fortunately, there are so many to acknowledge that to list them would fill a whole chapter.

I thank, too, all of the people who have taken the time and made the effort to endorse and comment on this manuscript and offer the important feedback that you have given me. Your validation means more than you may realize.

I want to acknowledge friendships that have been influential in the writing of this book. First and foremost, Rex Dickens, who has been an early explorer and constant advocate for the family of the seriously mentally ill, has been an inspiration and unequivocal supporter. From the very beginning, Rex's constant challenge to my unrestrained optimism, first regarding the concept itself of a triumphant family and then the possibility of a happy family, has led me to explore the capacities and limits of the family under the influence, especially the influence of mental illness. True friends tell you what you need to hear, not what you want to hear. Rex did just that and in the right balance. Thank you, Rex, for challenging my capacities and my limits. Hopefully, you the reader are the beneficiary.

Ralph Daniel, my constant Monday lunch companion for more years than I can remember, has been an ongoing source of encouragement. Teresa Seiler and Richard Blair, two of my heroes and dear friends with whom I have traveled to the far corners of the earth, have shown me through example the path to triumph. Bless you both. Our friend Beverly Grant has been a true supporter, as well as an irascible source of humor and passion.

Dr. Mary Lynch and Debra Harrison, cofounders of Consegrity, A Wellness Support Program, have not only introduced me to the world of energy, but they have given me a different lease on life. Now, I see things and feel things that I didn't before. Their humanity, love, and commitment never cease to amaze me. To them, I owe immeasurable gratitude. And especially you, Mary, a huge thank you.

Meredith Boyd, the most awesome and incredible administrative assistant a writer can have, has always been there when I needed her most. Her work in support of this book has been tireless and unswerving. She has always gone the extra mile, as she continued to do more than I could ever expect. I can never thank her fully or compensate her enough. You're the best, Meredith! And thank you for slowing me down and more important for taking the risk to tell me.

My dear friend Anna Lisa Story has given freely of her time, effort, skill, and heart. Her hard-hitting comments about an earlier draft were invaluable. Her generosity of spirit is much appreciated. I hope you realize your enormous contributions to me.

Gail Kearns again served me well as a content editor. Her resourcefulness is prized. Her suggestions have made for a more engaging book and a coherent read.

Others have greatly contributed to the flow of the book. Most important in this regard, Cynthia Crowder Coffee, a talented concert pianist, contributed enormously to the rhythm and cadence of the book. Where this is not present, I take full responsibility.

Laura Sanchez and Kathleen Barich also contributed to the editing process and found countless mistakes that I missed.

The contribution of Raymond Wilcove, who has informally served as an editor for all of my books, is appreciated beyond words.

Last and certainly not least, I want to once again thank my family, who continue to bear with me as I unfold my destiny. Their love and support can never be fully acknowledged. My three sons often gave up their time with their father as he pursued his passion and commitment to those less fortunate. Most of all, I appreciate the love and support of my wife, Leslie Ann, whose editing always makes my writing more accurate, softer, and gentler. Her sacrifice of our time together is a gift beyond measure that is offered to you, the reader. We both owe her a great deal of gratitude. Without her sacrifice, this book would not have been written.

—〰—

To the Reader

Take a moment right now and give yourself credit.

—ɯɯ—

If you have picked up this book on mental illness as a path to triumph, it is likely that you are dealing with some aspect of mental illness, and you probably fall into one or more of the following types of readers. You might be one of the 10 percent of the population who bears the diagnosis of mental illness. Your life is challenging and ripe for triumph, which always requires a serious challenge.

The most obvious mental illnesses are the more serious ones that include schizophrenia, bipolar disorder, major depression, and obsessive-compulsive disorder (OCD), all of which are believed to be biological or physical diseases. Serious mental illness has been traditionally defined by three variables: the diagnosis itself; the duration or persistence of the illness for at least a year; and the degree of disability, impairment, and incapacity.[90]

If you are a person who suffers from a serious mental illness, you are to be especially congratulated for continuing to read this book. Most likely, you are well into your recovery and are not in denial. If you are willing to take a moment *right now* and give yourself credit for the courage it takes for you to continuously work to overcome this illness, then you are even further on the trek toward triumph. Even so, it is still not easy to bear witness to the pain that the *disease* can generate in you, your family, and other loved ones under its influence or spell.[1, 9, 76, 90 148]

You may not be in the 10 percent of those who have one of the more severe types of mental illness, but in the 50 percent of all Americans who have at least one episode of a diagnosable psychiatric disorder in their lifetime.[135] If you are in either group of sufferers, welcome. You are certainly not alone. More than 54 million Americans have a mental disorder in any given year, although fewer than eight million seek treatment.[135]

Perhaps you are a family member, loved one, friend, or associate of someone with a mental illness. You, too, are not alone, as estimates indicate that there may be well over 100 million family members of those who suffer from serious mental illness alone. You may be glad to know that this book is largely about *your* experience.

There are excellent books[73, 95, 104, 130] describing the plight of the person with mental illness, or "the primary sufferer," as this person is often called, but there has been a shortage of information to acknowledge or address the needs of the family members and the loved ones, or "the secondary sufferers," that is, those of you under the influence* of the person who has the illness.

---

* "Under the influence" is a helpful metaphor for understanding the impact of mental illness. This is a term that originated in the field of chemical dependency, where it refers to the condition in which one finds oneself when under the influence of alcohol or some other drug. The influence can be primary, in which case the person is under the direct influence of the drug itself, or the influence can be secondary or indirect, stemming from the influence of the person who is involved in the illness. In the latter case, it is a loved one or family member who is under the influence (of the illness and the affected person). As with the illness of alcoholism, for example, the loved ones and the family experience an altered state of life as a result of living "under the influence" of the mental illness.

You may be a professional who works either with the primary or the secondary sufferer. Some of you may be working with both the family and the primary sufferer. I salute you! As a frontline worker, you are at the healing edge, a pioneer helping those on the path to family triumph. You are the vanguard leading to the effective utilization of a critical and seldom used resource, the family. Like the family members who pursue triumph, you are heroic, you are committed, and you are curious and ready to expand the limits of your knowledge. *And you are very much needed.*[135] Families under the influence require your skills and your humanity. There are not many of you *yet*. I am honored to share with you what I have been learning during the last thirty-five years as I have witnessed again and again the triumph of those under the influence of mental illness, which is so often accompanied and further complicated by addiction and other traumas.

Of course, nothing stops you from being a person in one or more of the following groups: a primary sufferer (the term "consumer" is often used, too) and a professional; a family member and a professional; or a professional, family member, and primary sufferer all at once. Then, you are really busy juggling roles. You have a lot on your plate. I hope this book will help you hold the weight of your extraordinary burdens and experience your triumphant survivorship.

You could also be a pioneer on another path of the journey to triumph. A warm welcome, too! You could be a primary sufferer, secondary sufferer, or professional who has a physical illness such as cancer, heart disease, chronic fatigue syndrome, fibromyalgia, multiple sclerosis, Parkinson's disease, Alzheimer's disease, HIV/AIDS, MCS (Multiple Chemical Sensitivity), or some other serious malady. You could also be someone with an addiction, such as alcoholism. Or, you could be someone who has endured an overwhelming life experience, or a series of them, whether from abuse, a dysfunctional childhood, war, poverty, or holocaust. None of these circumstances is easy to overcome; yet, each offers the opportunity to triumph.

You will find that the road to triumph is the same, regardless of the type of illness, addiction, or other trauma. In this sense, mental illness is but one of the many paths on the road to overcoming adversity. Also, as noted, all three often co-occur in the same family. There are only people on different paths, all leading to the same place: a sense of safety, a sense of meaning and importance, and a sense of feeling good about yourself and your loved ones.

Whatever path you are on, I honor your course. While this book uses the lens of mental illness to light up the route to triumph, the concepts and tools that are presented can be applied to life's most severe wounds. Therefore, it is ultimately a book of hope and possibility for the individual and for the family beset by any of life's catastrophic forces. As you will discover, triumph is a decision, one within the reach of virtually all of us. What is more, there are time-tested keys to unlock the doors to your triumph.

By reading this book, you are in store for a very special and rewarding trip. As you proceed, however, do not be fooled. You are embarking on a dangerous opportunity. Be aware that there are many setbacks on the road to victory. This book is a proposal for challenging work. There is nothing easy about finding the keys to deal with a life of adversity. Expect to be tired and to be discouraged. You might even want to give up at times, feeling lost and believing that you can never put into practice the book's many principles and suggestions. But you have a choice. You can curse your fate, or you can recognize your possibilities.

Most likely, you will have a wide variety of reactions and responses as you continue reading. By following the ideas in this book, you may feel uncertain at times and guilty for challenging the status quo. Even the experienced traveler is not immune to anxiety, culpability, or doubt. Your feelings can swing from despair to hope, from suspicion to certainty, from doubt to belief, from sadness to joy, from overwhelm to triumph. Because loss is an inevitable part of the journey, this book may evoke some of these feelings, all of these feelings, or a myriad of others.

Whatever your feelings, know that they are all natural and normal; they reveal your humanity as well as reflect your unique situation. Letting go of those parts of your life that no longer serve your best interests is a natural phase in the process of healing, but it also can be frightening. Saying good-bye to the familiar may bring temporary sadness, even as you know you are paving the way for your new future.

So, there are good reasons for the many feelings and reactions you may have. The messages in this book are powerful. No punches are pulled in describing the plight of the family under the influence of mental illness—or any serious, chronic situation. You will be invited to expand the range of your thoughts, feelings, and behaviors.

But don't be a victim. For example, find a safe environment, such as a local meeting of the National Alliance of the Mentally Ill (NAMI) or a twelve-step meeting, and slowly begin to talk about yourself and your situation so that you can know what to do next. Learn to trust yourself and at least one other person. Allow yourself to experience all of your feelings, which is the best way to minimize the possibility of acting them out in harmful ways.

Question, think, and, ultimately, dare to be the person you are capable of becoming by challenging the confining circumstance in which you may find yourself today. Create a compelling future for yourself. Let go of a crumbling past. While these concepts will be simple to grasp, they may be difficult at times to implement. Be patient. Change takes time. The difference between knowing how to do something and doing it separates those who fail from those who succeed.

Do not be deterred by the possibility that mental illness and its impact are not pretty sights. Mental illness is always a hurtful experience for those who suffer from it, and it is a hurtful experience for the family. Nothing can change this, but the experience can be transformed when understood, accepted, and embraced. Often ignored, its sufferers are commonly stigmatized, as are sufferers from other major adversities, such as addiction and the many types of abuse. Ours is a society that has not taken kindly to these wounds, often disenfranchising and denying its sufferers.

However, the winds of change are blowing. For those who have suffered for so long in silence, alone and ashamed, a growing awareness is shedding light on the nature of mental illness and its treatments. Federal laws have begun to institute a process of "parity," whereby mental disorders may receive the same access to reimbursement as do physical illnesses. The highest levels of government have officially recognized the impact of mental illness.[135] Encouraged by policy changes, open discussion, public recognition, and personal disclosure, its sufferers are becoming freer to come out of the shadows as media awareness is on the increase.

Witness the movie *A Beautiful Mind*, the true story of a Nobel Prize winner suffering from a mental illness. Earning four Academy Awards, including Best Picture of the Year in 2001, this landmark film brought national attention to mathematics genius Dr. John Forbes Nash, Jr. and his lifelong struggle to triumph over the debilitating effects of schizophrenia. While some incidents were fictionalized, the film chronicles Nash's life and transports the viewer into the mysterious world of mental illness. His shaky world of distorted images, false perceptions, and irrational beliefs form the foreground of this remarkable story, which humanizes schizophrenia in particular and helps reduce the stigma of mental illness in general.

Through the powerful medium of Hollywood, countless people are lifted out of their ignorance of mental illness, and given insight into what it might be like to have this disease, or live under its influence. Fear thrives in a climate of ignorance. We naturally fear what we do not understand. Being allowed to participate in Nash's world provides the audience with an awareness and understanding that fosters compassion for this exceptional human being whose theories continue to influence global trade negotiations, national labor relations, as well as breakthroughs in evolutionary biology.

This inspiring account of a brilliant person, who also happens to suffer from mental illness, challenges the stereotypical judgment of the mentally ill as morally weak, corrupt, defective, dangerous, or undeserving of love and respect. This film serves as a model of triumph for all people under the spell of mental illness. Breaking through the stigma that has perpetuated these misconceptions, it highlights the importance of the family's and other loved ones' acceptance, love, and involvement in the healing process. For, when appropriately and skillfully directed, the family can become a crucible of healing for every member, whether for the primary or secondary sufferer.

The backdrop of the film illuminates the power of love. Nash's wife, Alicia, is resolute in her support. Her love and shelter provide him the opportunity to go forth from her arms to confront his demons and to return to her for respite from his battles with the illness. She serves as an anchor for him, as he fights to free his life from the grip of schizophrenia. Together, they triumph over mental illness in this modern, heroic story. However, she remains in the shadows—visible, but just out of reach. This is the story of John Nash, the brilliant mathematician.

Wouldn't a movie about *her* life be interesting, too? Does she not inspire the audience to go beyond its preconceived limits, as does her husband? What knowledge, what skills, what attitudes, what behaviors, what feelings enable John Nash's loved one to triumph over the mental illness? What allows Alicia to support John in a way that enables him to receive a Nobel Prize for a theory he had formulated in the presence of his illness? What makes her extraordinary? Is someone simply born that way? How does she rise to heroic proportions?

While not diminishing John Nash's hard-won struggles, this book is Alicia's story and the story of the tens of millions of family members just like her who journey through the tortuous and turbulent labyrinth of mental illness alongside their loved ones. Too few people know of the family's suffering and pain, rendering the family even more fragile and vulnerable. As one family member said: "We're the invisible victims."

This is a book written for the mothers and fathers, the wives and husbands, the offspring and children, the brothers and sisters, the grandfathers and grandmothers—in short, this is a book for *all* the loved ones of the mentally ill person. This is a book about *their* story and the possibility of *their* victory.

The family's plight may be the only thing more hidden than the suffering of the mentally ill person, because the majority of people today remain uneducated and misinformed about the reality of living under the influence of a mental illness. Mental illness still remains locked behind closed doors, and many of its victors, let alone victims, are afraid to come out.

A realistic portrayal of the plight and the subsequent triumph available to each member of the family, this book is a nonromanticized account of the family's wounds, not a book about emerging without scars and bruises from the ravages of mental illness. It depicts how the loved ones of the mentally ill, as well as those who may be suffering under the influence of other major afflictions, can craft full, meaningful, and productive lives of their own.

At the same time, this is a book about the power of the family. The family, our most ancient institution, offers unique incentives and motivations, for it contains untapped seeds and kernels for healing that are unparalleled. The resources of the family, when family members are trained and not blamed, honored and not dishonored, seen as valuable and not problematic, can become a commanding key to unlock the door of defeat, opening instead the door to a life well-lived for its members, regardless of circumstance.

Together, we will find that within the family lies an undiscovered treasure that is clearly displayed in front of everyone, ready to be put to use, but all too often the family remains unaware of its influence. This enormous force for strengthening, revitalizing, and healing is largely hidden, too often underutilized and undervalued.

The family may be the best-kept "secret" we have to triumph over mental illness. Like so many natural resources, the family needs to be developed before its abundant source of energy can be tapped. This is a book about its development. One family member stated: "Before we found out what happened to us after our son got really sick, the family was like a gigantic sinkhole, and everybody was drowning. Knowing what happened has really made a difference."

Maximizing triumph is a team effort. The most obvious players are the patient, the doctors, and whatever mental health machinery can be put into play. Too often, the least obvious player is the family. Yet, the family is a major player. It has the ability to "entrain" its members, not unlike the movements of energy of great clocks, which harmonize each other and move together. In addition, the family is the context in which the illness waxes and wanes.[58]

Just as the fish tank supports the life of the fish within, the family supports its members as they sink or swim in the sea of life. Triumphing over mental illness often requires more than individual effort, and this book will point to a model of helping the team surrounding the mentally ill person. For when the team is strong, its resilience permits the members to harness capacities that lie dormant within them.

Just as a chain is as strong as its weakest link, a family is as strong as its strongest member. In this sense, the book is more an "us help" than a "self-help" book, speaking simultaneously to the sufferer and to the sufferer's family and other loved ones. Because individual identity emerges in the context of family interaction, the focus is on the attainment of the highest good of all involved.

The movie *As Good as It Gets*, which brought best actor and actress awards to Jack Nicholson and Helen Hunt, portrays how the energy of *us*, or love, can bring forth those qualities the ill member most needs. In a particularly poignant scene, the main characters, Melvin and Carol, are sitting at dinner. Fumbling to express his feelings toward Carol, Melvin nervously turns to her and says, "You make me want to be a better man!" Not until that moment does *she* feel valued and acknowledged—and perhaps loved. So acknowledged, she is *now* more able to be present in ways that spur his recovery. He begins to get better and *their* relationship is forever changed.

With acknowledgment, each person begins to heal. Melvin's healing accelerates and Carol's life is enriched. Her young, ill son receives better medical treatment, as does their injured friend, Simon. Even the dog triumphs. Everyone triumphs together! Everyone gets better together! There were still problems to be solved, conflicts to be handled, and a mental illness with which to deal. But there was also the possibility for a happy ending and certainly the possibility of a fuller life. While it must be stressed that love, or even a happy and triumphant family, cannot cure mental illness, it can form a matrix of nourishment for all of its members. It becomes a container, a crucible.

Poignant films and compelling memoirs focus attention on the plight of the mentally ill, such as Kay Redfield Jamison's *An Unquiet Mind,*[73] the true story of her triumph over bipolar disorder, as well as William Styron's *Darkness Visible,*[130] which chronicles his fight with depression. Few focus on the impact of mental illness on the rest of the family. This is the heart of *Unlocking the Doors to Triumph,* a blueprint to your personal triumph.

—ⱳⱳ—

Introduction

Dare to snatch victory from the hands of defeat.

—⁕—

A long time ago, in a faraway place, a king once owned a very large, beautiful diamond of which he was proud, for it had no equal anywhere in the kingdom. One day, this diamond incurred a deep scratch. The king was heartbroken. He called in the most expert diamond cutters in the realm, and he offered them a great reward if they could remove the imperfection from his jewel. But none could. Soon, a gifted craftsman came to the king, promising to make the diamond more beautiful than before. Impressed by his confidence, the king entrusted the precious gem to his care. With superb artistry, the craftsman set about to engrave a beautiful rosebud around the imperfection, using the scratch as the stem.

Unlocking the Doors to Triumph is about two unlikely partners: mental illness and triumph. It is an invitation to move beyond the limiting beliefs that may hold you captive to mental illness. Some believe that mental illness and triumph cannot co-exist, that this juxtaposition of terms is inappropriate, or that the possibility of triumph holds a false and unrealistic promise for people suffering under the influence of mental illness. Others believe that speaking of mental illness and triumph in the same breath can trivialize the experience of both, offering only reassuring platitudes to anyone under the influence of mental illness. Still others have experienced firsthand their own personal triumph over mental illness. Those who have triumphed over (and under) the influence of mental illness are the new family heroes. They are fighting the treacherous demon of mental illness and its dangerous twins, trauma and addiction.

The Paradoxical Nature of Triumph

The American Heritage Dictionary of the English Language[3] defines triumph as follows: "to be victorious or successful; to win; prevail." Just as courage is the ability to act in the face of fear, so triumph is the ability to proceed in the face of our problems, particularly to proceed against great odds. No adversity, no triumph! Triumph occurs when unrelenting circumstances do not stop you from loving fully, living meaningfully, and having a productive life. To triumph in the midst of mental illness is to move forward in a positive manner in the midst of all the burdens it brings.[55]

Triumph unfolds as we use the scratches of life's wounds to etch a portrait of meaning, value, and grace.

Overwhelming evidence from the writings of philosophers, mystics, poets, mythologists, artists, scientists, even entrepreneurs, suggests that the seeds of triumph are found in life's misfortunes, and they are forged from the crucible of adversity.[57] Showing that a life of triumph is a genuine possibility, not in spite of difficult circumstances but because of them, the sacred writings throughout all of history impart eternal truths whose application can enhance our daily lives. They emphasize that each of us *already has within ourselves* all of the resources we need for unlocking the doors to our triumph. Such a view, far from being passive, activates and inspires us not only to explore life's depths, but also to aspire to the heights of a life well lived. It reveals that to triumph is to rise above the limitations of a situation, to discover that life is worth living, and to realize that life's losses are worth enduring.

A Life Worth Living and a Loss Worth Enduring

Until one has experienced the presence of opposites, one can't distinguish them. Just as the calm and splendor of tropical islands owe their very existence to the turbulence and rage of volcanoes, the more severely disturbed the family, the greater the potential for its growth and development. The new sciences, as well as texts from ancient mystics, remind us that order always arises from disorder, just as the great mythical bird, the Phoenix, after being consumed by fire, rose from the ashes, renewed and more remarkable than before.

Mental illness, as well as any other major family trauma or loss, need not prevent loved ones from living triumphant lives, loving fully and passionately, and experiencing a meaningful and productive existence. Family members can have lives worth living and losses worth bearing. They can come to grips with what they have to accept, which is the illness, while discovering what actions they can take to make life better, which means, among other things, becoming an expert on the impact of illness, addiction, and trauma because the family is often exposed to this triple threat.

Accepting the chaos and weathering the destruction, those who embrace life refuse to allow mental illness to become the event that defines who they are and what their choices are. Where there is no triumph, family members try instead to change what they should learn to accept, namely their loved one, not noticing what they themselves can do that will improve *their* lot, which is to take care of themselves as well as they take care of their loved ones.

A life worth living is a life worth awakening to, a life that adds a larger purpose to your day, and extends beyond just yourself. It is a life of significance, whether you have a mountain to climb, are a dedicated activist, or have a project to finish. Your intention may be as simple as to bring joy, comfort, and laughter to another soul, one important only to you, such as a child who needs to be raised. A life worth living carries the excitement of knowing that new possibilities are forged every moment, and believing that you are a vital part of this process. It is a life savored, nuanced, and tempered by the inevitable blessings *and* woes that life serves to all of us. A life worth living is one more of life's countless triumphs that remind you of the preciousness and sanctity of life.

On the other hand, a loss worth enduring could be watching, day in and day out, a loved one who never reaches, or even begins to approach, his or her potential. It could be the realization that you may not see your youngster graduate, not for lack of intellectual ability, but because your child doesn't possess the emotional or biological wherewithal. A loss worth surviving could be the possibility that the family line stops with this child, because this child will not marry and will not have children. A loss worth enduring could be the realization that never again will there be the kind of equality and partnership that you once knew, or wished for, with a mate.

Another such toll could be the distress of a dwindling retirement plan constantly being drained, too many times to count, by unexpected circumstances requiring your immediate attention. There are countless losses worth tolerating, which may appear as chisels chipping away at your humanity. In accepting this inevitability with grace, you endure, perceiving the "chisel" as a means for shaping and unveiling your ultimate and true character.

Knowing that it is your choice to shape any obstacle into a challenging opportunity for growth is to have a life worth living and a loss worth overcoming. This is the uncanny union of two seemingly strange companions. It is to live a triumphant life. It is the route to a new life, and invariably a second life. At its simplest, transforming hurtful negatives into consequential positives is to be more alive and to live more fully.

The Many Faces of Triumph

Triumph, a victory born of disaster, does not depend on heredity, for no one is born incapable of it. Poverty is no stumbling block to triumph, nor are wealth, race, or background. Lack of physical health is neither an obstacle to triumph, nor are age and gender. Lack of education is no bar to triumph, for living life to its fullest is in itself an education. Creating a life of triumph depends not upon *what* we have, but upon *how* we use what we are given, especially the brain, which can so easily become hijacked by feelings. Triumph is available to virtually all of those who fall under the influence of mental illness.

Paraphrasing the famed French writer Victor Hugo, triumph has many names. For the weak it is impossible. For the faint of heart, it is unknown. For the valiant, it is hope. All family members deserve to have an attainable vision of rising above the horrific impact of mental illness and prevailing over mental illness despite their circumstance. The King James Bible reminds us in Proverbs 29:18, "Where there is no vision, the people perish."

In a more modern note, it is said that Helen Keller was once asked if there was anything worse than being blind. She replied, "Having no vision."

Not to be confused with those who display an incessantly dull positive attitude, triumphant family members have tears, a pounding heart, and shaking hands. They are sad *and* happy, fearful *and* loving, confused *and* clear, troubled *and* free, upset *and* calm, cowardly *and* courageous, cautious *and* trusting. They are not only one way *or* the other; they are *both* one way *and* the other. Such opposing or "biphasic personality traits" allow people to be more adaptable, rather than limiting themselves to being only one way or the other.[122] The ability to carry all at once such apparently paradoxical feelings is crucial for building a strong and balanced foundation. Any negative episode in the aftermath of mental illness does not preclude triumph.

Triumph does not imply a life free of pain. Joy, peace, and happiness can be found to *coexist* with the illness. Triumph unfolds when family members find the opportunity, *as well as* experience the loss, in the wound. The great writer Ernest Hemingway reminds us that we become stronger at the places where we have been broken. Certainly this is one of the most profound and touching of human miracles.

What is more, the skills necessary to move toward triumph can be acquired. Each and every person can increase her or his skills to deal with adversity, and can learn to strengthen his or her abilities to triumph under virtually any of life's circumstances. Further, triumph can reach beyond the individual to embrace relationships, whole families, even communities, and perhaps society itself. Just as an entire family can be affected by one member's traumatization, so, too, can an entire family be affected by one member's triumph. Perhaps never before in history has it been more important that we learn the skills needed for us to triumph and prevail.

Meet the Hartleys

It was a dismal winter afternoon, during the heart of their darkest moment, when they first walked into my office. Tom and Morgan Hartley were in tears as they sat in my office. Stunned by news that Morgan had accidentally become pregnant, they were terrified that this unborn child, too, might inherit the disease that had plagued both sides of their families for generations. Their first child, Malcolm, was diagnosed with childhood schizophrenia on his sixth birthday. While Tom and Morgan were aware of the possibility of the genetic transmission of mental illness, they were distraught that he was among the rare 2 percent of individuals who experience schizophrenia in their formative years.

Because their sense of stability was already shaken by Malcolm's illness, they were like two cats on a hot tin roof with anticipation and dread. They felt overwhelmed and confused. Should they proceed with this new pregnancy? They believed that life had just grabbed them by the throat, but this time they didn't know whether they could endure another blow. Had they been able to put their feelings into words, they might have said: "How are we going to make it? We feel so defeated!"

Both Tom and Morgan already knew the perils of living in a home engulfed by serious mental illness. Tom's father had suffered from major depression throughout his life, which ended tragically in his suicide when Tom was only ten years old. Morgan's mother has been ill with the disease of schizophrenia for as long as Morgan could remember.

Vividly recalling the shame, the embarrassment, the loneliness, and especially the terror that each of them had felt while growing up, Tom and Morgan thought that they had moved beyond the likelihood of its harrowing and tormenting devastation. They valued their escape from the wreckage that can befall offspring of the mentally ill.[31] But they were not free of the dread for their own children.

Exposed to their parents' psychoses and alcoholism from a very young age, they had learned to walk on eggshells in their own scarcely imaginable traumatic childhood homes, believing it was their obligation to be the caretakers of their mentally ill parents. Little came easily for Morgan or Tom, although both were endowed with intelligence, initiative, humor, and loving hearts. They had worked long and hard to overcome the deep hurt and anguish of their childhood traumas, and when they met each other, they felt they had finally found the love and safety they had so desperately wanted. The early years of their marriage were everything they had hoped: they spent time with each other, cared for each other, and understood each other as few could. They thought that they had moved beyond the "adult child syndrome," the constellation of traits of those who have grown up in a dysfunctional family.

When Malcolm was conceived, Tom and Morgan were apprehensive, but they wanted children so much that they chose to accept the risk. Overjoyed by Malcolm's birth, Tom and Morgan were in complete agreement that they could provide him with a childhood better than either of them had survived. They believed that they could beat the odds again

But Malcolm appeared to be unusually quiet and withdrawn, showing little enthusiasm for anything, and he was developing slowly in most areas. Behaving strangely as a toddler, he was ill at ease when Morgan and Tom touched him, and when Malcolm began talking primarily to Sam, an invisible family dog, they knew something was terribly wrong.[134]

At first, Morgan and Tom rallied around this latest tragedy, bouncing back as they did so many times before. They finally found a doctor who appeared sympathetic. Although already knowledgeable about mental illness, they read everything they could find on childhood schizophrenia. Paradoxically, the more they read, the more they felt encouraged *and* discouraged, which only added to their confusion.

The onslaught of their son's illness soon wore them down. It created stress, loss, grief, exhaustion, guilt, and a host of other feelings beyond anything they could have imagined. They began to argue more frequently about what was best for young Malcolm, and wondered how much they should tell other family members and friends. What about discussing his illness with his teacher at school? Tom was convinced this was essential, but based on her own experience as a child, Morgan believed that Malcolm would be shunned. Should they place him on medication? Again their opinions differed. Tom thought Malcolm was too young, that the medication might permanently harm him. Morgan just knew it was the right thing to do.

Before long, Tom and Morgan were constantly arguing with each other. They spent less and less time together. Their sexual relationship, once a source of closeness, tenderness, and expression, began to suffer. Tom started to have trouble sleeping. Many of his old childhood fears surfaced again, and he had nightmares of being unable to work. His doctor wanted to give him antidepressant medication. Morgan, who had always been available to Tom, was having her own problems. She found herself resenting—sometimes even hating—Malcolm, and she became irritated with the least provocation. She constantly felt guilty, blaming herself for problems that were beyond her control, just as she had done in her childhood. To make matters worse, she thought there must be something wrong with her because she had these feelings.

Morgan and Tom could not deny that their loving, once-solid relationship was in dire jeopardy. Nevertheless, the exhaustion they felt was no rival for the tenacity of these two people who had triumphed over their own childhoods and found the love of their life in adulthood. Despite their desolation, they knew that they could not give in to the emotional storm of mental illness.

As the Hartleys told me their story, I recognized the all too familiar core patterns of families under siege: terror, despair, hurt, anger, hopelessness, dispiritedness, and isolation from others. But they also refused to give up. Even though they felt defeated, they were committed to moving forward with their lives in the midst of inconceivable fears.

When I suggested that they could rise above, even triumph over, the current dread about the fate of their children, they looked at me intently. "If you take a tablespoon of salt, stir it into a glass of water, and drink it," I said, "the water will be undrinkable because of the taste of the salt." "On the other hand," I added, "if you take the same tablespoon of salt and mix it into a clean mountain lake, you could take a glassful of that water and drink it, and you wouldn't taste the salt." Tom and Morgan quickly got the message: pain and suffering are not caused directly by the event, but by the size of the "container" that holds them. I added that together we could explore ways to create the container that could hold their defeat. While puzzled, they continued to listen closely.

Expanding Your Container for Healing

"But how do I build a bigger container for my healing?" Morgan asked while Tom listened closely. (Ah, I thought to myself, this is exactly what you are here to learn.) "You will need to go on a journey, sort of a family odyssey, one not much different from the one that heroes and heroines of yesteryear took. You might not yet understand all of this right now," I added. "You might need to be further into the experience of it before you get a really good feel."

To whet Tom and Morgan's appetite and rekindle their hope, I continued to talk, slowly and intentionally. "For now, it is enough to realize that the job of creating a meaningful life can be done; so, for now, be open to the possibility that you really can be victorious over the mental illness and its wake, regardless of the circumstances."

"Most important," I said, "learn that if you are not part of the family's solution, you are part of the family's problem. Be solution-oriented by getting a damn good education. Educated families are part of the solution; uneducated families are part of the problem."

This simple, profound, and pivotal truth opens the doors to both triumph and healing. "Making a bigger container," I told the Hartleys, "is focusing your attention on what you can do, not on what you can't do. The focus is also on you, not just on your loved one. Making a bigger container is building a future so compelling, so inviting, that it can pull you forth toward it. Don't try to hang on to or save a past gone forever."

As their curiosity mounted, I went on to say: "Making a bigger container is consciously and purposely learning to focus on what you can do, rather than focusing on what you can't do. The goal of 'container building' is always to seek out and enhance the positive, not fight the negative. Strength is used in the service of weakness." I added: "Your body's muscles grow stronger by the resistance they encounter. Use the strength you have, and you will have even more as a result. By being strong you become yet stronger. Those who are strong became that way by applying what strength they had, over and over. And so can you."

After they paused to take in the many ideas presented, I asked Morgan and Tom whether they would consider it a triumph if the mental illness were no longer the defining event in their life. I asked them whether they could imagine the day when their major—and often minor—decisions didn't always revolve around the illness. I asked them whether they would consider it a triumph if they could find some value for the illness, and I asked if they could conceive of their life as worth living and their loss as worth overcoming, regardless of the prospect of further or future traumas.

I suggested that a *yes* answer to any of these questions could lead to a triumphant life, reminding them that this did not mean they would have to be continually cheerful. They could shed tears, feel sadness, express grief, and even be overwhelmed at times. They would only need to get up one more time than they fell down!

As Tom and Morgan looked at me in a quizzical way, I invited them to consider what qualities would enable them to move forward with their life in the midst of such a formidable adversity as mental illness. "What fosters the inner resolve to deal with life's great tragedies?" I asked. Harsh conditions often lead us to ask powerful questions such as: Who am I? Why am I here? What is my purpose? Is there a God?

We have many more choices than most of us realize. "There are many things over which we have no control," I acknowledged, "such as a loved one's mental illness—or life and death, or whether it rains or shines; yet, there is much we have to say about how we live our lives."

Continuing, I noted: "We can avoid responsibility by assuming unwarranted blame, moving through life as victims; or we could accept responsibility for what is happening, reject blame, and move toward living a sacred life. By accepting our plight, we can follow the path that has been taken by heroes, shamans, and mystics for thousands of years. We can see our struggles as our initiation, our gateway, into a fuller life."

After listening closely, Morgan asked, "Does this mean we can still have a happy and meaningful life?" "What an important question," I responded, knowing that there is no easy answer. "Doesn't happiness," I continued, "come from the word 'happenstance,' which is a fleeting and circumstantial situation?" Happiness is a word that is often misunderstood.

According to Dr. David Myers, an expert on the pursuit of happiness, a strong sense of controlling your own life is a more dependable predictor of feelings of well-being than any of the objective conditions of life.[98] In other words, what is going on inside of you is more important than what is going on around you in your outer circumstances. Drama occurs when you get stuck in your individual situation. Dr. Myers reminds us that a great many people benefit from their experiences of disaster and have more rewarding, rich lives as a result of them.

I went on to say: "If you can learn to accept what all the great writings in religion and science, philosophy and literature, teach us, broken dreams can be keys to unlocking the doors to a life more fully awake. A wounded life can still be a full life. The disquieting truth may be that nature never intended that we live life exactly as we hoped."

Life is always more and less than we expected. I quoted Job (I'll quote almost anybody to help a family), the biblical epitome of grace under fire, who said to his wife when she implored him to curse God: "Shall we receive good at the hands of God, and not receive the bad."

Because Morgan and Tom were already familiar with Alcoholics Anonymous (AA), I then went on to share one of my favorite stories about Bill Wilson, its cofounder. (An expanded version of this story appears in Chapter 18.) "It seems," I continued, "that Bill W, as he was called, was in a major depressive episode when he met a Jesuit priest named Father Ed Dowling."

Bill was taken by this priest and shared his dissatisfaction with life. When he felt comfortable enough, he asked him if he would ever experience satisfaction in life. The old priest came back with "Never" and proceeded to tell Bill that there was only divine dissatisfaction *and* it would keep Bill on the journey in life he was destined to take.

While Morgan got less than she expected from her happiness question, she got more than she bargained for. To drive the point home even further, I shared the following passage from *The Gospel According to St. Matthew*: "Blessed are they which do hunger and thirst." A new door opened for Morgan, one that is much brighter. She slowly began to develop a very different relationship with her pain and a new, broader definition of happiness.

To deal with their latest trauma, Tom and Morgan Hartley would have to discover a new way. "Major blows do not end life; they redirect it," I said. Saying she understood, Morgan jokingly quipped, "Yes, but is that the light at the end of the tunnel, or is it the light of an oncoming train?"

A Full Life

As the session neared its end, I told Tom and Morgan about positive psychology, which focuses on mental health as opposed to mental illness.[119] Positive psychology proposes that we can live four kinds of lives: a pleasant life, a good life, a meaningful life, and a full life. A pleasant life is one in which the person pursues the positive emotions of bodily pleasures, such as comfort, warmth, and orgasm, and the higher pleasures such as bliss, glee, and joy. The good life is one beyond the pleasant life: in the good life, the person uses "signature strengths"[119] to engage in activities that bring satisfaction in work, love, play, and parenting.

Discovering and using your signature strengths in all endeavors that you value characterize the good life. Two of my signature strengths, for example, are helping others and the love of learning. By engaging in clinical practice and writing, I have built both into the fabric of my life. As with all signature strengths, when using them, I am at my best. Attending to the details of life is not one of my signature strengths. When I engage in these activities, I feel drained.

The meaningful life adds one additional component to the good life: namely, using your signature strengths in the service of something greater than yourself, or connecting with a presence beyond your everyday life. Finally, the full life consists of experiencing all three, the pleasant life, the good life, *and* the meaningful life. You have positive emotions about the past and future, enjoy positive feelings from the pleasures, derive gratification from your signature strengths, and use these strengths for some larger meaning or purpose.

Concluding our first meeting, I asked the Hartleys which of these lives they would want. They had an option, I pointed out. Would they be willing to risk all they have for the possibility of all they could become? Would they be willing to give up the familiarity and comfort of an unpleasant but well-known situation for the potential of an unknown situation, likely uncomfortable, yet potentially satisfying and meaningful? Would they get up one more time than life threw them down? If they were willing to examine their core beliefs and to experiment with new behaviors, I knew they could have a rich, meaningful, and full life, albeit not an easy one.

Ordinary People with Extraordinary Challenges

Tom and Morgan are ordinary people who have been given an extraordinary life situation. They live under the influence of one of life's true adversities: mental illness. The struggle with mental illness, a word that often conjures up a host of negative images, becomes a deeply buried secret in countless homes. Mental illness can cause untold damage, often costing people their livelihood, their homes, even their freedom. In our country, 40 percent of the homeless and at least one-third of those in prison are people who are mentally ill.[99] All of those under the influence of mental illness can be robbed of the possibility for a full life.

Mental illness typically is an enduring, often lifelong circumstance, its many twists and turns frequently shaping the emotional terrain of present and future generations. Mental health experts describe mental illness as an extreme or catastrophic stressful situation.[28] Catastrophes overwhelm your abilities to cope, permanently altering your life and rocking the foundations of your world. They can shatter your beliefs, expose your deepest fears, and thrash your sense of safety, security, and comfort. Catastrophes carry the capability to transfigure you, your loved ones, and everything familiar to you.

But you are not alone. With help, you can find a new and even more meaningful life. While you can't change the past, casting light on its shadows can help you to build a new future and live a full life. Past horrors can prepare one for present challenges—if there is the right opportunity.

The Hartleys chose a course of triumph over mental illness. This decision will propel them on an odyssey, a journey far from the beaten path traveled by many under illness' influence. They are among the growing number of triumphant survivors[128] who have chosen not only to survive shocking circumstances, but also actually to thrive in the midst of them.

Triumphant survivors can learn to explain their ability to cope based on overcoming a catastrophe, rather than explaining their inability to cope based on being victimized by it. Struggle is not a problem, not an indication that something is wrong, but part of the solution of our inherent drive to make sense of our experience and move toward a more universal and encompassing vision.

Embarking on Your Own Triumphant Journey

This is a book about hope—and direction—for mental illness can also become the occasion for triumph. Accompanied by trauma and loss, triumph stops these twin horrors from becoming the determining events of your life. With triumph, what once defined your life recedes into the shadows of a life poorly lived. With triumph, you learn to see beyond the immediacy of the situation, and you have a vision, a purpose, a higher meaning that keeps pulling you forward and expanding your horizons. With triumph, you learn to give birth to opportunity and possibility in the midst of debacle and disaster. You learn to take your own heroic journey, just as our ancestors did, to discover the opportunity in the wound, or as one family member said, "the gift in trauma's other hand." One more time, you dare to snatch victory from the hands of defeat.

This book describes the quest to move forward in the face of life's major adversities, to conquer rather than being conquered. As I have listened to the many stories of the sufferers of illness, addiction, and other traumas and have walked beside them on their journey, I have found the following beliefs central to the appreciation of their struggle:

- Adversity is ever present and everywhere in life; it can appear at any time; and it is unavoidable. Almost all of us suffer one or more severe hardships, whether mental illness, physical illness, addiction, or other trauma. We differ primarily by which difficult events we incur.

- All adversity has a ripple effect or wake—a visible track of turbulence left by the hardship. Severe conditions affect and impact the primary sufferer *and* the secondary sufferer. Thus, mental illness, like alcoholism, is a family affair, as are all major adversities. Few escape the influence of harsh times. And when there is major unrest in the world, such as war and economic uncertainty, the influence of any adversity is always magnified, for trauma makes us all more vulnerable.

- Adversity and triumph are inseparable. If necessity can be considered the mother of invention, then adversity and trauma may well be the father of triumph. Triumph and adversity live side-by-side, like night and day or black and white. Just as courage is the ability to proceed in the midst of fear, triumph is the ability to act in the presence of adversity.

- Connection facilitates the expression of triumph. The greater the connection, the greater the opportunity for triumph. Relationship to self, others, and something beyond our everyday experience makes life worth living and loss worth enduring. Therefore, it is easier to triumph in the context of loving bonds, whether those bonds are with oneself, one's family, or one's commitments.

- Virtually everyone can triumph, regardless of his or her circumstance. It requires no uncommon characteristics. The movie *Life Is Beautiful* illustrates triumph even in the midst of conditions as severe as a concentration camp.

- Triumph can be learned and there is a clear path to follow. This path can be found in the great works of art, literature, and science as well as athletics and business.

- The cornerstone of this path is the interpretation given to the situation. Much more than reframing an event, the story you bring to bear to comprehend your life will determine its impact on you. The storyteller Isak Dinesen writes, "All sorrows can be borne if you put them into a story." People don't need new facts—they need a compelling story or "container." As you shall discover in a later chapter, meaningful stories can actually change the way your brain works. Ancient sacred texts remind us: "Man is made by his beliefs. As he believes, so he is."[132]

- Mental illness is such a complex issue, involving biological, psychological, sociological, cultural, and spiritual components, that the knowledge and wisdom of a variety of different disciplines are needed in order to triumph. No one branch of learning is sufficient. For this reason, I have used the principles and concepts from ten different fields of knowledge, which are described in depth in the chapter called "My Path to the Work."

- The philosophy and principles presented in this book are in no way intended to minimize the traumatic effects of all adversity, especially mental illness. Rather, what they emphasize are hope, possibility, and transformation by creating a life worth living and a loss worth enduring through channeling pain into something consequential and constructive.

You will learn that life's meanings are often made clearer by a particular circumstance. Of many such life-transforming events, one of the most hurtful and eye-opening is the presence of mental illness, for from that situation a mission can emerge that alters one's life.[68]

It can raise a host of questions, many of which are unanswerable, especially those such as, Why me? What did I do to deserve this? By working through these questions, strength emerges. Unexplored beliefs are uncovered. New purpose and direction can emerge, and a fresh orientation for life unfolds through the stories that you consciously and intentionally create, rather than those you might inherit or be given.

Unlocking the Doors to Triumph will teach you to construct your own personal story of triumph by confronting the essential elements that make up your beliefs. As you get to know the people in these pages, you get to know you; we are all much more similar than we are different. One family member eloquently put it this way: "In the difference of your situation, I discovered mine." This principle of universalization lets us know that it is in each other that we find ourselves.

In the process, you discover that a fundamental shift in your consciousness can occur as your own story becomes enlarged and is seen in the broader context of all humanity, all other stories. Rather than seeking only to change behaviors, you can learn to change the consciousness that created them. You will learn that changing your consciousness occurs when you change your beliefs. By changing your beliefs, you change your perception, and then you change your experience. Remembering this can change everything, especially your life.

Grounded in well-known psychological principles as well as clinical research, *Unlocking the Doors to Triumph* offers you a creative, fresh approach to overcoming adversity through the time-honored concepts and principles espoused by the heroes of old as well as the originators of the new. It presents essential information leading to practical tools that will invite you, the reader, to redefine what it means to triumph over one of life's greatest injuries, mental illness, by revealing the underlying nature, nurture, and structure of triumph. The concepts presented have been honed by over three decades of clinical experience with many hundreds of individuals and families under the influence of all types of adversity.

Rather than temporary or quick fixes, *Unlocking the Doors to Triumph* offers permanent and lasting benefits to be gained by facing adversity, and it provides the route to a rich and rewarding life in spite of horrific circumstances. This book provides antidotes to the pervasive sense of helplessness and hopelessness that so often accompanies the diagnosis of mental illness. It emphasizes a sustainable path to success and offers new ways to manage the perilous odyssey through mental illness with its ever-present challenges of loss, uncertainty, unpredictability, and chaos. What is more, it reveals that anyone under the influence of mental illness can have a full life, even a happy life, although not necessarily an easy one.

Each of the twenty-five chapters of this book presents a different facet of the diamond of triumph and a distinct dimension in your blueprint for the journey to a life lived fully. You will discover a pragmatic guide for dealing with chaos and creating a life worth living and a loss worth overcoming. You will learn to reengage with life in a way that is significant and enriching. You will learn how to move forward, especially against heavy odds. Understanding the struggle of each family member, you will learn to deal with life's excruciating blows and to harness the forces of the awakened and triumphant survivor. In the humorous words of writer Kathleen Norris, you will learn: "All that is necessary is to accept the impossible, do without the indispensable, and bear the intolerable."

By discovering the many facets of triumph, you will discover the truth behind Alexander Graham Bell's assertion: "When one door closes, another opens, but we often look so long and regretfully upon the closed door, we do not see the ones which open for us." These and countless other words from the sages will point you in the direction of triumph, a realistic and multifaceted path that reveals and illustrates solutions, helping you to see solutions where you had seen only problems.

Supplementary Resources

A word should be said about the many supplements to this book. The nine appendices that follow the body of the book can help you make better use of the text. The first appendix contains two self-help questionnaires that can aid you in assessing the degree to which you might be influenced by mental illness or another of life's major calamities (Common Errors in Thinking by Family Members and Danger Signs for Family Members). The next appendix offers a list of Useful Distinctions that can enrich your understanding of the readings. The remaining appendices offer useful summaries for many of the concepts described.

Following the appendices, there is a Glossary of Helpful Terms, because you may be unfamiliar with some of the terminology used. A different languaging system is used throughout the book, and familiar words may appear in unfamiliar contexts. The power of language will be used to evoke and awaken your capacities and talents.

A word should be said about referencing or annotating this book. Many readers will not want to be distracted by the citing of references. Some readers, however, might be interested in delving further into a particular topic and want its reference mentioned. To accommodate both, I have placed the appropriate references in the Bibliography as superscripts so they will not be intrusive to the reader. A biographical statement, About the Author, comes next. An Index of relevant topics concludes the book.

CHAPTER *1*

The Shocking Facts about Serious Mental Illness

You are not alone.

—⟋⟍—

Who among us does not know someone impacted by mental illness? When one includes alcoholism and other drug abuse as well as major trauma, whether physical, emotional, mental, or spiritual, there are even fewer people who haven't been impacted. In fact, mental illness, trauma, and addiction often exist together in the same family. And if one includes physical illness, there is hardly a soul who is exempt from the wake of one or more of these major tribulations. Life is certainly not made easy. "It's no walk in the park," the father of a thirteen-year-old boy who has schizophrenia and bipolar disorder remarked.

Overview of the Problem

Tens of millions of people in this country are deeply affected by serious mental illness.[135] In addition to the painful impact of

1

the illness itself, those who experience mental illness additionally experience anguish because they are stigmatized, shunned, and marginalized. What is even less recognized by our society than the plight of the primary sufferer, the one who bears the disorder, is the acknowledgment of the plight of the secondary sufferers, the family and other loved ones, who endure the burdens of the illness and its symptoms. Together, they number perhaps as many as 125 million people in this country alone.

Many stresses inherent in our complex modern life further complicate and aggravate the symptoms of mental illness. A recent survey, for example, suggests that we receive an average of almost two hundred communications each day from phone calls, pager calls, faxes, mail, e-mails, and unplanned conversations. Using the average of two minutes for responding to each contact, we could be devoting more than six hours of our day exclusively to this task.[57]

In addition, you have to fix your car when it breaks; you have to maintain your home; you have to generate tuition money for your children; you have to pay taxes. Along the way, you have to deal with the births and deaths of loved ones, find jobs and lose jobs, move to a new house or a new city. In other words, life demands your attention to an unending stream of situations. All of these stresses and strains can influence the waxing and waning of mental illness.

And if postmodern life were not enough, millions of Americans were traumatized by the terrorist attacks on the World Trade Center, the Pentagon, and the plane crash in Pennsylvania on 9/11. Estimates indicate that more than 80 percent of all Americans witnessed the destruction of the Twin Towers on television in which more than 4,000 innocent and unsuspecting people were suddenly and violently killed. These horrific deaths, in turn, precipitated a serious grief reaction in hundreds of thousands more.

Many of these viewers were repeatedly traumatized, transfixed by their televisions and radios, reliving the tragedies time after time. At least half of these viewers developed a "critical incident stress reaction," and up to one-third of the television witnesses may develop a post-traumatic stress disorder, which is commonly called PTSD.

The repeated display of these attacks showed the enormous potential of the media to traumatize any one of us. Those under the influence of mental illness have been especially influenced, however, because their prior experiences with trauma and loss make them more vulnerable to all subsequent trauma.[136] An already hard life can be made almost impossible when family members come under the influence of mental illness. Feelings of persecution have increased in the post-9/11 atmosphere of suspicion and fear.

Those with a serious mental illness are people we love and grow old with. They include kinsmen who have been diagnosed with a severe disorder, especially schizophrenia, bipolar disorder, major depression, obsessive-compulsive disorder (OCD), or those with other persistent and debilitating mental disorders. Existing in a private world of strange meanings, words, and visions, the sufferers of mental illness live in a realm very different from most. In their highly idiosyncratic lives, they cannot distinguish the outer reality from their own inner fantasies or thoughts. Their perceptions of other people and of their environment are often grossly distorted. Their moods may shift dramatically from one extreme to another; and they can be tortured by thoughts and unwanted behaviors that are barely noticed by many of us.

Primary and Secondary Symptoms

The primary symptoms of mental illness are the core, overt symptoms that define and characterize each of the specific mental illnesses. In more technical terms, they are the symptoms that are "pathognomonic" of the particular disorder, which is to say that they characterize the disorder. Symptoms that are primarily addressed by medications, they can include one or more of the following: delusions and hallucinations as in schizophrenia; major mood swings as in bipolar disorder; severe and profound depression as in major depression; and clinical obsessions and compulsions as in OCD.[90]

Not only does the sufferer endure one or more of these *primary symptoms,* but there are also *secondary symptoms* associated with all of the disorders. They can include one or more of the following: anxiety, depression, guilt, lack of discipline, poor grooming, low motivation, demoralization, dejection, dispiritedness, disillusionment, slowness, alcohol and other drug abuse, and ultimately low self-esteem and disrupted relationships.

These secondary symptoms quietly perpetuate the insidious shadow side of mental illness. One family member simply calls them "collateral damage." They become an integral part of the whole picture; unfortunately, they are frequently neglected, despite the heavy toll they exact. The effect of these secondary symptoms is a pervasive and negative orientation toward life. Rather than a life affirming *yes* to existence, secondary symptoms result in a resounding *no* to life's wonders.

Shocking Numbers

The numbers of those who suffer a mental illness are staggering. Twenty-five million people in this country suffer one form or another. According to the World Health Organization, mental illness, including suicide, is the second most common debilitating disease among developed nations. Worldwide, as many as 500 million people have some form of mental illness.[90]

Recent research indicates the presence of mental illness in one out of every four families.[135] In any given year, more than 50 million people will suffer from a mental disorder. This is almost one-third more than the 20 percent who suffer from cardiovascular disease. More than 7 million children will be affected. Between 25 to 50 percent of those impacted by mental illness also have a substance abuse problem, with alcohol, cocaine, and marijuana being the most frequent drugs of choice, respectively. Problems with these and other drugs are the most common "comorbid," or coexisting conditions in people with severe mental illness,[35] complicating the already difficult process of healing and recovery.

For as many as 100 million people, they are the loved ones and members of their families. According to Dr. David Satcher's recent Surgeon General's report on mental illness, 90 percent can be helped, yet fewer than 30 percent receive treatment.[135] If this were any other illness, it would be called an epidemic. The outcry would shake the very foundations of this country.

Serious mental illness is a complex disorder because it can have neurological, biochemical, genetic, cognitive, emotional, mental, spiritual, and even sociocultural aspects. While biology is shown to play an increasing role in its origin, society defines the parameters of mental illness by establishing social policies and priorities, indeed shaping the climate in which families endure the multiple impacts of mental illness.[76]

Just as society's tolerance for unusual behaviors influences what is diagnosed as "abnormal," insurance issues define who is and who is not ill by their classification of problems that are eligible for insurance, or "reimbursable." If an insurance company does not cover a condition, it doesn't exist. Only in the context of the larger social order is it possible for us to understand the entire problem produced by serious mental illness.

Those with mental illness often also acquire serious, disabling *physical* diseases, diseases that are typically linked to a lack of positive self-care—for example, illnesses that are linked to smoking, poor nutrition, or self-abuse. Studies further reveal that mentally ill people are at risk because they are frequently homeless, on the streets, and in jails rather than in hospitals. On average, those with severe mental illness die at least ten to fifteen years earlier than those in the general population. Being diagnosed with a mental illness is now considered a risk factor for premature death.[135] The unemployment rate for those with psychiatric disabilities is the highest of any distinguishable group. Within the decade, depression will be the number one cause of disability. For countless millions, these casualties are their very own family members, the people that they love the most and with whom they have the most contact.

Probable Cause

Serious mental illness does not result from a dysfunctional childhood or from poor parenting, although they can affect its course.[89, 90, 134] It is a medical illness, and while not contagious in the usual sense of the word, it has a great impact on everyone, especially the family and other loved ones. Considering mental illness simplistically as a disease or merely the result of a biochemical imbalance in the brain, however, ignores information that indicates *it is directly and indirectly affected by many nonbiological variables.* The problem of mental illness, therefore, has consequences far greater than are first apparent. All members of the family and other loved ones share in the misery that mental illness can cause.

Affecting the present while simultaneously influenced by the past, mental illness can collide with the future. Take the example of

Lillian. She is an attractive thirty-eight-year-old woman who grew up in a family under the influence of schizophrenia. Never having been in a long-term relationship, she was terrified of closeness and intimacy. Upon inquiry, she revealed that during her childhood, her mother was often taken to the hospital when her psychosis got out of control. Experiencing enormous insecurity, she believed that "had I been a better girl, she never would have left me."

No words were given to her horror. Lillian was never told why her mother "just disappeared," because her father believed that she could not understand and thought it would be better if she did not know the truth. As Lillian ruefully commented: "The roads to hell are often paved with good intentions. So, instead of knowing, I lived with the unknown terror that I could awaken, and mother would not be home." To a young child, when a parent is absent, it is as if the parent is dead. As an adult, she now lived with the pervasive fear that anyone she loved would die or leave her. Afraid of the future, she was hesitant about marriage, despite many proposals, and she vowed never to have children, fearing that she would pass the illness on to them.

Like many, Lillian did not link the terror and humiliation of her childhood with the fears and insecurities of her adult life. It took years of psychotherapy for the connections among Lillian's myriad of problems to be uncovered and resolved. Speaking for countless other family members, Lillian tearfully lamented, "We're victims without a voice. People care about us even less than the ill." Family members of the mentally ill are often stigmatized and ignored, as we have seen, often withdrawing into a world of shame, secrecy, and silence, where they do not receive the attention or help they deserve *and* need.

Reciprocal Causation

We now know that not only does the person with mental illness influence virtually all of the other members of the family, but those family members in turn influence the person with the mental illness. To focus on the problems of only one family member, to the exclusion of others, is to miss the bigger picture.

Yet, when most families are asked what the problem is, an ordinary family will typically answer, "My Johnny [that is, my loved one] is the problem. If only he didn't [or did] . . ." What most families fail to recognize is that "the problem" is much broader than Johnny. The real problem, the important problem, is what has happened to the loved one *and* to the family, not just to Johnny; what *is* happening now to the family, not just Johnny; and what *will* happen to the family in the future, not just Johnny.

Too often, when the problems of "the identified patient," or the primary sufferer, are the only problem that is identified or addressed, the result is a limited view of the predicament. Soon, we shall examine the consequences of this issue. First, however, it is necessary to understand more clearly the many wounds that result from mental illness.

CHAPTER 2

The Wounds

Mental health experts describe mental illness
as an extreme or catastrophic stressor.

—⁓—

There is no escape from life's wounds. Wounds are unavoidable, inevitable, and also potentially useful on the journey to find the person we were born to be. From all of the great writings, it is clear that the consequence of wounding is far more profound than it first appears.[55, 57] Their message is clear: we can permit an event to utterly destroy us, or we can perceive the same event as a summons—in mythological terms, a "call" to act courageously, which results in extraordinary growth in the process. Each of us may have examples in our own experience that point to the relationship between the wound and the development, or lack of development, of our self.

How many of us know others who, judged by all objective conditions, have little or no reason to be happy and they are? Conversely, how many know still others, who seemingly have everything, yet nevertheless they suffer horribly? What distinguishes these two different types of people? They clearly perceive their wounding in very different ways.

The study of classical mythology teaches us that wounding exists in two basic forms. Wounds can be "profane," or they can be "sacred." The distinction of profane and sacred wounding becomes a key entry point into the stories we ourselves create, and a central method to enlarge our personal stories, particularly those limited stories in which we tend to think of ourselves as helpless, passive victims who are also hopeless, with few, if any, choices.[35, 55, 71] Consequently, the distinction between a sacred wound and a profane wound is one of the most important concepts that can unlock the door to triumph as well as healing.

Profane Wounds

Unfortunately, most of the wounds that we incur are profane wounds. These are wounds that make us pine and whine: Why me? What did I do to deserve this? What is wrong with me? Am I bad? Profane wounds invariably create shame, the experience that there is something fundamentally wrong with us at the level of our very essence. They breed secrecy, darkness, and concealment. Profane wounds are an assault and an affront to the ego's unrealistic belief in its supremacy. There is always struggle and little, if any, acceptance of the situation.

Profane wounds create suffering,* a state of endless agitation, with no beginning, middle, or end, which means suffering perpetuates itself with little or no possibility of triumph. At their core are a lack of accountability for our life and the formation of many maladaptive emotional defenses, none of which

---

* I craft a fundamentally crucial distinction between pain and suffering from this point forward.

can lead to corrective experiences. Because they appear interminable, profane wounds teach us little about anything. Hence, we don't learn from our behavior, let alone from our mistakes, and we go through the same repetitious behavioral patterns time and time again.

The state called suffering is one in which few commitments are made. We engage in passivity or aggressivity, blame others or the situation, and are often in denial about our ability to respond. Our thinking is typically exclusive and polarized: we either believe the problem is our fault, which can foster excessive guilt and continued self-absorption, or deny our ability to respond, which promotes avoidance and apathy as coping styles.

Take Mary. She recently lost her sister, Ann, who committed suicide while in one of her many episodes of major depression. Mary was left with many mixed feelings toward Ann: love, guilt, anger, and confusion, to mention but a few. Questions, too, such as, Could I have done something more? haunted her. She wanted desperately to talk to the other members of her family, but based on prior experience, she believed no one could listen and told herself she couldn't bear one more loss. So, she withdrew into the silence of her loneliness and aloneness. In the darkness of the host of these negative feelings, she suffered on top of her pain. Because she could not talk, she could not grieve, and because she could not grieve, she could not heal.

The language of a profane wound is one of limitation, hesitancy, helplessness, and hopelessness. Almost hallucinogenic, it can weave such a dark spell that in its grasp, we see no solution. Victimization and unconsciousness mark it. A profane wound is always full of drama and exaggeration. As one family member said, "We put our problems on a pedestal and worship them. No wonder they seem overwhelming."

What is more, we come to believe that we are the only one who has such an unfair plight, thereby engaging in further unproductive self-pity. To make matters worse, we tend to take the injury personally—very personally. However, as noted, we tend to do little about it and avoid personal responsibility for doing something about it.

None of these behaviors associated with a profane wound move us forward in the face of adversity. Such beliefs can become pervasive and invade every aspect of our life. In addition, we become remote and increasingly withdrawn. In the process, life becomes meaningless and we become dispirited and disillusioned. Eventually, we lose contact not only with others, but also with ourselves.

The Unabel family, whom we will meet in the upcoming chapter "The Power of Us," exhibits a profane wound when mental illness first strikes. Plucked from the shredded narrative of their old existence, they were tossed into a new life of chaos and terror. Until there was an intervention, little good could come from the devastating injury to the family. Little possibility of a life worth living and a loss worth enduring could be fashioned from mental illness until they could learn a different way. Without help, profane wounds most often bring out the worst in almost every member of the family. What is tragic is the lack of awareness, for awareness can bring out the best in each person.

A profane wound occurs when we freeze-frame a particular—and usually horrible—scene. We store the wound in our mind just as it occurred, and we relive the negative circumstance again and again. It lingers as a still photograph in what should be a motion picture of our life. This is why so many trauma survivors say, "I feel like it [the traumatic experience] is still happening to me!" The behavior persists and the trauma remains unresolved. All growth in that area stops.

Two examples help to illustrate this important principle. The first is an old-fashioned record. If it were to be scratched deeply enough and then played, the phonograph needle would fall into a groove, and the free flow of the music would stop at the point where the scratch begins. What would be heard is the same sound over and over again.

The second is a movie or a slide projector that gets stuck or jammed. The same scene is played over and over again. Trauma occurs in a similar way. The same image, sound, even smell, is played over and over again in the person's mind. Suffering a type of tunnel vision, in which the person can no longer see the positive scenes preceding or following the trauma, the person is left with that particular distressing image or experience and all of life becomes a constant replaying and reactivating of that one experience. This negative event is not only the person's past and present, but also it becomes his or her future. It becomes the template upon which all new experience is projected.

Sacred Wounding

On the other hand, when a wound becomes sacred, it is as if the frozen frames of the movie can move forward again. As the movie in the mind begins to evolve from frame to frame, we get to see the whole of the movie. In the process, we see, hear, discover, and understand things that were unavailable in that one, single frame. As we struggle to enlarge our view, we find and create meaning for our negative experience.

Another useful analogy to understand the expansion of our view of self when we create a wound as sacred is a plate filled with food. If we have a small plate and it is full of food, there is no room for anything else. If we extend our plate, or find a bigger one, then the same amount of food that was on the smaller one now occupies proportionately less space. By making our "plate of life" larger and larger, the original amount of food, or adversity, becomes smaller and smaller. The greater the number of connections we make beyond the limited self or ego and the more profound the meaning for our circumstance, the bigger the size of our plate, a finding that discoveries in neuroscience supports.[25]

Transformative in nature, sacred wounds lead us toward corrective experiences and literally help us reprogram our brain, as modern neuroscience demonstrates.[125] They awaken the seeker within us all and lead us to the essential truths in life, truths such as we are all one and division and separateness are illusions, truths that both modern science and the ancient sacred texts are now revealing.[88, 57, 141] Most relevant, they lead us to the discovery that life is not about circumstance; rather, life is about the meaning that we give to all of our different experiences.

A sacred wound is a creative act birthed by the soul instead of the ego. Any life-shattering event can be a modern-day sacred wound, a wound so profound that it pierces the soul and renders us open to a greater order. It exposes us to questions we hadn't needed to ask before, questions of God and Spirit, purpose, the unanswerable *why*, and the divine mystery of life. We do not get over a sacred wound; we are transformed by it. Like the mythological heroes of old, modern-day family members who undergo a sacred wound will emerge unmistakably changed by the ordeal.

Sacred wounding has many names. Some of them include divine dissatisfaction, fierce grace, divine enemy, blessed curse, and joyful unfulfillment. As these terms suggest, they all convey the notion of creating meaning out of life's adversities. It is analogous to the notion of making lemonade out of lemons. To create meaning offers the possibility of real transformation, shifting our problems from the domain of the profane to the domain of the sacred. In this shift from the micro to the macro, from the personal to the universal, there is both healing and triumph. This act of creation focuses attention away from the small or lesser self, and places it upon the realization of the larger or greater Self.

Like some acolyte in an ancient initiation, a person who has dealt with cancer, for example, can emerge from this ordeal, or modern-day initiation, fundamentally changed, having given birth to a higher self, one that is often unattainable to those who have not undergone the ordeal. Cancer, or any serious adversity, can provide us with the gift of a different vision, whether we are the primary sufferer or the loved ones.[83] In either case, it can filter out the static and noise of everyday concerns. It can lift the veil of musts, shoulds, and other expectations, revealing the marvel of life, proposing a panoramic view of the soul's essence. As mythologist Joseph Campbell says, "The demon you swallow gives you its power."[17] The greater life's pain, the greater life's reply.

Rather than feeling like a victim who has no control over the circumstance, a sacred wound offers the challenge of having power over how we respond and how we view the injury or illness. In the process, our struggle becomes elevated to the heroic. Instead of dwelling in our unconsciousness, we become more and more conscious. Instead of feeling alone and isolated, we feel connected to a larger universal pattern. Instead of shame, we feel more self-esteem. Instead of addiction and crippling attachment, we feel spaciousness and freedom. And most importantly, a sacred wound enlarges our view of life, raising our small story of what happened to a comprehensive perspective, one in which we can find our place in the greater community or whole.

A sacred wound also offers the possibility that tragedy carries a gift in its other hand, when we are mindful to remain open to the grace that is available to us all. Tragedy remains tragedy, however, and pain remains pain, even with a sacred wound. You still feel the pain and you still feel the injury when you incur a sacred wound. Nothing removes the pain. But the pain in a sacred wound is a very different experience than the suffering in a profane wound. The pain offers lessons to learn, unlike suffering, which offers only a dead-end experience that must be endured. Once the lesson is learned with pain, you can move to life's next lesson, rather than recycling through the same issue over and over as in suffering. You are now accountable and can be entrusted to take effective action, even if you didn't cause the situation. Heroism and consciousness are the earmarks of pain.

In suffering, there is no learning, no forward movement, and therefore no triumph. In true pain, however, one moves forward with acceptance and surrender. The pain in a sacred wound offers the opportunity of an expanded awareness of self and others as a result of the experience, while suffering evokes only the possibility to be engulfed. Do not be mistaken, however: dark days still occur with pain. Yet the descents into darkness, when approached as a sacred opportunity, can lead to a place where the sweetness of life can be savored without denying the darkness.

With the suffering of a profane wound, you *want* to believe in miracles; in the pain of a sacred wound, you *do*. While both wounds injure you and can and do change you forever, the latter invites you to a deeper, more profound, and reverent view of life and the former disempowers you. One opens the door to limitless possibilities; the other closes it. One activates healing; the other activates dysfunction.

One woman was grief stricken by the diagnosis of schizophrenia in her eight-year-old daughter. She cried and cried until one day, as she described, "my tears filled up a whole river and I was finally able to float out. Afloat," she continued, "I could see the other side where my husband and two children were. From that moment on, they never looked the same and I never treated anyone the same anymore." The unconsciousness of her once-profane wound transformed to the conscious appreciation of her whole family.

Other examples of sacred wounds can be found virtually everywhere. Alcoholism, for example, becomes a sacred wound when the alcoholic achieves sobriety in the sense of living, not merely talking, a twelve-step program. One woman's wound of losing her child became a sacred wound when she opened to a deeper mission and connection with life. This woman is Norma Phillips, whose son was killed by a drunk driver. She inspirationally writes: "Dean's death was the worst tragedy of my life. At first I thought there was no place to turn for the comfort and support I needed. . . . But I found help in a nearby Mothers Against Drunk Driving Chapter (MADD)."

In 1985, Ms. Phillips was elected national president of MADD. "The day I took office," she says, "I recommitted myself to the goals of reducing the incidents of drunk driving and the pain and suffering it causes." While her efforts didn't take away the pain, it gave the pain a focus and direction, which in turn gave her life new meaning. While she still experienced great pain, the suffering was significantly diminished.

Theresa Saldana, an actress, was brutally stabbed in an attack that required more than a thousand stitches in her body. The result was a long battle with pain, rage, and terror. In her book, *Beyond Survival,* she writes, "My rage gave me the drive to keep fighting death, pain, and the sick wishes of the person who harmed me."[115] It was her anger toward the treatment that survivors receive at society's hands that led her to form an advocacy group called Victims for Victims. She needed to know that the trauma she endured was not a total waste and "served some useful purpose."

Fortunately, living a heroic life is more common—and accomplishable—than we might realize, as the above examples attest. Heroes and heroines are all around us. I have been a cycling enthusiast since I got my very first bike. So, one of my heroes is Lance Armstrong, who developed testicular cancer in 1995, at the height of his career as a racing cyclist. He is the first and only American to win (he has won five times in succession) the Tour de France, the 2,290-mile road race that is considered the single most grueling sport event.

In his biography, Armstrong describes through living example his philosophy of making an obstacle an opportunity. He writes: "By now you've figured out I'm into pain. Why? Because it's self-revelatory, that's why. There is a point in every race when a rider encounters his real opponent and understands that it's himself. In my most painful moments on the bike, I am at my most curious, and I wonder each and every time how I will respond. Will I discover my innermost weakness, or will I seek out my innermost strength? It's an open-ended question whether or not I will be able to finish the race. You might say pain is my chosen way of exploring the human heart."[6]

Later, in discussing the cancer, Armstrong said that he would have chosen cancer over winning the Tour de France. When asked why, he asserted: "What I mean is that I wouldn't have learned all I did if I hadn't had to contend with the cancer. I couldn't have won even one Tour [all five of his victories in the Tour de France came *after* the onset of the cancer!] without my fight, because of what it taught me. I truly believe that. I had a deep sense of illness, and not only wasn't I ashamed of it, I valued it above everything."[6]

Tipper Gore and Rosalynn Carter are examples of prominent women who have allowed the wounds inflicted by mental illness to become an acknowledged and active part of their functioning daily life, affirming the triumph of both of these heroic women over their adversities. No family is immune, no matter how successful, rich, famous, happy, or sad. As we have seen, mental illness is an equal opportunity destroyer.

Tens of millions of men and women have been thrust into roles in which there lies the opportunity for them to choose between sacred or profane wounds, between meaningful or meaningless lives. How many family members have chosen similar but different paths, and have become advocates at the local and national level and campaigned for rights and liberties for their loved ones? How many ordinary people have been thrust into this journey of mental illness and become extraordinary along the way?

In order to develop a sacred wound, it isn't necessary to write a book, establish a foundation, lecture widely, or devote time and money to a needed cause. The Abel family, whom we will also meet in the chapter "The Power of Us," developed a sacred wound. Almost all families have the capacity to create a sacred wound. They expand their plight from the limitations of being passive, helpless, and reactive to being active, heroic, and proactive. They possess within themselves the potential to open their hearts and their spirits, embracing the universal nature of their dilemma and experiencing the pain and triumph of all families, for they know that harm befalls all families.

Family members generate sacred wounds by allowing the mental illness to penetrate their souls, to open their very beings and their innermost selves, and use their wounds to bring them to an appreciation of life that they could never have imagined. They can do this by creating a new and powerful story that holds the unique meaning for the circumstance in which they find themselves. This principle is embodied in the often quoted statement by German philosopher Friedrich Nietzsche: "He who has a *why* to live can deal with almost any *how*."[57]

One family member, for example, would create a game in his mind whenever his child experienced psychotic rages. He would ask himself the following questions: If the universe were setting up challenges for him called psychotic rages, how would he behave? What would he do? He would then organize his behaviors around these answers. To flesh out this story, he believed that all the members of the family were students, or players, in what he called "Soul School." There were lessons in this cosmic school that were aimed directly at him and were meant to provide the instruction that he came to earth this time to accomplish. While this may seem like California mumbo jumbo, the different stories he created in his mind all had the same theme: his rite of passage to the journey he was born to make.

More importantly, these stories calmed him down, and they instilled a source of comfort from a higher level that was more powerful than anything else that he could imagine on the human level. Sacred wounding, the hero's journey, and the mythical meaning of betrayal as one of the greatest agents of the sacred became core concepts in his healing, and he used them as living metaphors. They provided the focus and direction he needed when he was in the midst not only of his child's monsters, but his own as well. "How can anyone deal with the darkest side of humanity without the benefit of some supreme power?" he would ask me.

Triumph, as it lives through a sacred wound, is not a matter of mind over matter. It is not a matter of willpower, and it is not simply positive thinking. Rather, it is the age-old alchemical process of transforming the poisonous lead of our horrific experience into the shining gold of our destiny to manifest our most sacred self. By undergoing this alchemical process, or journey, we transform our profane injuries into sacred ones. Like the heroes of old who accepted a sacred "call" to save the realm, the modern family hero accepts the call of the illness. Not everyone, however, chooses to accept the call for such a journey. When the call is refused, the result is always the same: a disaster of some major proportion for the individual. For the refusal of the call is a betrayal of the self.

The Jones family is an example. When their daughter suffered OCD on her sixth birthday, both Mr. and Mrs. Jones were horrified. Convinced they were being punished for some unnamed transgression, they began attending religious services compulsively. When this failed to impact their child's actions, their compulsivity increased as their responsibility decreased. They slowly began to isolate from family and friends alike. Soon, they were held hostage by the cleaning rituals of their daughter. They couldn't enter the house without washing themselves, and their child's behaviors continued to deteriorate. A vicious cycle of their own compulsive actions resulted, which only exacerbated the symptoms of the OCD. Unfortunately, this family, like some families, retreated behind a wall of ignorance, shame, fear, and guilt. Rather than finding a purpose or meaning in their circumstance, they drowned in a sea of self-pity. Rather than seizing the illness as an opportunity for growth, they sank deeper and deeper into anger, resentment, and despair. And rather than becoming heroes, who responded courageously and creatively to a tragedy, they reacted by becoming victims to their child's illness.

Betrayal as a Sacred Wound

Betrayal is a pervasive theme in mythology as it is in life. As seen through a mythological perspective, betrayal is not only common but, more importantly, it opens your eyes. Of all the wounds to the soul, betrayal can be one of the greatest agents of the sacred.[71] It closes the door on naiveté, and marks the end of the destructive effects of blind trust. It opens you to reflection and greater consciousness. By opening you to the darker sides of life, you can become more discerning. Betrayal, therefore, initiates the next step in your growth by opening you to new, expanded possibilities and realities.

Betrayal occurs virtually every day in the family under the influence of illness, addiction, and trauma. It happens whenever parents (it could just as well be spouses, siblings, or children, especially adult children) say one thing and do another. It happens when family members make promises to take their medications, act appropriately, take better care of themselves, stop eating, stop drinking, or stop working so hard—and they don't. It happens when family members tell others they will not hurt them, and they do, or when members tell others they won't be mean or cruel, and they are. It especially happens when loved ones are not able to perform and function like active participants in the family. The seeds of betrayal unfold with each broken promise and each broken dream.

The message in betrayal is that its consequences are much more far reaching than they first appear to be. We begin to separate appearance from truth, or small story from larger story, discovering in the process that appearances are but a small part of what things really are. Loss of idealization exposes knowledge. When a son's trust in his father is betrayed, for example, he learns more about the world and discovers he can have the courage and strength to rise above the wound.

As psychologist James Hillman notes, the person can remember the "wounder" (he calls it "traumatic remembering") and become stagnant—lost in the shallowness of a small, trivial story—or the person can remember the circumstances of the wound, discover them to be occasions for change, and grow into the maturity offered by a large, meaningful story. Out of this betrayal, the possibility of a stronger person arises. We move from one developmental level to another when we are thrust out into an unprotected existence.

Myths show us that trust always contains the seeds of betrayal.[71] Our closest relationships form the backdrop for betrayal. It is inevitable that everyone, eventually, will let us down or fail us in some way. It is betrayal that marks our revocation of complete trust. Only when Jesus is nailed to the cross, deceived and abandoned by those closest to Him, does Jesus feel the full human depth of the betrayal. He cries out: "My God, My God, why hast thou forsaken Me?" But it is only at the end of primal trust that Jesus becomes available to the fullness of the human condition. In the Christian faith, Jesus dies, gestates for three days, and is reborn with fuller love. There must be death before rebirth as the process of a sacred wound unfolds.

Classical myths reveal that it is in the larger story that the betrayer, or perpetrator, is an instrument of transformation. We find the betrayer and the betrayed bound together in a mutual narrative. And if each of their separate stories were known, we would find that their paths are surprisingly similar. Remember the story of Luke Skywalker and Darth Vader in the *Star Wars* trilogy. At first, we think the two are diametrically opposed, but later we realize the father and the son tread the same path.

Betrayal and trust are such strong themes in all the great religions and myths because each can serve as an opening of divinity for the other. It is the human gate to higher experience, for it can initiate experiences of God. Thus, for all its agony and suffering, betrayal extends our consciousness more than naive trust. It challenges us to go beyond everyday circumstance and enlarges our vision. It is as we move from idealization to betrayal and then to forgiveness that we arrive at maturity.

There are always two great betrayals. The first betrayal occurs from the circumstance. It may be faulty genetics, which predisposes the person to inherit something negative or horrific. It may be a poisonous environment, whether parental or societal. Such a betrayal, however, need not end in calamity or disaster. As bad and as harmful as this type of external betrayal can be, however, it pales in comparison to the second betrayal. The worst betrayal of all occurs when we betray ourselves. This self-betrayal unfolds as we refuse to become what we can be by cheating ourselves, making flimsy excuses and rationalizations.

Self-betrayal can appear in disguise, for instance, when we criticize ourselves without mercy. We may deny our needs and belittle ourselves. We may ignore our "real self." We become skilled in telling ourselves why things will never work. We can refuse to become what we can be, and we plunge into suffering, a pit with no bottom. Suffering is our refusal to embrace the pain. Such behaviors always lead to what one of the greatest evolutionary thinkers, Dr. Carl Jung, calls inauthentic suffering—an endless suffering that offers a dull, boring, meaningless existence punctuated by cynicism and apathy—that is, a profane wound.

For the person who dares to choose triumph, there is an alternative. This passage always involves moving through our "dark night—indeed our dark nights—of the soul." As Joseph Campbell has stated: "The labyrinth is thoroughly known. We have only to follow the thread of the hero path, and where we had thought to find an abomination, we shall find a god. And where we had thought to slay another, we shall slay ourselves. Where we had thought to travel outward, we will come to the center of our existence. And where we had thought to be alone, we will be with all the world."[18]

As living under the influence of mental illness is not for the weak of heart, so triumphing is for the daring and the brave of spirit and soul. As Dr. Jung said, "There is no birth of consciousness without pain." Pain awakens the seeker within. There is no escape from life's wounds. Triumph is a resounding *yes* to life regardless of circumstance. It is being lifted to a better place, not emerging without scars and bruises.

Life Is Not as It Often Appears

There is a story about a man who was in his room when it suddenly filled with light. God appeared, telling the man that He had work for him to do, and showed him a large rock in front of his cabin. God explained that the man was to push against the rock with all his might. For years, he toiled from sun up to sun down. Each night the man returned to his cabin, sore and worn out, feeling his whole day had been spent in vain. Since the man was showing discouragement, Satan decided to intervene by placing negative thoughts into his weary mind, suggesting that the task was impossible and that he was a failure. These thoughts disheartened the man. "Why kill myself over this?" he thought. "I'll just give the minimum effort." One day the man decided to take his troubled thoughts to God. "God," he said, "I have labored long and hard, giving all my strength to do what you asked. Yet, after all this time, I have not even budged that rock. Why am I failing?" God responded: "When I asked you to serve, I told you to push against the rock with all of your strength. Never did I mention I expected you to move it—just to push. And now you return with your strength spent, thinking that you have failed. But, is that really so? Look at yourself. Your arms are strong and muscled, your back sinewy and brown, your legs have become massive and hard. Through opposition you have grown much and your abilities now surpass those you used to have, even though you didn't move the rock.

When you hear a word from God, you tend to use your own intellect to decipher what He wants, when actually what God wants is your best interests. When everything seems to go wrong, just PUSH. When people don't react the way you think they should, just PUSH. When people don't understand you, just PUSH—or *Pray Until Something Happens.*

As valuable as prayer is, there is an old tale that reveals its darker side. There was once a farmer who was caught in a terrifying storm. The rains poured into a horrible onslaught. Soon, the rain turned into a flood that surrounded his house. Two men in a rowboat came by and offered to take the farmer to safety. "Don't worry about me," yelled the man. "God will provide." But the rains continued and the water rose even higher. Soon, another rowboat appeared and the farmer was again offered a ride. "Don't worry about me," yelled the man. "God will provide." But the rains continued and the water rose even higher. Soon, the water was so high that the man had to climb on top of his chimney. Then, a helicopter came by and he was offered another ride to safety. "Don't worry about me," yelled the man. "God will provide." Well, the rains still continued and the man drowned. When passing through the gates of Heaven, the farmer saw one of God's angels and bitterly complained. "I have been a pious man all my life," he grumbled. "I prayed regularly and often. Why did God forsake me?" he cried. The angel said, "God didn't forsake you. He sent you two rowboats and a helicopter." As one of my favorite maxims from Alcoholics Anonymous states, "When you pray for potatoes, reach for your hoe."

We next turn our attention to beliefs that are vital to triumph. You will explore how they are formed and developed. Most importantly, you will learn to create stories or explanations that will help you to overcome huge obstacles against great odds, such as living under the influence of serious mental illness, or some other serious traumas and addictions. In the process, you will learn further how you can form new neural networks and expand the neural circuitry that you already possess. This uplifting possibility can apply to both the primary and the secondary sufferer alike.

CHAPTER 3

The Sufferers

Anxiety, depression, and even terror permeate the family home.

—ɯ—

Just as in every heroic epic, there is always a group of characters that appear in the story of the family that is under the spell or influence of mental illness. Regardless of the character, however, everyone usually suffers under the effects of mental illness. There are two central characters in the family: the primary sufferer and the secondary sufferer.

The primary sufferer is often called "the identified patient." While the primary sufferer is the one who is inflicted with the overt, distressing, and debilitating symptoms of the illness, secondary sufferers are the family members, loved ones, friends, and associates who are affected by the behaviors of the person with mental illness. Each has his or her unique role, although sometimes it can be hard to distinguish who is who in terms of pain and suffering.

The Cast

Together, primary and secondary sufferers *are* the family. As the recipients of the various symptoms of the illness and its consequences, both primary and secondary sufferers directly experience stress, trauma, and loss. All of those involved also experience trauma indirectly. Secondary sufferers watch their loved ones undergo stress, trauma, and loss. Primary sufferers, in turn, can see the trauma of their loved ones as they suffer the effects of the illness.

There is little question that the primary sufferer usually carries the main weight of the injury. Secondary sufferers, however, have their own unique pain and suffering. At the core of their experience is powerful grief as well as the burden that comes from witnessing and enduring the daily problems, challenges, and assaults that are typically associated with mental illness.[89, 90] Secondary sufferers are inflicted with the fallout of pain and suffering, in addition to the attempts of the primary sufferer either to involve them in some of their disordered behaviors or exclude them from others.

For example, secondary sufferers may be asked to give money, provide shelter, become part of a loved one's delusional system, or even bullied and coerced into cooperating in the compulsions of a loved one. When family members do not comply, the primary sufferer can become hurt and depressed as well as upset and hostile. Not infrequently, secondary sufferers become the targets of their loved one's behavior and are victimized by the symptomatic behaviors of their relative.

Negative Spells and Deep Trances

Often, when one member of a family has a mental illness, it is as if the whole family is cast into a very deep, powerful, and negative spell or trance, complete with all the alterations in perception shown by anyone who is in the midst of any spellbound, hypnotic, or altered state experience. The word "trance" sometimes evokes the enigmatic, even the mystical. Most of us seem to have an intuitive grasp of what a trance is. I have found that families can relate easily to the notion of a trance, because their loved ones frequently seem so far away and dazed or detached from their physical surroundings. Understanding what a trance is, therefore, can be very empowering to all members of the family.

Trance is a natural response to any event that captures and focuses our attention.[37, 149] We are in one trance state or anther much more than we realize. We don't recognize that we are entering and exiting trance states all day, every day. Indeed, life can be seen as a process of entering and exiting a wide variety of trances. Whenever we are swept up by strong emotion, we are in a naturally occurring trance state. In such highly fixed states of awareness and absorption, there is both increased attention to certain events and a corresponding inattention to others. Under the deepest effects of such a spell, called a somnambulistic state, we have no awareness of being entranced. [38]

Because traumatic events serve as powerful activators of our capacity for trance,[33] trauma can cast a spell over everyone in its shadow. The dialectic of trauma, or its rules of logic, reveals itself in complicated, contradictory, and uncanny altered states of consciousness. These altered states can result in elusive, dramatic, and often strange problems. Typically, people don't even realize that they are under trauma's spell; yet, they show all the classic responses of a trance, such as age regression, time distortion, amnesia, anesthesia, dissociation, and even hallucinations. In response to trauma, the mind develops extraordinary capacities that clearly resemble those of trance states.

For example, when hypnotized, one of many types of trance states, a person can see things that aren't there. This is called a positive hallucination. On the other hand, a negative hallucination occurs when the person doesn't see something that is present. Everyday examples include the person who is experiencing love when there is none (a positive hallucination), or the person who is not experiencing love when it is present (a negative hallucination, which is akin to denial).

A person can suddenly feel small and powerless when in an "age regressed" trance. I remember when I used to visit my parents many years after I had moved away from home. I would walk down the corridor to their apartment. It seemed that with each step, I got younger and smaller and the adult part of me receded into the background with each stride. Another normal trance phenomenon is the ability to remember some things vividly while simultaneously ignoring others. Still another is the ability to dissociate, or disconnect from others or a situation.

All of these trance phenomena are distinguishable from the psychotic experiences of the seriously mentally ill by their degree of distortion and severity. In a trance, the ordinary relationships between mind and body, reality and fantasy, fact and misperception may be disrupted, creating altered states of consciousness that can foster an array of problems *or* opportunities, but they generally lack the bizarreness of the symptoms of psychosis.

All trance states vary in duration. Some are short, lasting seconds, and others develop over a lifetime, like loss of self. They can also vary in intensity. Some are so strong, like rage, that they seem almost hallucinatory in their hold. When under their spell, little else can exist and no other understanding or possibility is present. Depending on their intensity and duration, some trances are relatively easy to exit, while others are very difficult.

Understanding behaviors as trance states can be empowering for many families. A common adage reminds us that the beginning of wisdom is to give the correct names to our experiences, thoughts, and feelings.

Family members under the influence of serious mental illness are engulfed and overwhelmed by horrific experience. One family member described her experience as "feeling like I am being pulled into the blades of a giant propeller." When describing the behaviors of a loved one, another said that it is "like an octopus with huge tentacles sucking me in."

Ironically, the core and heart of the experience of living under the influence of mental illness, or any chronic illness, can be surprisingly similar for the primary sufferer and the secondary sufferer. Some of the words that I have heard used *by both* the primary and secondary sufferers to describe their experience include: *frightening, terrifying, threatening, confusing, exhausting,* and *demoralizing.*

I have also heard how grief-stricken, heartbroken, confined, consumed, isolated, belittled, mocked, beaten up, guilty, joyless, misunderstood, and lonely they *both* feel. Home life is described more as a war zone than as a place to replenish and go forth again with strength. As a family member once asked me, "How can you separate the hurting person from the hurting family?" Both the primary and the secondary sufferer, therefore, experience many of the same feelings. They do, however, have very different capacities to deal with them and can live in very different worlds.

Clearly, mental illness can weave a web of doubt, confusion, and chaos around *everyone* in the family. Neither by conscious design nor intention, the disturbing and at times bizarre behaviors of the primary sufferer can weave a spell of trauma and grief in the family. The primary sufferer can further traumatize loved ones through control, intimidation, and fear. Anxiety, depression, and even terror can permeate the family home. Addiction, instability, separation, divorce, and desertion are frequent outcomes. Domestic violence, elder, parental, child, sibling, or spousal abuse can also occur. As one family member stated: "This is no home. This is a place to run away from!" Another said: "I feel like I'm being swallowed up by how much this hurts; I'm drowning!"

The effects of trauma on the secondary sufferer are documented in studies of traumatized hostages, as well as in studies of the spouses of combat veterans, police officers, firefighters, and other emergency personnel.[40] These studies reveal the impact upon the loved ones through a host of symptoms and additional ills that can be incurred. As trauma specialist Dr. Don Catherall writes: "The effects of traumatization are easily passed on from parent to child, as well as from child to parent, from spouse to spouse, or even from friend to friend. An entire family can be affected by one member's traumatization."[20]

CHAPTER *4*

The Family

There is a great and often hidden treasure in the family.

—⚏—

The family unit has been in a rapid and accelerated process of change, especially during the last four or five decades.[53] No less is true for the family that lives under the spell of mental illness, because significant numbers of adults suffering from mental illnesses depend on their family members for support. Such support may be emotional, financial, residential, or social, and may include a variety of activities to assist in providing care for, and enhancing the welfare of, the ill family member. This swift growth in family involvement was an unintentional consequence of what has become known as the "deinstitutionalization" movement of the 1960s, when large numbers of sufferers with mental illnesses were released from state institutions into the community.

The Burden of Care

The failure of the mental health system to provide the promised adequate community and family services has forced family members to tackle the burden of caring for loved ones. The lack of community service has impelled family members to adopt more responsibility for their loved ones. Family members did not choose to undertake this tremendous responsibility, nor were they equipped with the knowledge essential to accomplish such a difficult task. As mentioned before, estimates suggest that as many as 100 million family members have been placed in the position of potential providers of care and support. Typically, they are overwhelmed and undersupported.

Despite these vast numbers of sufferers, the response of the mainstream mental health community to the plight of family members historically has been one of blame, neglect, and exclusion. This trend has continued. As surveys show, significant numbers of family members express dissatisfaction with the mental health system's inattention and insensitivity to their special needs.[68, 90]

The neglect of family members by the mental health system has been the impetus for grassroots organizations that have formed outside the traditional sources of help. Examples include NAMI, which was founded in 1979, as well as other self-help programs and organizations, including AA and Al-Anon, which is an organization for the family and friends of those suffering from the disease of alcoholism. All of these programs have flourished apart from the professional community.

The plight of the family, as well as its potential to become an agent for triumph, has received insufficient attention. This situation is changing as more mental health professionals recognize the family's influences on mental illness. The interested reader is referred to the work of the following pioneers: Diane Marsh[89, 90] for the study of serious mental illness in general; E. Torrey Fuller[134] for the study of schizophrenia; Michael Goldstein and David Miklowitz[94, 95] for the study of bipolar disorder; Demitri and

Janice Papolos[104] for the study of bipolar behavior and depression; Barbara Van Noppen[137] and Marlene Cooper for the study of OCD. All have heralded the impact of mental illness on the family and loved ones.

We have learned, for example, that negative reactions, particularly criticism, hostility, or overinvolvement and intrusion by family members, can exacerbate or worsen the mental illness and create a greater risk for recurrences of the disorder. Called "expressed emotions" in the mental illness literature, these aversive behaviors add to an already stressful family atmosphere.[68, 89, 90] This is documented in schizophrenia, bipolar disorder, major depression, and OCD. In addition, studies consistently show that patients with the best prognosis are those supported by family members who take an active role in their loved one's treatment.[82] In fact, nontreated families are a risk factor in the relapse (and other types of trouble) of their loved one, while the treated family is a positive prognostic and preventative factor.

The family is the major context in which mental illness waxes and wanes. Because it often provides the arena in which the illness unfolds, the family also offers the possibility of becoming an extraordinary healing environment. We human beings, as social animals who are group oriented, congregate around and depend upon the family. Our family may be the most important group to which we will ever belong. An Irish proverb reminds us, "It is in the shelter of each other that the people live."

There is a great and often hidden treasure of love, support, strength, commitment, caring, and wisdom in the family. One of the most neglected resources, families may also prove to be one of the most powerful assets in treatment. There are beneficial results for the mentally ill family member when this resource is harnessed, and the positive effects on the entire family are substantial. Rather than falling into a morass of shame and secrecy by continuing to deny the family predicament or the pervasive influence of mental illness, it is time to bring the potent force of the family to the forefront and utilize its inherent strength.

To discover how what once has been a shameful secret can now become the catalyst for unlocking the doors to triumph in the family, it will be helpful to understand the concept of "family systems." Before we can fully appreciate this important concept, however, it will be useful to look at just how powerful the family can be.

CHAPTER 5

The Power of Us

"Being family" seems to provide protection
from many of life's worst ills.

—⚏—

Neglecting the family may be one of the most limiting factors in dealing with mental illness. A definition of family that I have heard again and again by family members who live under the influence of mental illness is a form of the following: "We are a group of related people, all of whom suffer alone." You do not have to suffer alone anymore. Triumph is within reach of the vast majority of sufferers.

Clinical research and common sense both attest to the well-established scientific finding that a strong and informed family may be the best resource a sufferer can have.[127] It is clearly documented that those with the disease of alcoholism, for example, have a better prognosis when the family is involved in the recovery process. Similarly, the prognosis for individuals who have a serious mental illness improves when family members are provided with the information and support they need. (It is important to note that the same finding occurs with virtually every other illness or negative life condition.)

Proof That Family Matters

Summarizing state-of-the-art reviews of research assessing the effectiveness of family therapy, Professor Jay Lebow at Northwestern University writes: "A resounding body of research now points to the vastly superior outcomes achieved by families-based therapies for treating adult schizophrenia and bipolar disorder when compared with treatment with other psychotherapies or with psychopharmacology alone."[82]

Studies also show that the healthiest and hardiest among us are those who are embedded in a structure in which members are able to stay together throughout their lives, call upon one another, remember one another, gather at emergencies, celebrate life's joys, and console each other about life's miseries. "Being family" seems to provide protection from many of life's worst ills. It is not independence that is the ultimate measure of health, as has been recently thought. Rather, it is interdependence, or dependence coupled with personal responsibility and accountability, that is the highest level of functioning. Dr. Stephen Covey, an international authority on the family, writes: "Dependent people need others to get what they want. Independent people can get what they want through their own efforts. Interdependent people combine their own efforts with the efforts of others to achieve their greatest success."[24]

Two Different Families, or Are They?

To illustrate the "power of us" principle, consider the following two scenarios: in the first, John is an intelligent twenty-one-year-old man who was born into a family we shall call the Unabels, a pseudonym to protect the real family upon which this example is based. He has just been diagnosed with schizophrenia (or bipolar disorder, or major depression, or OCD; the diagnosis is not the key variable because the story is the same). Because of the bizarre behaviors he has exhibited since he stopped taking his medication, the police have placed John in a California hospital for this illness.

The hospital treatment team is meeting to consider the course of his stay as well as his prognosis. Right now, John is very suspicious, confused, and disoriented. He nervously and angrily refuses to give the hospital permission to contact his family. No one in the family knows where John has gone. He has been missing before, so little attention is given to his absence now. The rules of confidentiality, designed to protect John, prevent the hospital from communicating with or even informing his family, so there is no way for them to be notified that he has been involuntarily placed in a hospital.

The Unabels—John's mother and father, as well as a younger brother and sister—are an unhappy family who have difficulty expressing the love or commitment they feel toward each other. Because of a family history of alcoholism, the family environment is often inconsistent, arbitrary, unpredictable, and chaotic. At times, it is terror-filled and physically dangerous, because Mr. Unabel will strike his wife or one of the children. Family members do not communicate directly or openly with each other, and there is a strong tendency to blame each other for their misfortunes. Mrs. Unabel believes she is being punished for her sins because she has been angry with God. Life is seen as a series of crushing experiences that must be endured by everyone in the family.

As a result, the Unabels have little contact with each other or anyone outside the family. They tend to act as separate individuals, rarely asking or expecting anything from one another. Dependence is a four-letter word in this family, and everyone lives in his or her own private world. Currently the family has limited financial resources as well, because Mr. Unabel can't keep a job. While John's grandmother also suffered from "a strange and peculiar condition," the current generation of the Unabel family has incurred its share of chronic illnesses and poor health—actually more than its share. In short, this family is a clinician's nightmare—unmotivated, uninvolved, and impoverished.

Consider the second life situation. Joe is an intelligent twenty-one-year-old man born into a family we shall call the Abels. He also has been diagnosed with schizophrenia (or bipolar disorder, or major depression, or OCD). Joe's bizarre behavior since he stopped taking his medication is a clear signal to his parents that he needs help. They respond by placing him in a hospital setting that they believe offers the most support for him. The treatment team is meeting to consider the course of his stay as well as his prognosis. Right now, Joe is very suspicious, confused, and disoriented, but he has waived his right to confidentiality. He relies on his family and wants them involved in his life. Consequently, the hospital can speak with his family.

The Abels—Joe's mother and father, as well as older brother and younger sister—have a functional family system. They act as if they "belong to each other," as one family member said, and they know that each member profoundly affects the whole family and the whole family profoundly affects each member. They are openly affectionate, and enjoy showing their commitment and respect for each other. They communicate directly, without using other family members to communicate for them. They trust each other, confronting their problems openly and straightforwardly. They don't have a large extended family, but they have a group of friends who are there when they need them. They attend religious services regularly and are united in their belief in either a "higher power" or some force beyond them (which no member seems able to define). Some members of the family call this God; one of the children calls it "the Force." Although the family members each describe this presence in different ways, they have learned to be united in their faith and belief that this force, while a harsh teacher at times, is essentially benevolent.

The Abel family has learned to be optimistic, viewing life as a series of challenges to be met, rather than tragedies to survive. The family members are action-oriented, nonblaming, and accountable. More than intelligent, they are open and curious and all have a strong desire to learn. They view disease, death, and suffering as "taxes for the gift of life." While Joe's grandmother also suffered from "a strange and peculiar condition," the current generation of the family has incurred its share of chronic illnesses and poor health—actually more than its share. But there is no active alcoholism or other drug abuse, and their respectful nature toward each other precludes violence and abuse as coping strategies.

Given roughly similar symptoms, diagnoses, ages, genders, and intellectual capacities, which person, John or Joe, will have the more favorable life? If you had to choose, which life would you choose to live? Obviously, for both John and Joe, the course of treatment, the prognosis, and how each will fare throughout his life depends on much more than the diagnosis. How often is the family overlooked as a source of help in the overall treatment and prognosis? An old maxim states: Take a sick person, place him or her in a healthy environment and the person will get better. On the other hand, take a well person, place him or her in a sick environment and the person will get sick.

Consider what would happen to the Unabels under the following circumstances:

- If both John and the Unabels were included in their son's care.

- If the Unabels could find a professional who greeted them respectfully, understanding their needs without judging them.

- If this professional were able to involve the family in the healing process.

- If the Unabels joined a psychoeducational group (such as NAMI, a national mental health advocacy organization) to understand their son's illness.

- If the Unabels acquired the information, skills, and support they needed for their long trek through life.

- If the Unabel family decided it would benefit them *and* their son if they were to participate in family therapy.

- If Mr. Unabel's alcoholism was diagnosed and treated.

- If the abuse and despair of the family was addressed.

- If the Unabels could learn communication skills, stress reduction techniques, assertiveness, conflict resolution, problem solving, symptom management, and how to deal with insurance companies and other bureaucracies.

- If the marriage between Mr. and Mrs. Unabel improved.

- If the marriage did improve, what effect would that have upon John.

For sure, something very important would happen to every member of the family. Certainly, each member of the family would gain a greater perspective and understanding, laying the foundation for potential healing. And what might happen to both Joe and to the Abels if they were greeted in a similar way? What would happen if their role in their son's treatment, rehabilitation, and recovery were fully utilized as the vital resource it is instead of being marginalized, minimized, or ignored?

No matter what your experience of family, there is something about being in your family, something about being a part of an "us," that is riveting, that is indelible. I can be a part of you that carries you through life's most trying moment and teaches you the most enduring lessons. The family is the basic building block of our world. It is the most fundamental unit of society, and it forms the very core of the human experience.

Instead of a group of people conspiring to keep the illness secret from a shame-inducing society, instead of a group of people who conspire even among themselves to keep aspects of the illness secret from each other, could the family instead prove to be the key to unlocking the doors to triumph for every member?

- What if the family became more about "us help" than "self-help" and "we-sight" instead of insight?

- What if the focus of the family shifted from "I, me, and mine," to "we, us, and ours"?

- What if there was a shift from dealing with life on an individual basis, the world of the survival of the fittest, to a world based on an invisible connection with everyone and everything on the planet?

- Would this shift make a difference in everyone's life?

- Could the family be the missing key to securing a favorable long-term prognosis, including maximizing the possibility of its loved one's immediate treatment?

With this background, it is now time to turn to the important concept of family systems.

—w—

CHAPTER 6

Family Systems

*Behavior is typically both the cause
and the effect of members' responses.*

—⚒—

The notion of the family as a system—or the "family systems" approach—began to emerge in the 1950s as clinicians and researchers studied the complex situations and conditions under which the family functions. The influence of the family came under careful scrutiny, which led to an explosion of recovery and treatment options, the most important of which is that every family can be viewed as a system.[148]

Briefly, a system can be defined as two or more interrelated parts, and thus a family system is two or more related people. These people do not have to be in ongoing physical contact to affect the lives of each other. When the various parts of a system (family) work well, the system (family) works well. When the parts do not work well together, the system does not work well.

A sports team is another example of a system. When the team members play well with each other, cooperate, and support each other, the team usually wins. While the play of each team member is important, the cohesion of the team is more significant than the play of any single member. Everyone can think of a team of great players who could not win because the "chemistry," or sense of interdependence, was not there. They could not function as a healthy system.

Systems Theory

Approaching the treatment of mental illness from a family systems perspective involves a number of underlying assumptions. A vital premise is that the whole of the family is greater than the sum of its parts. When the parts of the system do not work well, the system fails. Not only is the whole of the family greater than the sum of its individual members, every member mutually affects the other as well as the whole. Thus, there is a reciprocal nature between the parts and the whole. In terms of the family, this means that you cannot separate the hurting person from the hurting family. As one family member so compellingly said to me, "This isn't something that is happening just to my son; it's happening to me, too!"

Another key assumption in family systems theory is that causation is circular rather than linear, that behavior is typically *both* the cause *and* the effect of members' responses.[148] This suggests that the context in which a given behavior occurs is often more important than the actual behavior. In other words, any given behavior cannot be understood only by understanding the event(s) that precede or follow it. For example, John withdraws from Mary because she yelled at him, but Mary yelled at John because he didn't listen to something that was very important to her. But he didn't listen because Mary wasn't giving him the love he wanted. Systems theory states that John's yelling at Mary is a "recursive loop"; in other words, you have to understand the whole chain of communications to understand either person. No one person is right; each person shares the responsibility for the communication.

Unless there is blatantly harmful behavior, such as physical violence or sexual abuse, there is generally no "right" or "wrong" way to respond, or to feel, from a family systems perspective because every act is influenced by every other act. Instead of a focus on blame, the focal point is on behaviors that yield (or do not yield) positive results. By removing accusations and normalizing the circumstances and the behaviors, family members are not labeled and their actions are not described in pejorative or derogatory terms when viewed from a systems perspective.

Because mental illness affects the family on the systemic level, rules and patterns can be discovered that can dictate the behaviors of every family member. For example, all families have rules about the expression of emotion, which are typically implicit and unspoken.[10, 61, 140] Family rules can govern how, when, where, by whom, and even which emotions are permitted to be expressed or suppressed. In one family, the mother may cry and express the sadness, while the father may explode with hostility and express the anger. The daughter may become frightened and express fear and anxiety, while the son may feel abandoned and express the depression. On an individual level, their reactions appear very different, but on a systemic level each person is expressing his or her feelings in accord with the family's rules regarding gender and age.

Systems theory posits that all behaviors are influenced, and perhaps even maintained, by the larger system in which they occur. And given that the family is the primary situation in which mental illness occurs, the possibilities for healing expand radically when viewed from this perspective. We shall continue to see that one-dimensional solutions rarely are effective in changing multidimensional problems.

A systemic or interpersonal view of mental illness offers greater potential to help sufferers and their loved ones by acknowledging that there are many paths in mental illness. These paths go beyond biology to consider family and broader social factors. This perspective can enlarge the range of considerations about the nature of mental illness, its full impact, and its treatment. As with any systems approach, the individual family member's experience is part of a network of interrelated components, each component affecting all of the others. As a result, no single component can be isolated and studied realistically without also considering its interplay with the others.

A Bigger System

It is also important to recognize that the family system cannot be understood apart from the larger society. Society defines mental illness and provides diagnostic labels. It establishes social priorities and policies, determines the focus and nature of mental health services, and creates the climate in which families live. Mental illnesses can never be separated from their social system, or social context, as they are dependent on social standards and cultural values.[76]

Like every institution in society, the family reflects broad cultural values and is deeply shaped by them. For better and for worse, as a society we have decided that when a person is troubled and can no longer manage life, it is primarily the responsibility of family members to struggle with their loved one's problem. We have fostered an attitude that privatizes human problems by expecting families to solve them, largely out of public view.

The segregation and placement of care within the family are not a cultural accident. It is the structural analog of America's political decision not to bear responsibility for all the groups and individuals in need of care. The cultural soil in which families grow does not favor their development. Families have been ignored and left without knowledge of the tools needed to solve the increasingly difficult problems of their individual members. In applying a version of rugged individualism to the family, society has further isolated its oldest and perhaps most vital institution, one whose health requires nourishment through public, social, and legislative support.

In addition, as noted earlier, the events of the September 11th terrorist attacks have created a shift in governmental priorities, further eroding the already tenuous support for families living under the spell of mental illness. There are fewer funds for the seriously mentally ill now than before 9/11, and even less financial resources are available for families. Families have been left in the precarious position of needing more help than ever in the midst of fewer and even reduced funding priorities.

Expecting family members to care for each other in a society that shows so little care and regard for the family's plight is a prescription for illness and pathology. The fate of families and the fate of society are intertwined, because we are a nation of families. If family members are to extend compassionate care to each other during times of vulnerability, crisis, and illness, then society itself must help by providing models of care and nourishment. If families are to get the help and care that they need and that they deserve, their fate must be viewed as a national problem and therefore a national priority. It becomes the responsibility of federal and state governments to intervene and to revitalize troubled families. This would produce an enormous positive impact.

Unfortunately, as we have seen, this has not been the case, and families have had to absorb with little aid or support the impact of mental illness.

The Disabel Family

The Disabel family illustrates the vital interaction between the family system and the social system. An elderly couple, Abe and Mary Disabel live on a small pension left over from Mr. Disabel's business. They had lost much of Mr. Disabel's retirement when the NASDAQ crashed. Their thirty-five-year-old son Sam has suffered from schizophrenia since he was twenty and he understandably has had a lot of trouble supporting himself. The county day care program was a godsend to all three of them, because it kept Sam out of the psychiatric hospital on a number of occasions. When the state in which they lived suddenly experienced a multi-billion-dollar budget shortfall, many county mental health services were cut, including the day care program that kept Sam out of the hospital. Since they could no longer depend on day care for Sam, their lives have not been the same.

Beyond Family Systems

Understanding the family as a system, both in its narrow and broadest sense, serves both the field of mental health in general and the family of those under the influence of all illness, addiction, and trauma in particular. Providing an extremely helpful way to view the impact of events that can go beyond the individual, a systems approach in fact has been a distinguishing feature of family therapy. It stresses the value of seeing the individual as a product of his or her whole family, as well as the totality of the person's generations, emphasizing that the family is the basic and fundamental treatment unit.

There is nothing incorrect about the tenets of family systems; they are just incomplete. While the concept of the family as a system is useful for appreciating the influence of illness, addiction, and trauma on the family, the next chapter, which explores the concept of belief systems, may be even more crucial for acquiring the keys to unlock the doors to triumph.

—⟳—

CHAPTER 7

Belief Systems

Beliefs are the lenses through which we view our world . . .
the bedrock from which each of us constructs our lives.

—⚶—

We need to remain aware of how each family member is influenced not only by other family members, but by the larger society that surrounds him or her as well. As useful as it can be, the idea of family systems itself can limit our ability to see clearly. There is an enormous flow of ideas from the larger culture, one that is outside of the family and its system. These prevailing ideas often have an impact on our beliefs systems, an impact we may barely be aware of.

In the 1990s, a number of experts in the field of family therapy began to see beyond the family as a self-contained system. These pioneers portrayed the family as a "crossroads," a juncture often of two genders, partners, and usually two generations, each inhabiting different worlds and speaking bafflingly different languages.[105] Because each word in our language can have vastly different meanings and connotations for each member of the family, communication is complicated.

The contemporary family is, as never before in our history, more than an interrelated system; it is a crossroads—one from which its members go forth and to which they return from different worlds where different languages are spoken, different stories are told, and different parts of themselves are employed. This new focus of family as crossroads as well as systems acknowledges an atmosphere of interdependency, one in which all members of the family are in roles that are mutually supporting, roles that are both multidimensional and multidirectional. What tasks in living and loving could be more comparable to the challenges of our mythical hero or heroine's journey?

Particularly valuable when viewing the family as a crossroads is the presence of an interpreter who is aware of the family as a group of interconnecting parts. The pioneers of this treatment perspective,[34, 46, 105, 142] with its focus on meaning, have shifted from a systems approach to one in which they see family members more as storytellers, spinning yarns to explain and interpret the world. It is the job of the healer, or therapist, to serve as a skilled questioner who brings forth the knowledge and experience that is carried in the stories of the people with whom he or she works. There must also be a clear focus on the meanings, the ideas, and the practices at play by each family member.

The Importance of Story

Beliefs organize our experience and largely, if not entirely, determine *what* we experience and *how* we experience it. Beliefs are the lenses through which we view our world (for no two worlds are ever alike). The bedrock of our behavior, beliefs form the essence of our feelings. They are the blueprints from which each of us constructs our lives. In daily life, the best medium for understanding our own and others' beliefs is through the stories we tell.

Beliefs are embedded in the stories we exchange in our conversations with one another. Therefore, stories may be perhaps the largest carriers of our beliefs. They form and create the containers that hold our lives. They can either be like boxes, confining and limiting our growth and well-being to outdated knowledge, or stories can be the bridges to newer and greater realities.

It is not uncommon for family members under the influence to believe that their plight is more horrific than most others. I remember one compelling moment when Mr. Unabel was cursing his fate. He thought few experienced the pain and suffering that he was forced to endure. This belief was a hindrance to his moving forward. All logical attempts to dissuade him fell on deaf ears. When he seemed especially receptive, I shared the following story: A young man was at the end of his rope. Seeing no way out, he dropped to his knees in prayer. "Lord, I can't go on," he said. "I have too heavy a cross to bear." The Lord replied, "My son, if you can't bear its weight, just place your cross inside this room. Then, open that other door and pick out any cross you wish." The man was filled with relief and said, "Thank you, Lord." Doing as he was told, he entered the other room, and he saw many crosses. Some looked so large that the tops were not even visible. Then, the young man spotted a tiny cross leaning against a far wall. "I'd like that one, Lord," he whispered. The Lord replied, "My son, that is the cross you just brought in."

Recall Mr. Unabel whom we met earlier in Chapter 5, "The Power of Us." This story meant more to him than any of my previous words that were intended to provide a perspective for him to examine his belief that his life was more horrible than most, if not all. He was able to use this particular story to shift a belief that had held him captive for a very long time. For as long as he believed his cross was too much to bear, it was. And, as we now know, the burden of his cross was felt by other members of the family, and became a part of their reality, or cross, too.

The Science of Belief

We can further appreciate the nature and function of belief systems through the science of quantum physics, which exposes the many properties of subatomic particles. One of its major tenets shows that the "reality" of an event is not static.[56, 106] It is made distinct and active by the observer becoming a part of what is observed. In fact, the very act of observation changes the nature of what is observed. In addition, the event can't be separate from the observer's *internal* construction of meaning for that event.

Everyday examples of this principle are common. Have you noticed how often someone who is spewing with anger will find others with whom to be angry, as if anger begets anger? Angry people have an amazing facility to attract people to be angry with. Analogously, loving people seem to attract and experience much love. Have you noticed, too, that when you are worried that people will spill their drinks on your new carpet, most often they will?

Therapists who stand outside of the family system, making "objective" assessments and interventions, sacrifice opportunities to help the family. As contemporary science demonstrates, the therapist is *a part of* the very system undergoing therapy. It is foolish to think that therapists can be separate from it.

Rather than serving as problem solvers, as systems theory asks, therapists can help elicit stories that are personally compelling to the family, stories that connect family members to something of greater significance than the personal self, which is limited and bound by time. The focus of the therapist in a beliefs-based system is to encourage new stories that generate solutions, rather than dwelling upon outdated and limiting stories that perpetuate problems.

The Psychology of Belief

Dr. Jill Freedman and Dr. Gene Combs,[46] contemporary leaders in the field of helping people create powerful stories, assert that therapists who champion triumph think of themselves as working "to help people notice the influence of restrictive cultural stories in their lives and to expand and enrich their own life narrative." As people free themselves from the constraints unwittingly maintained by their old and inhibiting stories (which they typically inherit from their family and the broader culture), they can begin to create transcendent new stories within which they can live out new self-images, new possibilities, and new futures.

Drs. Freedman and Combs go on to state, "We strive to find ways to spread the news of individual triumphs—to circulate individual success stories so that they can keep our culture growing and flowing in satisfying ways."[46] This perspective on triumph, which focuses on creating meaningful narratives or stories, opens the door to a different way for family members to comprehend themselves. This is why we are engrossed in such current real-life stories of Dr. John Nash's triumphs over mental illness, or Christopher Reeve's[114] and Lance Armstrong's[6] many triumphs over physical illness.

The keys to understanding their plight lie in stories filled with wounds that become sacred and journeys that become heroic. Like the tales of old,[11] which convey important messages for transformation and successful living, there are limitless stories awaiting our creation, calling us to a full life, one in which we use our signature strengths in the service of something greater than our personal selves.

This exciting new field of "narrative" therapy, or storytelling,[46, 105, 142,146] has direct relevance to helping all members of families under the influence of mental illness in their journey to triumph. In this healing-edge application of some of the latest psychological theories, which are compatible with both the stories told by mystics of old and the neuroscientists of now, problems can arise if the stories that people invent, or create, to explain what is happening are insufficient in representing their fully lived experiences.

Problems can be narrow and constricted stories that point to few possibilities other than suffering and victimization, which are prominent characteristics of the stories of many families who are not in recovery. We have seen that when adversity strikes, it can weave its insidious spell around all family members, creating stories for each that can be often more horrific than the external events or circumstances themselves. (Why me? Poor me? Damned me! Damned you!) It is very different to look at problems as limited stories, as opposed to true and unalterable situations. Which way offers the most possibilities? Which way can lead to peace and comfort?

Triumph, on the other hand, unfolds through the process of storying or restorying people's lives and experiences in a way leading to powerful inquiries that address life's great questions and dilemmas. (Why not me? Is this another initiation, test, and trial leading me to the person I was meant to be?) The story and stories chosen, or created, can lead either to a life of dysfunctional behavior or triumphant living. Unfortunately, many people today have few powerful stories to guide them.

It is interesting to note that before the modern era, all peoples of the world attempted to answer life's major questions through stories. As Drs. Alan Parry and Robert Doan, leading proponents in the field of narrative therapy, write: "It was the *meaningfulness* of the answers given, not their factual *truthfulness,* that gives them their credibility.[105] The hearers of the story believed that it was true because it was meaningful, rather than it was meaningful because it was true." Recall, if you will, that beliefs are a function of the observer as well as the observed.

Such an interpretation offers the possibilities of creating new avenues for triumph. For example, remember the Academy Award-winning movie *Forrest Gump*? What if Forrest Gump's mother had said to him, "Life is like a bed of snakes" instead of "Life is like a box of chocolates"? Most likely, his outlook on life, others, and even himself would have been quite different. The resulting changes in Forrest's character would have had far-reaching effects.

The Biology of Words

As we have seen earlier, words can actually alter biological functioning, including the DNA within the nucleus of the cell.[88] Let me give you an example. (Please note: THE SENTENCE THAT FOLLOWS IS NOT TRUE.)

Immediately to your right, there is a large tarantula (spider) that is perched, ready to grab hold of your face. It is vicious and dangerous; it will hurt you.

If you believed me, how would you feel? What thoughts would you have? Now, whether there really is a tarantula next to you or not, the point is this: if you believed one was there, you would think, feel, and behave *very* differently than if you believed that there was no tarantula present. Unless your family raised spiders, especially tarantulas, your beliefs and actions would be independent of your family system, and based on your belief systems.

The field of psychoneuroimmunology describes the interactions between the brain, the endocrine system, and the immune system. A person who can experience high purpose with determination—the heart and soul of triumph—will enhance the effectiveness of the immune system, which, in turn, increases the person's overall resistance to illness and injury.[5] Perhaps this is one of the reasons why families living with mental illness who have "small stories" as opposed to "large stories" about their experience (for example, they are being punished as opposed to being called to a higher purpose in life) often develop so many physical symptoms.

The Meaning of Beliefs

In an analogous way, the *meaning* of the beliefs regarding the diagnosis given to family members—whether mental illness, post-traumatic stress disorder, or physical illnesses such as AIDS, cancer, or Chronic Fatigue Immune Dysfunction Syndrome—are keys to unlock the force of triumph. For example, some families believe illness to be a challenge, while other families believe the illness is punishment. Similarly, diagnoses can unite families (everyone in our family has back pain), while other diagnoses are more likely to isolate family members (for example, mental illness, abuse, or AIDS).

An assessment of a family's experience with illness is incomplete without a thorough understanding of each family member's beliefs. Norman Cousins, widely remembered as the man who laughed his way to triumphing over two major physical illnesses,[22] places the importance of our beliefs in perspective. He writes, "What we believe is the most powerful option of all."[21]

Thus, certain beliefs may conserve or maintain an illness; some may make symptoms worse; others alleviate pain and suffering. Summarizing his work on mind-body-spirit connection,

Dr. Cousins (he holds the only honorary degree in medicine from the Yale University School of Medicine) states that our beliefs become our biology. He goes on to say: "The responses of individuals to the world around them, touching off hopes or fears or joys or despairs or expectations in general, has physical reality. . . . It doesn't mean that medical treatment should be supplanted by psychological or emotional approaches, but that the effective reach of the physician can be expanded by awareness of emotional and psychological factors involved in the cause of disease and in a comprehensive strategy of treatment."[21]

The Language of Beliefs

Words link together and become the building blocks of belief systems. Guiding people toward their triumph requires not only an understanding of the family as a system but as a self-created world of words, symbols, and meanings. Triumph (and healing) implies a fundamental reorientation to the nature of reality. This new awareness acknowledges that our lives take place primarily in a world of meanings and are seen through our belief systems (or "schema," to use a psychological term in common usage).

The stories we tell are the stories we believe, and both are infused with the beliefs we have formulated. We develop our identities within our families, professions, and communities through the belief systems that we share (and do not share) with others. We live our lives only slightly aware, and sometimes not at all aware of our beliefs and the effect they have on our own lives and the lives of others.

The irony and the challenge of life is that to survive and move forward in the world, *one needs both a commitment to strong beliefs and the ability to question those beliefs when they are no longer useful.* This occurs as people create meaningful lives for themselves by drawing distinctions and sharing stories. Although writing primarily about physical illness, Drs. Wright, Watson, and Bell, leading authorities in the field of family health, note that "it was the beliefs about a problem that were the problem when families experienced difficulties with an illness."[146]

If a family is under the influence of cancer, for example, it is often the beliefs about the cancer—its origin, the likely outcome for the person and the family, what treatment means—that can create as many difficulties as the physical nature of the cancer itself. When the family believes the cancer is a punishment, or the work of the devil, for example, it has a completely different illness experience than the family who believes that the cancer is a wake-up call, inviting them to a more appreciative consciousness of life. The influence of beliefs is pivotal, profound, and palpable.

That the family creates its world through words and language takes into account the primacy of language in human interactions, providing a solid basis for developing sound principles for effective help. Language is not separate from action; it is a particular form of action. Words and symbols are as vital to human growth and development as are claws and teeth to animals of the jungle.

Recent developments in the field of neurology show that the creation of meaning and the creation of brain cells go hand in hand. A brief insight into the inner workings of the brain will clarify our understanding of the process by which our brain is constantly changing in response to our words and beliefs.

The Neurology of Beliefs

Neuroscience is the science of the nervous system. It helps us to understand the process by which the brain is built and shaped by early experiences, particularly interpersonal experiences. Health professionals and other sources of support that work with families who live under the influence of mental illness can create an interpersonal environment, a milieu that is capable of actually rebuilding brain cells. While this concept may appear revolutionary, Sigmund Freud, the father of modern psychotherapy, suggested it at the end of the nineteenth century. Neuroscientific studies reveal that our brains, far from being locked into predetermined patterns by our DNA, are always changing, constantly producing new circuits and pathways (that is, new ideas and feelings) in response to our experiences and our perceptions, which in turn affect the circuitry of the brain.[25, 125,147]

The brain is continually building and rebuilding, modeling and remodeling itself from birth to death. That the brain can produce new cells in the later years of life is now a generally accepted fact. Everything we learn, every sensation, every human contact we make causes millions of neurons to fire, creating physical interconnections called *neural maps* or *neural networks;* this constantly changing circuitry forms the architecture of all our experiences.

Neurons, the tiny processing units that make up all parts of the nervous system, are organized into neural networks, which can range from just a few neurons (in a simple animal) to trillions of neural interconnections in brains such as our own. There are approximately 12 billion neurons in the brain, each possessing from ten to one hundred thousand synaptic connections, which create an almost inconceivable variety of associations. These neural networks encode and organize our behaviors, continually changing the encoding and organization of our behaviors.

Changes in the brain's structure are a function of the stimuli triggered by our response patterns. As we develop a history of responses, we literally alter the molecular structure of our brains. New pathways and neuronal networks are constantly being formed. This ability to grow fresh neurons (that is, brain cells) provides genuine agility, flexibility, and adaptability in a changing world.

One of the more exciting new developments in neuroscience is the research by neuroscientists Drs. Andrew Newberg and Eugene d'Aquili,[101] who are presenting evidence that we are "hard-wired" to believe in God. They have proposed a biological theory of spirituality, which they believe provides a neurological basis for the human hunger for God. Their theory has propelled Dr. Newberg (Dr. d'Aquili died before the completion of their book, *Why God Won't Go Away*) into a leading figure at the age of thirty-six in the emerging science of neurotheology, which explores the links between spirituality and the brain.

The two researchers used SPECT (single photon emission computed tomography) scans, which are very sophisticated ways to map the workings of the brain, to examine the brains of Tibetan Buddhists while meditating and Franciscan nuns engaged in deep, contemplative prayer. These scans photograph blood flow in the brain, indicating neuronal activity, snapshots of the brain nearing a state of mystical transcendence. The fascinating outcome of their research revealed that at peak moments of prayer and meditation, the flow of blood in the brain was dramatically *reduced*, showing less brain activity in the region that is responsible for drawing the line between the physical self and the rest of existence.[101] When the self, or ego, is pushed aside during meditation, true "reality" is revealed.

Drs. Newberg and d'Aquili believe that reduced activity of the personal, "thinking" brain could produce a range of milder spiritual experiences, such as the awe experienced in watching a sunset. Their research suggests that all of these experiences are rooted in the genetically arranged wiring of the brain, rather than in emotion, or in wishful thinking. Transcendent experiences, they assert, are born in a moment of spiritual connection that is as real to the brain as any perception of "ordinary" physical reality. This suggests that God is a perception generated by the brain, and that we are wired, under the right conditions, to experience the reality of God.

Mystics state that true reality is witnessed only when the self, with its limited awareness or consciousness, is quieted, as during meditation. This theory of neurotheology suggests that the brain experiences two realities. In one reality, awareness reaches the thinking mind through the filter of the self, while in the other, the self is swept aside and awareness becomes spacious, comprehensive, and unified (that is, transcendent). Mystics experience this transcendent state as more "real" than ordinary reality.

Research in neurotheology points to the mysterious nature of life. Albert Einstein wrote: "The fairest thing we can experience is the mysterious. It is the fundamental emotion that stands at the cradle of true science. He who knows it not and can no longer wonder, no longer feel amazement, is as good as dead." Other great scientists, all giants in the field of quantum physics, such as Niels Bohr, Max Planck, and Werner Heisenberg, share Einstein's view.

Psychotherapy and the Brain

What is more, the field of psychotherapy itself is on the verge of an explosive new paradigm: namely, the psychotherapist as neuroscientist. The power of psychotherapy to effect change in the brain is in direct proportion to the psychotherapist's ability to recognize and alter poorly integrated, or inadequately regulated, neural circuitry. According to neuroscientist Dr. Louis Cozolino,[25] who is a professor of psychology at Pepperdine University in California, psychotherapists are clinical neuroscientists who create an individually tailored environment enriched to enhance brain development. "We use a combination of language, empathy, emotions and behavioral experiments to promote neural interaction," he writes.

Psychotherapy (actually, all effective learning) is a means of creating or restoring neural network integration and coordination. Stated differently, neural growth and integration are strengthened and changed by psychotherapy. Psychotherapy can be understood as an enriched environment specifically designed to enhance the growth of neurons and the integration of neural networks by the use of stories that make positive sense of our experiences. Drs. Parry and Doan write: "The therapist uses the power of carefully crafted language to bring a hitherto subjugated story into the forefront of the client's life; this story replaces a story that is not the client's own, but into which she/he has been recruited."[105]

Successful psychotherapy may be helpful because of its very ability to change brain chemistry in a manner that amplifies neural plasticity and flexibility.[147] In the context of an emotionally meaningful relationship, such as psychotherapy, language itself is a key to resculpting and modifying neural networks. You may recall that optimal levels of arousal and stress result in increased production of neurotransmitters and neural growth hormones, which enhance learning and cortical reorganization.

"Therapy evolved because language organizes the brain in some primary, fundamental way," Dr. Cozolino writes. He goes on to state, "What we know of the brain suggests that therapy is successful to the degree to which it builds and integrates neural networks. . . . Therapy is a process of helping clients *rewrite the story of their lives* [italics added] while simultaneously building neural networks and reorganizing neural integration."[25]

Our Beliefs Are Our Story

We will soon discover how other fields of inquiry, such as classical mythology, help us to rewrite powerful stories, stories that change not only our emotional lives but our brains as well.[4, 17] Recent advances in the field of neuroscience demonstrate that the stories we create and recount to ourselves can affect the structure and functioning of the brain. The actual language used in the stories appears to be a key mechanism of this new integration. Behavior, emotion, sensation, and conscious awareness combine to maximize the integration of a wide variety of neural networks in the process of listening to and telling stories. Stories, therefore, serve as powerful tools to bring about neural network integration at a high level.[4, 25, 125, 147]

A clear and compelling story line, accompanied by verbal and nonverbal expressions of emotion, activates and enhances both the left and right hemispheres of the brain as well as facilitates higher- and lower-level brain processing. As vehicles to explain actions and define both the social and private self, stories are emotionally meaningful sequences of facts and consequences linked together that aid in the organization, maintenance, and evaluation of behavior. The healing power inherent in stories has been recognized for centuries.[18]

Neuroscientist Dr. Daniel Siegel[125] writes: "Storytelling is central to every culture, and when you find that kind of universality, you know it's not just social learning but reflects something deep-seated in our genes." He goes on to state, "The neurological subplot of the well-made story involves the integration of the brain's left and right hemispheres. Coherent stories are an integration of the left hemisphere's drive to tell a logical story about events and the right brain's ability to grasp emotionally the mental processes of the people in those events."

In a more earthy tone, author Barry Lopez,[87] in his classic children's story *Crow and Weasel,* writes: "I would like you to remember only this one thing, said Badger. The stories people tell have a way of taking care of them. If stories come to you, care for them. And learn to give them away where they are needed. Sometimes a person needs a story more than food to stay alive. That is why we put these stories in each other's memory. Never forget these obligations."

In a different vein, author Leslie Ann Gravitz, who also happens to be my wife, writes in *Choosing Life,* an adult allegory of life: "You have been given the ability to create beautiful stories, and the most magnificent story could be your own. Humans are the only mammals who have the will and mind to see whatever they want: fairies fluttering their translucent wings, wishing you well through your moments, dropping purple rose petals along our path; mermaids swimming with you below the turbulent waters to the Kingdom of Neptune, and returning with you upward, guiding you to the cool breezes of the sea. I hear some voices that object that this is child's stuff, and they are right. Child's play is what lightens the human spirit and adds mirth to the human drama."[66]

CHAPTER *8*

The Impact on the Family

*Family funds and emotional resources can be exhausted
in efforts to provide care for an ill member.*

—⁂—

The family is the major shock absorber between the individual and the rest of world. As the first line of defense, it may be the only place where any of us are irreplaceable. A well-functioning family is the base from which we can go forth renewed, ready to face the world, and to which we can return for rest and nourishment. When this vessel of stability and safety is weakened by the stress of illness or shattered by the trauma of illness, each member can suffer. As you shall discover, the impact of the illness may be devastating in the early stages, manageable in the middle stages, and positively transformational for everyone in the latter stages of healing.

Trauma in the Family

The family, like any system, becomes altered in reaction to the traumatization of any member. In the resulting system, the world is no longer as benevolent, as kind, as just, or as controllable. Life often lacks purpose and meaning. Nothing is ever the same, and no one is as safe as he or she once was. As one family exclaimed: "Our world has been turned upside down. We have become hostages to our son's fits and moods. We are captives. We are afraid—no, terrorized—by his actions."

As a systemic illness, mental illness can severely distort the contours of the family structure. [9, 31, 61, 68, 76, 79, 89, 91, 95, 99, 118, 103, 134, 135] It often results in members taking on dysfunctional roles, such as the overresponsible family member, the hero, the scapegoat, or the placating family member. It can also foster dysfunctional rules. For example, "Don't make waves." "Don't bring anyone home." "There is nothing wrong here, and don't you dare tell anybody that there is anything wrong."

Nearly all primary sufferers will involve their parents, spouse, children, or siblings in their illness, which is often itself a traumatic situation for the secondary sufferer. One child who had OCD would cry hysterically until each member of the family washed carefully before coming into the house. An adolescent teenager who was hospitalized for delusions of persecution would threaten his younger sister if she didn't screen all of his phone calls. Family funds and emotional resources can be exhausted in efforts to provide care for an ill member.

Trauma and the Family Environment

The mental illness can soon dominate the family environment. Every event and every family member's life can begin to revolve around the primary sufferer and the illness. Minor decisions, such as what to eat and where, as well as major issues, such as child rearing and choosing a career, may become funneled through the disorder, as the illness becomes the defining event in the family's life. Many times I have heard family members say, "It is as if the family has been put into a negative spell by the illness and everyone is under its control."

The presence of mental illness typically produces a particular family atmosphere, or culture, which is a complex interaction among the three following variables: first, the type, severity, and nature of the illness; second, the individual member's developmental level and the specific assets and liabilities he or she possesses; and third, the response of others, especially members of the family and the broader culture. The magazine *Psychology Today* published an article[58] that I had written, "Binds That Tie—and Heal: How Families Cope with Mental Illness," in which I used the following themes in describing the family environment:

1. **Impending stress and frequent trauma.** A consistent research finding is family disturbance, disruption, and tension. Family life is typically chaotic, unpredictable, and rife with misunderstandings. Relatively inconsequential events are often cast in life-and-death terms; each day is crisis-oriented; members are on "red alert," constantly walking on eggshells. There is unrelenting uncertainty. Thoughts of the future are generally filled with dread, doubt, and fear, while memories of the past are marred by regret and guilt. Trauma for the family invariably coexists with mental illness. The family system is typically riddled with conflict and indirect communications, as family members disagree and argue among themselves regarding what should and should not be done about events that cause tension. "There's just no peace," one family member said, describing her family life.

2. **Unrelenting sadness and ever-present loss.** A partial list of losses for families under the influence of mental illness reveals the depth and breadth of their injury. There is loss

of relationship and relationship potential; there is loss of peace and quiet; there is loss of emotional security; there is loss of financial security; there is loss of privacy; there is loss of an ordinary life and a sense of normalcy; there is loss of control; there is loss of dignity; there is loss of freedom; there is loss of opportunity; there is loss of healing memories (there may be no promotions, graduations, grandchildren); and eventually, there is the greatest loss of all, the loss of self, or spiritual bankruptcy, as it has sometimes been called. Many family members compare their plight to the biblical character of Job, whose faith was tested by a constant onslaught of adversities.

3. **Chronic sorrow and ongoing grief.** At the heart of the family experience is a powerful and prolonged grieving process that stems from the ongoing traumas and losses. Grief can show itself in ways other than sadness and depression. It can appear as anger, irritability, withdrawal, passivity, loss of motivation, and despair, as well as sleep deprivation, fatigue, and many psychosomatic disorders such as headaches, abdominal distress, back pain, or sore muscles. The family's grief is most commonly "disenfranchised," or unaccepted by others. Unlike the grief that follows a death or a similar tragedy that is socially sanctioned, the grief of family members under the influence of mental illness is not supported by society. There are few, if any, rituals that allow family members the permission to experience and to work through their grief; consequently, the grief seems endless. One of my clients described the grief as "a funeral that never ends and that nobody even cares about." Grief's reality is a life forever changed.

4. **Widespread guilt.** Most individuals in the family feel bad about something. Primary sufferers often see and hear the pain and suffering they—or more accurately the illness—are causing. These people are mentally ill;

they are not unintelligent. Family members and loved ones, too, feel guilt, for they are constantly wondering whether something they are doing, or not doing, is causing their loved one such torment. The father of a schizophrenic boy aptly summed this up when he said, "I just can never do enough!" An overwhelming burden can be created by not knowing how to communicate directly and lovingly in ways that could reduce the impact of the illness. Pain occurs, which is unavoidable; on the other hand, suffering, or being caught in the drama of the illness, mounts, which is avoidable when the family is trained.

5. **Constant fatigue and persistent exhaustion.** The family under the influence of severe mental illness gets little rest. Members can be on call twenty-four hours a day, seven days a week, with little or no relief in sight. There are few breaks, and even fewer vacations. The persistent stress can leave all family members physically and emotionally exhausted, bringing out the worst in everyone. As Vince Lombardi, the legendary football coach of the championship Green Bay Packers, wryly commented, "Fatigue makes cowards of us all." Family members lack the strength needed in order to deal with the illness in a triumphant manner. A far too common consequence is a dampened immune system. The health of family members suffers, followed by a host of physical and emotional ills. Often, family members may be blind to the effects of the illness on them, as they are unaware of being so involved in their loved one's problems. As one family member so aptly asked: "Affect me? How does my daughter's illness affect me? She's the one who is suffering!" Another stated simply, "My heart is worn out!"

Families under the influence of mental illness share at least one and often all five of these characteristics as core ingredients of their painful family culture. These five negative recurring themes will occur in virtually every family that is under the influence of illness (whether physical or mental), addiction, or trauma. Some family members will experience these various conditions more often than others will, and they may also feel them in differing degrees of intensity.

CHAPTER 9

The Impact on
Individual Family Members

*Certain themes are likely to be more consistently associated
with certain family roles.*

—⁓—

In any discussion of the impact of mental illness on the family, it is important to note that the different members of the family—the parents, spouses, siblings, offspring, and grandparents, as well as friends and associates—tend to experience the mental illness of a loved one in different ways. While recognizing that both the shared and the unique concerns of the various family members can only be described broadly, certain themes are likely to be more consistently associated with certain family roles. Rex Dickens,[30] a pioneer on the impact of mental illness in the family, summarizes the impact upon each family member in the following ways:

Parents

Dickens calls the parents "anguished souls." Grief and loss are the focus of the parental experience. Bereavement is especially intense when a child is afflicted, because the child is a treasury of love, hope, aspirations, even immortality for the family. More symbolic than real, such as in death, the loss for parents is the potential of a meaningful and productive life for, and with, their child. Their wound most often comes after they have had opportunities to mature, develop, and acquire adult coping skills as well as normal defenses. In many cases parents will have someone else—their spouse—with whom to share the pain and the burden of the child's illness.

Often, however, there is major conflict and outright fighting between parents, even regarding minor decisions affecting their child. There is also social role transformation. Instead of pride and satisfaction in producing competent children, parents often feel shame, facing ostracism from their own family as well as from the larger society. They frequently feel devastated by their inability to love their children into a return to health, or to protect them from the ravages of the illness. Parents also can experience profound guilt, and emotional desolation can ensue with the prospect of a lifelong responsibility.

The experiences of parents have been studied more than that of any other family member. They are most likely to serve as the primary caregivers, and have the most contact with health care providers. Importantly, the emotional health of the children in a family is significantly affected by the emotional relationship between the parents. When the couple's relationship is warm and supportive, children are more likely to feel safer, be healthier, and appear to be happier.

Spouses

Spouses, the husbands and wives or other life companions, are often "engulfed souls." They are also "alone" and "lonely" as well as "overwhelmed" souls. The marital couple is the basic building block of the family and the basic unit of reproduction, as well as the core of intimacy and love. The spouses typically define the stability of the family; yet, their experiences are less well documented than the experiences of the parents. Spouses are more likely to be ignored and excluded by the health system, and typically face crushing responsibilities compounded by a loss of intimacy. It is through intimacy that we are most able to be ourselves: when it is lacking, the partner(s) may suffer a profound loss of comfort, relaxation, and the ability to deal successfully with stressful situations.

Spouses have to deal not only with their own loss and grief, but must learn also to manage the illness of their partner, meet the needs of the children, and continue to work and fulfill the household responsibilities. As the sole adult resource for the family, they frequently are responsible for everything and everyone. Sometimes described as the "ultimate acrobats" who struggle to maintain their high-wire balancing act, spouses fear that if they lose their balance, the whole family will fall with them. However, like parents, they have usually had more time to develop their personalities and coping skills and have more resources than siblings or offspring. Regardless, they are vulnerable to drowning in the sea of chaos that becomes their life: the daily, ongoing experience of loss of a mate, loss of true intimacy, and loss of equality.

Marital discord, often compounded by intense sexual difficulties, can plague spouses when mental illness is present. Consequently, couples under the influence have divorce rates that are six to nine times higher than for the general population. I have seen that the most favorable variable for a successful marital experience lies in the ability and willingness of the ill member to be accountable to his or her illness, spouse, and children, if present. As the wife of a man who suffered from bipolar disorder said, "When my husband starts getting irritable and restless, I know he needs to increase his meds. He used to argue with me when I told him, but now he has learned to trust my judgment, and that has made all the difference in our relationship." Chemical addiction, like alcoholism, which as we have seen is very common, and/or violence virtually ensures an unfavorable marital outcome.

Siblings

Siblings are "frozen souls." Their needs are often ignored and minimized by the family and the mental health system. The "plight of the healthy child" may be the one least validated and acknowledged in the family and the world at large. When the siblings are "the healthy ones," they often receive little attention, easily becoming lost in the shuffle, and find that they must grow up with little support. Healthy siblings often experience a triple loss—their mother, their father, and their brother or sister. Their age at the onset of the mental illness is critical. The younger the sibling, the more vulnerable he or she is. As children, typically they are unable to grieve. Even as adults, they can find themselves in a morass of grief, which is usually unacknowledged. Often thrust into the role of caregivers when young, they may, in later years, avoid the same sibling that they were called upon to care for as children.

True innocent bystanders, siblings are the family members other than parents most prone to experience guilt. Because they are not mentally ill, they are inclined to develop "survivor's guilt." Typically embarrassed in front of their peers, withdrawing and suffering low self-esteem, they often unconsciously assume positions of extreme responsibility in order to compensate for the illness of their sibling.

Siblings who are healthy need to be repeatedly told that they did not cause the illness, and that it is not contagious. In grade school, they need to know how to explain the illness to themselves as well as to others. As teenagers, they need to know their parents' plan for their brother or sister, as they often get the message or assume that they will have to forsake their own future for their ill sibling. As adults, they may often have difficulty in feeling trust and intimacy, and may experience a fear of rejection and abandonment, finding it difficult to commit to long-term relationships. They have a fear of becoming ill themselves, and this fear of mental illness can stalk them through adulthood, in addition to their concerns about transmitting the illness to potential offspring.

Children

The offspring, the children of the mentally ill, are "hallowed souls." As one young person said, "To be a child with a mentally ill parent is like having my identity tethered to a cyclone." The dance of development is for the child a dance with an absent or impaired partner. Because children experience the trauma and loss at the youngest age of any family member, they are the most vulnerable to injury and may suffer the most profound consequences of all family members; the younger the child, of course, the more shattering the effects of the experience. Survivors too young to integrate the trauma, they can face an adulthood in which they are, all too naturally, psychically numbed and disconnected from life.

Often, too, the children eventually inherit the job of raising their ill parent or parents. Through a process called "parentification," they are required to mature too quickly, losing their childhood in exchange for caring for their ill parent. The roles they adopt in order to compensate for the trauma of the illness may last a lifetime. They can feel betrayed by both parents: by the ill parent for abandoning them and causing them despair and by the nonill parent for not safekeeping their lives as children. As Dickens notes, children may experience a hole in their soul. In their consequent loss of self, they may feel bewildered, suffering serious self-image problems and experiencing low self-worth.

More importantly, neuroscience tells us that the early interpersonal environment may shape neural networks in the child's brain, establishing the biochemical set points for the brain circuitry dedicated to memory, emotion, and attachment. It is within the context of these parent-child relationships that neural networks dedicated to feelings of safety and danger, attachment, and the core sense of self are shaped. The first few years of life appear to be a particularly sensitive period for the formation of these networks.

The healthiest environment is the one created within intimate relationships with caregivers. These relationships stimulate the brain to grow and influence the form it takes. Although the brain remains plastic throughout life, those early experiences can have a lasting and powerful impact on later life. Because traumatic experiences can influence biochemical levels and neuroanatomical networking,[136] *both* siblings and offspring are at risk for unhappy and maladjusted lives, depending on their particular circumstances. (Anecdotal evidence, paradoxically enough, suggests that they have less rather than more physical illness, because they are unusually proactive concerning health matters.)

Grandparents

Grandparents are "helpless souls," because they often watch the plight of the family, failing to grasp what is happening. Either engaged or disengaged from their adult children, they are often mystified and don't know what to do. Typically the least trained members of the family, they can inadvertently foster (or enable) the illness and "do all the wrong things for all the right reasons," while simultaneously criticizing their adult children who are struggling to do their best as parents. Grandparents experience a triple whammy of losses: losses for themselves, losses for their adult children, and losses for their grandchildren.

Extended Family

Other relatives and extended family members can be "confused souls." In an atmosphere of the shame, secrecy, and silence, they have little idea about what is happening, often regarding their family member as rude, distant, or just not interested in them. Ironically, they often are very curious about what is happening, and could be enlisted to become invaluable resources in the hidden arsenal to combat mental illness, if given the awareness and the opportunity.

Friends

Friends and associates can be equally perplexed. The tendency of the family member is to withdraw and become reclusive. Like extended family, the irony is that many friends would gladly help if they knew they were needed. Instead, they, too, mistakenly withdraw and family members in turn feel even more rejected, reinforcing their feelings of shame, incompetence, and worthlessness. Family members forget to remember that healthy people feel good about themselves when they can give of themselves. A colleague of mine is fond of saying, "Giving is the first step in receiving."

Sadly, as we have seen, less than a third of all those who need treatment receive treatment. There are many important reasons for this. First, despite all the gains made by science and society, those under the influence of mental illness continue to suffer feelings of shame and embarrassment. There remains significant stigma despite helpful legislation such as the Americans with Disabilities Act. Symptoms and behaviors of primary sufferers are often invisible or minimized and ignored by loved ones, professionals, and the broader culture. Many sufferers are simply unaware that there is effective treatment and help available. Last, and certainly not least, is the fact that a great many under the influence of mental illness cannot afford private care, and insurance companies are either slow to pay or do not pay at all.

In concluding this chapter, it is important to reaffirm a central tenet regarding the intergenerational transmission of illness and trauma. Biology is not destiny. There is no rigid correlation between heredity and the occurrence of mental illness. Similarly, being the parent, spouse, sibling, child, or relative of a mentally ill person does not imply a life of damage or injury.

Not all parents who have a mental illness are poor parents; and not all children who have mentally ill parents become impaired or unable to cope. It cannot be stated too often that with appropriate information, support, and skills, loved ones can survive the influence of mental illness, and they can truly thrive. More will be said about such triumph, but first we need to explore further the potential costs in every arena for those who are close to a family member or a loved one who has a mental illness.

—∞—

CHAPTER *10*

Family Impact and Diagnosis

Each separate diagnosis of mental illness
presents its own unique challenges.

—⁓—

In addition to the universal signs of the family described in the last chapter, each separate diagnosis of mental illness presents its own unique challenges. For example, in the case of schizophrenia, males and females are affected in approximately the same numbers, but the disorder most often appears in the early to mid-twenties for males and in the late twenties for females. Consequently, women are more likely than men to marry and have children before the onset of the disorder. In addition, the prognosis for women is better than for men. [134]

In a similar vein, more males than females seem to get OCD in childhood, but the gender differences disappear in adulthood. Hence, more males with OCD tend to be single and unemployed, especially those who have a severe case. The onset of OCD occurs about half of the time in childhood and adolescence.

Consequently, these sufferers have issues that more resemble the long-term, life span issues of the person with bipolar disorder and schizophrenia.[75]

As opposed to schizophrenia, which is a *thought* disorder, and OCD, which is an *anxiety* disorder, bipolar disorder and depression are *affective* disorders. Studies have consistently shown that the affect or emotion of the primary sufferer can be highly "contagious," or can be transmitted to other family members.[95] For example, it is a common research finding that interacting with someone who is depressed can be a depressing experience. Similarly, while the primary sufferer's euphoria and elation from a manic episode may at first be infectious, in short order family members are subjected to the sufferer's irritability, anger, and aggression that quickly follow and characterize mania.[94]

Unlike schizophrenia and OCD, which are more or less constant, bipolar disorder and major depression are more likely to be episodic. Between episodes, there is a frequent return to the previous level of functioning, which requires families to shift roles, sometimes quickly and abruptly. Thus, those members with bipolar disorder and depression are more likely to work, to marry, and to have children than those with other serious mental illnesses like schizophrenia. As a result, the primary sufferer with these two disorders is more often a spouse and parent in the family, rather than an adult son or daughter, as is more frequently the case in schizophrenia, where the onset is typically in adolescence.[93, 94]

Sufferers of bipolar disorder, usually verbally assertive and better functioning in interpersonal and vocational arenas, often have significant relationship problems that directly impact their disorder. Expansive moods can place the family in financial as well as emotional jeopardy and danger, while depression can create an atmosphere of despair and hopelessness.[73]

Bipolar disorder is also a more *ambiguous* disorder than either schizophrenia or OCD. This means that affective symptoms can readily be confused with normal moods. Consequently, family members may be perplexed by the difference between the sufferer's mood and symptoms and can be more prone to see normal moods as abnormal, or feel a great deal of anxiety, even terror, in the presence of potentially positive aspects of behavior, like creativity or humor. Hence, it is easier to confuse the person with the illness, which wreaks havoc on the relationships in the family.

Conrad is a normally energetic, bright, and creative man who has his own successful business as a buyer of rare antiques. He also suffers from bipolar disorder. During his last manic state, he went on a long and expensive buying spree and purchased an excessive number of antiques for which he later had no use. He also started negotiations for three new outlet stores and made elaborate plans to renovate them. Now that he is on the proper medications, his business acumen and increased energy can allow him to use the talents he has in appropriate ways. However, his wife has a hard time shaking free of the frightening memories of his expansive and inappropriate moods, and she becomes terrified whenever he gets excited about any new business ventures. Conrad feels unfairly criticized, censored, and labeled as "mentally ill." The result can be major arguments between them as well as missed professional opportunities.

Primary sufferers can also have "dual diagnoses." While it is a term often associated with alcoholism, which we have seen is highly associated with mental illness, dual diagnoses exist whenever two or more core diagnoses are present or coexist in the same person. For example, many people with OCD also have major depression at the same time. A person can suffer from

OCD and bipolar disorder, or both schizophrenia and major depression. These situations happen much more frequently than we would like to think.

While generalization is often useful, mental illness is characterized by significant variability in terms of its outcome across diagnostic categories, within specific diagnoses, and even for a given individual at different times.[90] There is the potential for full recovery, partial recovery, or no recovery. It is virtually impossible to predict the outcome of a mental illness for a given sufferer at the time of the initial diagnosis. Consequently, all members of the family of the mentally ill person may experience uncertainty, holding the hope for a full recovery but fearing partial recovery or a recurrence, which are more likely outcomes.

In addition, the threat of relapse, or a return to symptoms, or more likely a worsening of symptoms, can keep family members in a constant state of tension, fear, or even dread. One of the ways family members survive the horror of mental illness is to adopt certain roles. It is to this aspect that we now turn.

—⟋⟍—

CHAPTER *11*

The Many Roles
of Family Members

Family roles:
scapegoat, responsible one, adjuster, placater, mascot.

—◊◊◊—

Research from the field of family therapy shows that family
members assume identifiable roles when adapting to prolonged stress.[10, 65, 140] These roles are taken on both to save the
family and to shield the person from the enormous fear and loss
that can pervade the household atmosphere. They are a part of
our instinctual nature. Recognition of these roles, particularly
the role or roles we have played, is the first step to liberation
and choice, because the roles that family members play out are
largely unconscious and out of their awarenss.

Virginia Satir, one of the great pioneers in family therapy, first
described the roles for distressed families *in general*. The emerging children of alcoholics' movement found them useful, and
some of the early pioneers of this movement further elaborated

on these roles. Before we examine roles more specific to families under the influence of mental illness, it is instructive to examine the more common roles.

One of the most obvious roles a family member under the influence of mental illness may adopt (or be given) is the role of the "scapegoat." As the name implies, the scapegoat is the family member with the problem. It is generally the person who is acting out or disturbed. According to role theory, the scapegoat takes the focus off of the *family* problems by running away, failing, stealing, drinking, using other drugs, or otherwise acting out and behaving inappropriately. He or she often appears consumed with anger, but the characteristic feeling is that of pain.

The "responsible" family member is almost a reverse image of the scapegoat. This is the person who begins to pick up responsibilities left behind by the trail of chaos. The responsible one operates from the unspoken mantra or principle, "In the midst of chaos, I'll take care of everything." This person is everyone's marvel. The responsible family member can appear as a martyr. He or she is a prime candidate for psychosomatic illness, for the body becomes the person's outer manifestation of the ongoing stress she or he endured.

The "adjuster" is the person who seems impervious to the effects of the illness, and she or he adjusts or adapts by detaching. This is the person who can sit at the dinner table, watch all hell break loose, and seem not to notice, continuing to eat without missing a single bite. This role is guided by the unspoken principle, "In the midst of chaos, I'll ignore it." He or she is a prime candidate for not being able to make or keep commitments. Little seems to affect the person, and little appears to matter, either.

The "placater's" guiding principle is "In the midst of chaos, I'll fix it and make everything better." Placaters fix people's feelings, worries, and troubles. They learn to be so sensitive and aware of what is happening that they can walk into a room, and without even consciously realizing it, figure out just what the level of tension is, who is fighting with whom, and whether it is safety or danger that predominates. And reflexively they begin to diffuse whatever tensions exist. They work hard at taking care of everyone's feelings and needs—everyone's except their own. They are often in a constant state of panic, anxiety, worry, and depression.

A fifth role is that of the "mascot." The mascot is similar to the placater, although much more of a clown and goof-off. Rather than resolving and helping people to work through their feelings, the mascot will typically alleviate the tension by doing something funny. His or her function is to create distraction in order to diffuse the tension. Performing this role exacts a huge toll and handicaps the person severely. Immaturity, hyperactivity, fragility, and emotional impoverishment are often outcomes. Relationships with others are less likely to be formed and are typically superficial.

As long as these roles are in place, the family is destined to remain stuck. Each member has his or her own unique function to sustain, reinforcing the unhealthiness in other members as well as in the family as a whole. These roles are progressive, becoming consistently more all-encompassing and confining unless they are interrupted. The same person may assume different roles at different times in life, and as one family member shared, "Since there was nobody but me, I got to play all of those roles at one time or another."

Roles and Gender

No cultural factor has greater weight or sheer force in determining roles in families under the influence of chronic illness than gender. In general, when both genders are involved in the helping process, the following occurs: mothers take on more responsibility than fathers; wives take on greater responsibility than husbands; and sisters take on more responsibility than brothers.[76] A woman's automatic assumption of greater responsibility is a clear example of gender-specific differences among family members.

Obviously, there are major differences in addition to culture and gender. Primary and secondary sufferers have significantly different functions. In a healthy or functioning family, *everyone* must pitch in to make the family work.[26, 27, 129] They must realize that they are *all* on the same team, and the enemy is the mental illness, not the person who has it or any other family member. In only very rare cases is the primary sufferer unable to contribute (for example, if he or she is physically incapacitated, or too young or too old). More important, it is critical to the well-being and self-esteem of the primary sufferer to contribute to the family.

Beyond the Role of the Primary Sufferer

In serious mental illness, it is always to be remembered that the primary sufferer has only *a part* of his or her brain affected. While most parts of the brain are *not* malfunctioning, significantly poor insight often ensues. Nevertheless, as has been noted, severe mental illness does not *end* life; it *redirects* it. Many families expect either too little or too much from their ill loved one and from each other. "There's a healthy and an unhealthy way to be disturbed," as one family member said to me. She was referring to *all* members of the family. Appropriate expectations of every family member are central to healing.

The following eight ways for the primary sufferer to contribute are critical to the overall level of family health. The more of these contributions the primary sufferer can carry out, the better for *everyone* in the family.

1. The primary sufferer helps the family by stopping the denial and acknowledging the presence of the mental illness. Overthrowing denial of the illness is a crucial turning point, signifying the beginning of movement in the direction of healing. (It is important to consider the work of Dr. Xavier Amador,[1,2] whose research provides evidence—at least in the cases of schizophrenia and bipolar disorder—that poor insight into the illness is a *neurophysiological symptom* of the illness itself. Poor insight is not evidence of resistance, noncompliance, or stubbornness, according to Dr. Amador.)

2. The primary sufferer contributes to the family by getting treatment if necessary. (Again, it is important to be mindful of Dr. Amador's research, which emphasizes that noncompliance in regard to treatment and refusal to take medication are common neurophysiological effects of the illness that are not to be confused with resistance or obstinacy.)

3. The primary sufferer contributes to the functioning of the family by entering into and remaining "in recovery." Serious mental illness cannot *currently* be cured; yet, there exists huge potential for recovery and healing, particularly when under the supervision of experienced helping professionals. Much recovery can and does occur for all members of the family who get the support and aid they need through such nonprofessional organizations as NAMI.

4. The primary sufferer accepts the impact of the illness on others, taking into account that the other family members do have their own feelings, stresses, losses, and upsets.

5. The primary sufferer is accountable—to the illness, to himself or herself, to the family, and to the larger community.

Whenever possible, the person is responsible to learn as much as she or he can about the illness and learn to care for himself or herself. While accountability, or problem ownership, is more complicated with children, they as well need to take age-appropriate responsibility for solving problems and for their actions.

6. The primary sufferer frequently creates or finds ways to help his or her loved ones, regardless of how small. The sufferer practices random acts of kindness. For example, drawing the bath water for a loved one can be an important contribution when the loved one is exhausted from either caring for the primary sufferer or has simply had a bad day. Remember that primary sufferers still have parts of their brain that are fine, even excellent.

7. The primary sufferer contributes by making the concerted effort to share the person he or she is *aside from the illness.*

8. Last but not least, the primary sufferer contributes by remembering that the earmark of success is to get up one more time than you fall down. His or her willingness to persevere in the face of difficulty cannot be underestimated. By contributing, primary sufferers will feel better about themselves, and others will feel better about the primary sufferer, reversing the vicious cycle that so often can occur in families under the influence of mental illness.

Beyond the Role of the Secondary Sufferer

Family members as secondary sufferers face a different but not necessarily easier set of roles. They must break away from the emotional roller coaster of pain, powerlessness, shame, guilt, confusion, fear, disappointment, exhaustion, and frustration. These emotions are often the currency of interactions, and they are the source of too many conversations among the family. More often than not, family members tend to care too much, rather than too little. It is to be expected that they will feel incredibly strong, frequently negative, and a host of other powerful and ambivalent emotions. Much of the insanity and despair that family members may experience is in direct proportion to their effort to manage and control the uncontrollable.

A frequent analogy that I use with families to point to their constructive role as guardians is that of a lighthouse. The lighthouse serves as a beacon or signal to aid navigation. When it is working correctly, it stands on the shore, anchored securely, with its inviting light, guiding ships safely into harbor. The lighthouse cannot uproot itself, wander out into the water, and take a ship by the stern, and say, "Listen, if you stay on your current path, you will break up on the rocks." No. The ship can choose to be guided by the lighthouse, or it can go its own way and crash on the rocks. It has its own destiny—just as we all do!

Leaving loved ones to their own fate may be one of the most difficult of all undertakings for the secondary sufferer. While this statement, of course, is dependent upon the age of the sufferer and his or her *current* soundness, it is nonetheless important. Even children have their own destiny. And while there is a great deal that parents can and must do to help their children, as sad as it may be, there is much they *cannot* do as well.

Acquiring this attitude, which is sometimes called "detachment," can take a lifetime of training to master. Without learning the art of healthy boundary setting, all family members will sink into the quagmire of the illness. To attain this skill, it is essential that family members relinquish the fantasy that they can or should change someone else. Only then can they claim the power that is truly theirs—the power to change themselves.

In order to serve as a lighthouse, that anchored guide so needed, *although not necessarily wanted* by their loved one, family members must attend to their own healing. This is the resounding and recurring theme of individual and family triumph and recovery.

Only with a clear understanding of the pervasiveness of mental illness, realizing that it is influenced from within and without as well as from their personal psyches and the psyche of the larger culture, can family members learn to become and to remain appropriately supportive of their loved ones.

CHAPTER *12*

The High Cost of Caring

A family member can easily feel despair and loss of hope
when he or she looks too far into the future.

—⟋⟍—

A realistic assessment of the family situation is a first step toward triumph. Further, to bring the family's full healing potential to the fore, family members must address their own wounding. For the family to become a key that unlocks the healing in *every* member, the impact of the injury must be acknowledged and treated. The gift within the problem has to be unveiled.[55] The proverbial elephant in the living room must be revealed for what it is. The pain of the family must be brought to light, legitimized, described, and treated, just as the issues of the family members of alcoholics have now been brought to light. Then, and only then, can the family move forward toward triumph.

Learned Helplessness

Unable to comfort and soothe each other, family members become prone to what one of the most eminent psychologists of the twentieth century, Dr. Martin Seligman, calls "learned help-lessness," a concept considered by the American Psychological Association to be the Landmark Theory of the Century. Learned helplessness is the "giving-up reaction, the quitting response that follows from the belief that whatever you do doesn't matter." It is caused by "experiences in which subjects [family members] learned that nothing they did mattered and that their responses didn't work to bring them what they wanted." Dr. Seligman goes on to state: "This experience taught them to expect that, in the future, and in new situations, their actions would once again be futile."[121]

Writing about what she calls "triumphant survivors," best-selling author Dr. Ann Kaiser Stearns says: "It is a characteristic of nonsurvivors, people who cope poorly with the day-to-day stresses and special crises of life, to conclude that one is as one will always be and therefore to make no attempt to change." She goes on to write: "Triumphant survivors, however, trade in the position of helplessness for a decision to take charge and search for options."[128]

The cancer of human endeavor, learned helplessness lies at the core of defeat and failure. To believe that your actions do not matter is a significant cause of fear, apathy, and depression; for the family snared in passivity and inaction this core issue is the antithesis of empowerment. When not addressed directly, as is so often the case, inertia and apathy can become contagious, and the failure to expose them often leads to a self-fulfilling negative prophecy.

Secondary Stress

A noted expert on the impact of trauma, Dr. Charles Figley documented the types of stresses and the resultant disorders that families under the influence of trauma can experience. The type of "empathic," indirect, or bystander stress that family members can experience is what Dr. Figley[40] calls "secondary or systemic traumatic stress." It has also been called vicarious traumatization, vicarious victimization, secondary trauma, secondary victimization, burnout, covictimization, depression fallout, emotional contagion, and countertransference. It is the response individuals manifest when hearing about or witnessing the traumatic experiences of others (e.g., family members). It is also the stress that results from helping or wanting to help a traumatized person.

Secondary or systemic traumatic stress is well documented *and routinely addressed* between emergency medical and disaster personnel. In fact, these personnel are often portrayed as heroes by society, because they help others, usually at the expense of their own welfare. Typically, the opposite occurs in families under the influence of mental illness, where members are more often criticized and secondary stress is more often *not addressed*. Yet, what family member cannot relate to the notion of secondary stress? In every family consultation in which I have participated, each family member has immediately recognized the concept—and voiced immediate appreciation and enormous relief to have it named. It is easy to underestimate the tremendous feeling of relief for family members when their experience is acknowledged by assigning its right name. Finding that their experience is not uncommon, they feel less crazy, sometimes even unexpectedly normal for the first time.

Dr. Figley notes that secondary traumatic stress, or STS, is the *least* studied and *least* understood aspect of traumatic stress, although it is the *most* potent and important source of stress for family members. Like secondhand cigarette smoke, its effects are real but not well documented. Some of the more obvious aspects of secondary traumatic stress are physical (shock, sweating, rapid heartbeat), cognitive (confusion, apathy, disorientation), emotional (fear, anger, depression), behavioral (passivity, drug abuse, sleep disturbances), interpersonal (abandonment, domestic violence, divorce), and spiritual (anger at God, questioning the meaning of life, loss of purpose).

Every family member is at risk of experiencing STS. Dr. Figley goes on to describe "secondary traumatic stress disorder (STSD)" as "the result of a buildup of STS that leads to emotional exhaustion and emotional burnout." Parents, spouses, children, and siblings may be at particular risk of the effects of STS because of the especially close, intense nature of these relationships.

Compassion Fatigue

The cost of caring, which Dr. Figley calls "compassion fatigue," is identical to STSD and is the equivalent of post-traumatic stress disorder (PTSD), or "the natural behaviors and emotions that arise from knowing about a traumatizing event experienced by a significant other."[40] While compassion stress is defined as the stress associated with exposure to a sufferer, compassion fatigue is a state of exhaustion and dysfunction—biologically, psychologically, and socially—resulting from prolonged exposure to compassion stress. Compassion fatigue is a form of burnout and arises from persistent exposure to chronic stress, trauma, loss, grief, and exhaustion—namely, the family atmosphere resulting from the influence of mental illness. Family burnout is the ultimate fatigue of loving, intimate relationships.[39]

Compassion fatigue is the disorder most likely to affect family members and loved ones, as its origin lies in their close involvement with one another. Because its transmission occurs through loving connection, the more severe and chronic the illness, the more likely one is to experience it. A natural consequence of giving care, it is normal and natural as well as logical and predictable. However, the negative effects of compassion fatigue can be mitigated, thereby accelerating recovery. It is preventable to a large degree and highly treatable. Prevention lies in social connection and education, the same ingredients researchers find necessary for families living under the influence of mental illness.

The symptoms of compassion fatigue are typically disguised and can vary widely. They range from depression to anger to resentment as well as from apathy to passivity, even physical illness. The impact of mental illness can be devastating, manageable, or, recognizing the opportunity that lies within, it can be transforming. The impact depends on the following three variables: (1) the characteristics of the *individual* (for example, the person's temperament, intelligence, or skills as well as the age of the person when the illness occurs), (2) *the nature of the illness* (for example, whether the impairment is mild, moderate, severe, or the course of the illness is acute, chronic, or episodic), and (3) *the response of others* (for example, the actions of the other family members, friends, neighbors, job, and governmental legislation).[55]

Overloaded and undersupported, family members experience a variety of common symptoms that are often not directly connected to the disorder of the loved one. The family becomes "the neglected affected" and is frequently ignored.[62, 63, 64] Families are six times punished: they are forced to watch the deterioration of a loved one, they are blamed for it, they are isolated from others, shunned, excluded from treatment, and forced to pay in many respects for it.

In addition, family members can be exposed to profound ethical and moral dilemmas on an almost daily basis. I have had family members tell me—and bear the horrific guilt—of their wish for a family member to die, to disappear, or to leave home.

I have seen family members express more than mere anger but raw aggression—and bear the horrific guilt—at a loved one and fall into a depression afterward. I have witnessed the agony—and the horrific guilt—of deciding whether to spend the money once more on another doctor, or one more treatment program. A family member can easily feel despair and loss of hope when he or she looks too far into the future. The overall stress on everyone can be crippling; very few are aware of the degree of stress and trauma to which they are subjected.

It is imperative for the family to learn that replenishing themselves is another key to unlocking the doors to triumph. Family members easily get caught up in giving that consumes them and caring that exhausts them. As one family member said: "Without taking care of ourselves, too, we find all our doing and caring and giving leaves us only frustrated, resentful, and self-righteous." She went on to say: "It is so easy to get so busy caring for others that we stop growing ourselves." The ancient Chinese sacred text *I Ching* tells us that "A healthy family, a healthy country, a healthy world—all grow outward from a single superior person," and instructs us to "begin by improving ourselves," a topic to which we next turn.

—〰—

CHAPTER *13*

Caretaking vs. Caregiving

Care provides the key to unlocking our potential.

—⚮—

Fifty to 70 percent of those who suffer with mental illness live at home with their families.[76] Families, therefore, are the backbones of support for the majority of mentally ill people of all ages today. At the same time, the act of caring for a mentally ill family member typically arouses profound and deeply complicated emotions, as we have seen. Being thrust into a foreign world of doctors, hospital administrators, government agencies, insurance companies, social workers, and sometimes even the police and the court system, compounds this already overwhelming and unfamiliar predicament.

The ill person is often unaware of the emotional intensity that her or his loved ones and other family members must typically confront. Further, as described earlier, society's harshness toward the mentally ill can create an extra burden for the entire family. If you are tending to a family member who has cancer, heart disease, or some other serious physical illness, most people consider you a hero or a saint. On the other hand, if your relative is mentally ill, you are often a suspect and treated as a perpetrator, who may be somehow responsible or culpable.

While virtually all of us, at one time or another, will care for a loved one, it is an art and science about which most of us know little. Author Arthur Frank expressed this most compellingly in his book *At the Will of the Body.* He writes: "As little as we know of illness, we know even less of care. As much as the ill person's experience is denied, the caregiver's experience is denied more completely."[43] Applying this concept to mental illness, his words are considerably amplified.

Two Kinds of Care

Because the family has become the most important source of care for the seriously mentally ill person, an important distinction must be made between caretaking and caregiving. They are the dark and light sides of service, respectively. These two different helping strategies can look similar, but they are fundamentally different and have considerably different impacts on the person with the mental illness and family members themselves.

When we have learned to distinguish the subtleties between these two deceptively similar "coping" strategies, we can acquire the skills most appropriate and healthy for all concerned. We can then apply them in a way that will be steady, ongoing, and consistent, being mindful that these skills are built upon qualities that can endure for what may be extensive periods of time.

Caretaking involves giving to another in order to prove your value, or giving to another in order to be accepted; caregiving is providing to another in order to grow and mature. Caretaking is a win-lose or lose-lose situation, while the caregiving is a win-win situation. Caregiving is an act of interdependence, while caretaking is an act without mutuality or reciprocity. Caretaking usually engenders additional impairment in the primary as well as the secondary sufferers; caregiving facilitates recovery in both.

One client expressed the distinction as the difference between "feeding" and "serving" someone. When I asked what she meant, she elaborated: "When you feed someone—or yourself—it's like you give them junk food, like a Hostess Twinkie. It satisfies the immediate hunger, but pretty soon it throws the body into upset. When you serve someone, you are giving them what they need." Caretaking, she went on to say, is "penny-wise and dollar-foolish."

Caretaking

Caretaking is all too often the more common expression of caring in families under the influence of serious mental illness, because often it appears to be the easiest. It is a negative and ultimately destructive form of helping. An aberration, caretaking is the dark side of protecting someone, and it involves doing for another what that person *can* and *should be doing* for himself or herself. By rescuing and controlling the afflicted person, it enables the illness to get a stronger foothold *on the whole family*. The origin of caretaking is the fear and guilt of the person offering help, and it breeds guilt and resentment in both the afflicted and affected family members.

Caretaking is in its essence a compulsive act, one that ignores the real needs of both the afflicted and the affected person. While seemingly an act of love and generosity, it is neither. In actuality, it is a demeaning and defeating encounter for the afflicted as well as a self-defeating experience for the affected. Under stress and strain, all family members can default to caretaking.

A useful acronym to understand the vulnerability of family members to fall into the habit of caretaking is HALT, a term that originated in the alcoholism field. Each letter stands for a different vulnerability: H stands for *h*ungry, A for *a*ngry, L for *l*onely, and T for *t*ired. Whenever the primary sufferer is hungry, angry, lonely, or tired, he or she is especially susceptible to regression or relapse. Whenever the secondary sufferer is hungry, angry, lonely, or tired, he or she is susceptible to becoming a caretaker. When used in the alcoholism field, the person under the influence of these four cardinal states is advised to go on "yellow alert," a state of high emotional discernment and vigilance.

Certainly, there are times when any family member would be overwhelmed by the behaviors, thoughts, and feelings of the mentally ill person. This is especially likely to occur when she or he is *too* understanding, becomes *too* sympathetic, comes *too* close, and does *too* much to help the other. In other words, when family members have poor boundaries and have trouble separating their feelings and thoughts from those of their loved ones, they are more prone to caretaking.

The caretaker does not realize that there are times when it is simply better for the mentally ill family member to be left alone, and it is also better for the nonill family members to leave them alone. Both need permission to detach at appropriate moments. This is just one reason why, without an extremely strong system of support, family members will have a very difficult time attending to their loved one constructively.

A term closely aligned with caretaking is "overcare," a term used by Doc Children and Howard Martin in their book *HeartMath*, which teaches the reader how to access the power of his or her heart's intelligence in order to promote the body, mind, and spirit's optimum functioning. According to these two scientists, "Worry and anxiety are the black sheep of the family of care. They're care gone awry." One of our biggest energy drains, overcare occurs when the heart is barraged by nagging worries, fears, and uncertainties, which "can degrade [care] from a helpful experience into a harmful one." Overinvolvement, overidentification, overattachment, poor boundaries, perfectionism, and the inability to leave a loved one to his or her fate are but a few of overcare's manifestations. The distinction between overcare and care is "the heavy, stressful feeling that accompanies overcare, while true care is accompanied by a regenerative feeling." When a family member crosses this line, trouble always follows, because overcare can make the situation worse for both the primary and the secondary sufferer.

Caregiving

Caregiving, on the other hand, stems from a more healthy position and concern for another, rather than out of fear of a reprisal from the person expecting care. Caregiving unfolds when the family member performs a given behavior for the ill member that the ill family member *cannot* and *is not able to* do on his or her own. As a result, the mentally ill family member is truly helped and the act facilitates the growth and development of *both* the primary and secondary sufferers. In the words of poet Ralph Waldo Emerson, "It is one of the most beautiful compensations of this life that no man can sincerely try to help another without helping himself."

An act of choice and loving kindness, caregiving honors the uniqueness of *everyone* involved. A function of how much consciousness we can bring to the situation, caregiving is based on service not bondage, freedom not compulsion, consciousness not unconsciousness, heroism not victimization, self-esteem not shame, and feelings of connection or universalization not personalization and undue responsibility. Mother Teresa, the epitome of a caregiver, says, "It's not how much we give, but how much love we put in the doing—that's compassion [caregiving] in action."[57]

To "care about" versus to "care for" lies at the heart of this important distinction. Caregiving is "wanting to serve," not "having to serve," because of the need to dominate, control, or manipulate. The following words by the great German poet Goethe further clarifies this key distinction: "If I accept you as you are, I will make you worse; however, if I treat you as though you are what you are capable of becoming, I help you to become that." Thus, it can be as important to see the ill family member for what he or she *can be* as well as who the person is in the moment.

For most of us, caregiving is not an automatic behavior. Caregiving is a learned behavior. While very few are born with this important facility, the attitudes and skills can be learned, birthed in the belly of the wound where our humanity is its purist and clearest. The caregiver learns to identify his or her own needs, asks for what she or he wants, develops a network of support, rests often, and is true to himself or herself while being loving. It is only after the person learns to say "no" that he or she can really say "yes."

Caregivers clearly understand the need for self-care. As one of my clients said: "I have to have me in order to help him." We are reminded of this self-evident truth every time we travel on an airplane. One of the very first things we are told is "In the unlikely event of a loss in cabin pressure, an oxygen mask will drop in front of you. Please place the mask first over *your* face, even if you are traveling with an infant." We can't help others until we help ourselves by paying attention to our own reactions and feelings.

It may be helpful to delineate some of the more important tasks of caregivers. To make the transition from caretaker to caregiver, the person must (1) determine appropriate obligations and boundaries between self and others, (2) recognize and acknowledge the intense emotions that arise throughout the illness and the caregiving career, (3) deal with the fear, bewilderment, and anger generated by mental illness, and (4) manage the central paradox of caregiving, which is the balance between care of self and care of another.

Care of the Self

Genuine care is one of the most rewarding acts in which a person can engage. Reinforcing our essential connection with others, it is an expression of the heart that inherently feels good, whether we are the giver or the receiver. Without care, love loses its meaning, for care has a restorative and uplifting effect on both. What is more, research from the HeartMath Institute, which conducts studies on the "intelligence of the heart," shows that when we merely touch another physically, there is an exchange of electromagnetic energy, which can be actually measured, that is transmitted to the other person's brain and vice versa. The heart's signal in one family member is clearly reflected in the brain waves of another. That is to say, the electromagnetic energy of the heart of one family member may be picked up in the brain waves of another. One can only imagine the effects of "emotional touching," the currency of family life.

The implications of findings such as these are profound for families under the influence of major adversity. How family members deal with loved ones has a pronounced effect not only on their mood but their physiological functions, especially the balance of the endocrine system, the immune system, and the entire nervous system. True service, without agendas or attachments to the outcome, generates "coherence," or harmony and order among the different physical and emotional systems of the person, while the heart's electromagnetic field of energy dramatically changes for the worst and becomes "incoherent" when the person experiences negative emotions like frustration, anger, or resentment.

Care provides the key to unlocking our potential. It is not care and caregiving that stops most family members from caring; rather, it is caretaking and overcare. And it is important to remember that family members have to care in the first place in order to get to caretaking and overcare.

Guidelines for Care

The National Association for Children of Alcoholics (NACoA) distributes a series of kits describing the impact of alcoholism on the family. In one of their most recent kits, NACoA talks about the Seven Cs, which include the four Cs of Al-Anon. These useful guidelines for caregivers of any illness to keep in mind are as follows: you didn't *c*ause it; you can't *c*ure it; you can't *c*ontrol it; you can help take *c*are of yourself by *c*ommunicating your feelings, making healthy *c*hoices, and *c*elebrating being yourself.[100] Family members are served by remembering these Seven Cs.

Caregiving and caretaking involve attitudes and behaviors that one not only offers to another, but also offers to himself or herself. Thus, it is important to realize that we can caregive or caretake ourselves as well. We can be as mindless toward ourselves as toward others. We can do the wrong things, even for the right reasons, for ourselves as easily as for others. Thus, in our efforts to relieve our own frustrations, we can consume unhealthy food or indulge in excessive drug usage.

At still another level, the difference between caretaking and caregiving, like all division, is artificial. Primary sufferers and secondary sufferers, albeit at different times, *both* need care, nurturance, protection, and love. *Both* need their efforts, their courage, and their strength mirrored back to them; *both* need to appreciate and be appreciated. Those living under the influence of any chronic illness, an altered state of life, may well need to rely upon new and different styles of relating: greater authenticity, honesty, adaptability, flexibility, and, ultimately, acceptance.

In the final analysis, all of those involved are in the "soup" of family, each retaining his or her own unique flavor and yet coming together in one grand mélange. As each loss is grieved by the individual and by the family, the path is readied for the creation of new dreams to match the newly emerging, and constantly changing, realities of everyday life.

In conclusion, the relationship between the ill, whether the physically ill or mentally ill, and those close to them may be the quintessential case for examining the moral and social foundations of all human relationships. It exposes the limits of empathy, understanding, sympathy, responsibility, and obligation in all relationships. As one family member put it, "Sometimes it boils down to a choice between my needs and theirs." Another aptly said, "We're finally grown up when we stop trying to fix everybody."

This dilemma posed by the illness speaks to the question, "What do we owe each other?" One family member stated her predicament in the following way: "How much of me do I owe you?" Questions like these, which are always raised in the context of living with any chronic illness, whether mental or physical, are tough ones to answer and have few simple or "right" answers. They require wisdom, not just information. Care for self, others, and something beyond the self are soothing tonics for the human experience, while opening the doors to triumph.

—ɯ—

CHAPTER *14*

The Core Dilemma of Caring

What do we owe each other?

—⁂—

The primary dilemma between the family member and the sufferer is the conflict between caring for self and caring for other. There is an often razor-sharp line between the family member's need to take care of himself or herself and the parallel need to take care of the loved one. The fundamental bind and the main source of ambivalence for family members lies in striking a healthy balance between attending to their own personal needs and appropriately responding to their responsibilities for their loved ones.

Individual vs. Collective Responsibility

The stakes in the undertaking to find a befitting accord between individual rights and collective responsibilities can be quite high. Primary sufferers can hold the threat of life and death over their loved ones. They can do so directly with actual threats of suicide or even homicide; and they can do so indirectly, because they could easily fall in harm's way without help. The judgment calls that family members are so often summoned to make "require the intelligence of an Einstein and the diplomacy of former president Jimmy Carter, who won a Nobel Peace Prize," said one particularly insightful father. Another family member described the constant tension and pressure so frequently inherent in life and death decisions "as a nightmare you don't wake up from."

The core dilemma of family members is made even more difficult by a society that apportions conflicting and inconsistent messages to its members. Loved ones often feel confused by the discrepancy between cultural messages about obligations to self and commitments to others. The conflict between my need to take care of you and my need to take care of myself arises from two powerful and contradictory cultural messages. The first one is to love, protect, and care for family members *regardless* of the personal cost to the self. The second message is that family members have the right—indeed they have the responsibility—to pursue their own personal happiness and self-fulfillment: that is, they are obligated to place the self over others. Family members are given further discomforting messages from a society that does not value caring work (for example, teaching and caregiving), privatizes family life, and withdraws structural support from a family system already dramatically overloaded with obligations.

The conflict between "my needs" and "your needs" is not a cultural accident. The political decision to stress individual over collective rights fosters a cultural philosophy to avoid responsibility for all the groups and individuals in need of care. This underlying principle stands in marked contrast to the values honored by Scandinavian societies, for example, which have chosen to place the responsibility for the welfare of individuals squarely within the domain of the government.

A Cultural Perspective

The United States is struggling for a consistent way in which to care for the poor, the ill, and the dispossessed. As a society, we cannot agree whether it is the individual's responsibility, or whether it is ultimately society's duty to care for the disadvantaged. The cultural values of *self-fulfillment versus fulfillment in service of others* are represented in all forms of the arts, as well as in political and educational institutions.

The resulting basic tension or dialectic—closeness or distance, dependence or independence, giving oneself to others or preserving oneself by disengaging, self-centeredness or group-centeredness—is the reoccurring theme heard in virtually every discussion about coping among family members. It is no wonder that family members are confused about boundaries, having been taught to believe simultaneously in the sanctity of the self *and* of attachments to others. Family members are constantly in the bind of choosing between their needs and those of their loved ones. "What about me?" is the silent cry of so many family members.

Closer inspection reveals that underlying tension in modern society is the message for persons to be involved and uninvolved, connected and disconnected, all at the same time. As a society, we are told that we find our selves only through connection with others. We learn that selflessness is the route to Self-realization. We are trying to incorporate the spiritual message that all things and all people are part of a seamless web, that independence is an illusion, and that spiritual enlightenment and happiness are less likely to be found in self-reliance than in the spirit of mutual alliances. Yet, simultaneously, we are also instructed that there can be only one winner, that rugged individualism is the backbone of our country, and that only the fittest survive. It is no wonder that

the whole family has taken a backseat to other forms of treatment; yet, as is so clearly being pointed out, the family may be
the tie that binds all of healing together.[59]

The dark side of family involvement can be seen as entanglement and as a debt to be paid at the cost of no less than one's
own self. There is a much more empowering way to see this dilemma, however. First, it is more helpful to see the issue not as
an impasse between the needs of primary sufferers or the needs
of secondary sufferers, but to view the needs of the whole family.
Rather than viewing the bonds of family as those of the binds of
indebted obligation, it is far more triumphant to create them as
pathways to opportunity. What can be offered now is the opportunity to learn and love with those who have given you life and
with whom you can share a common life, whether you live in the
same house or across the world.

Words of Caution

A caveat throughout *Unlocking the Doors to Triumph* has
been that there are times when the needs of the individual certainly come before the needs of the family, or the needs of the
family come before the needs of the individual. For example, I
have seen secondary sufferers, especially spouses, so distraught
that if they didn't leave the home or insulate from the relationship, they themselves might become shattered or devastated.

The concepts of "tough love" and "detachment" underlie the
need at times for separation. Sometimes, it is even necessary and
appropriate that the primary sufferer be hospitalized or stay at a
recovery center in order for the rest of the family to recuperate.

At the same time, a central theme of this book has been that
the most effective help for *all* family members is more often than
not "us help," rather than "self-help." As the basic principles of

family systems indicate, the whole is greater than the sum of its parts. There is strength and resolve in looking through the family lens as opposed to the individual lens whenever it is possible to do so. Family triumph invariably promotes individual triumph, and family healing invariably promotes individual healing.

The renowned Elisabeth Kübler-Ross, who single-handedly virtually brought the study of death out of the closet and into the light, wisely noted, "All true benefits are mutual." It is an amazing paradox that when the best care is provided either for the family, the primary sufferer, or the secondary sufferer, everyone in the family seems to benefit in the long run.

—ɯ—

CHAPTER *15*

Family Healing

I should have started by changing myself.

—〰—

Serious mental illness bears the potential for catastrophic injury to every member of the family. As a system that is besieged by biochemical and traumatic assaults, the family can be witness to the horrors of mental illness on a daily basis. Dr. Diane Marsh, one of the nation's leading authorities on serious mental illness, describes two kinds of ongoing burdens, both of which place enormous pressure and tension on family members.[90] As a result, virtually everyone concerned requires some form of healing when a loved one is ill and suffering.

Objective Burdens

Healing is needed from the *objective* burdens of the illness, or the practical onslaught of problems and conflicts that stem directly from the illness. These could include the need to deal with family disruptions caused by symptoms of the disorder, whether dealing with a loved one's hallucinations or delusions, managing major mood shifts, coping with bizarre behaviors, or witnessing obsessions and participating in compulsive rituals. Objective burdens also include overwhelming caregiving responsibilities, failures of the mental health service system to meet your needs or those of your loved ones, and the harsh attitude exerted by our culture's ignorance, and ensuing stigma, toward mental illness. Describing these burdens, one family member acknowledged: "So much of my time is taken up by my son's illness. No matter where I turn, I am dealing with one damn problem or another."

Subjective Burdens

The weight of these objective burdens leads directly to the experience of *subjective* burdens, or the personal suffering experienced by family members in response to their loved one's illness. According to Dr. Marsh, it is common to experience intense feelings of loss, sorrow, and grief, in addition to trauma, shock, guilt, despair, rage, and a host of other overpowering emotions. One parent aptly summarized subjective burdens in the following way: "There is just no escaping my constant feelings of dread from the dread of the illness!"

As we have seen, learned helplessness and compassion fatigue are virtually universal symptoms developed by family members in response to mental illness. Whether a family member succumbs to these symptoms is determined by two factors. The first is a sense of achievement that depends upon the extent to which the helping family member is satisfied that his or her efforts relieve the suffering of the loved one or family member. When family members find that their best efforts are not sufficient, they can feel helpless, impotent, and often hopeless. The second factor is the degree to which one disconnects from the suffering family member. Healthy detachment can arise from the sense that one has done everything possible, and is entitled to live one's own life. When family members find that they are incessantly thinking of their loved ones, reading books that their ill family member should be reading, or continually dwelling upon their loved one's plight, then it is not possible to coexist in a healthy, separate way.

A clear understanding of the insidious and potent forces at play can give family members the powerful advantage needed to mitigate the consequences of mental illness and its wake. By learning as much as possible about the illness, finding a community of support that understands the illness, and acquiring the skills needed to cope with the illness, family members can surmount, or even avoid, many negative outcomes. Ironically, however, when available, help has been geared more toward aiding the secondary sufferer to facilitate the healing *of the primary sufferer.* Few programs have been designed to help secondary sufferers learn to heal their own afflictions.[62]

Information Is Transformation

Only by achieving a healthy balance between their own needs of self and the needs of others is it possible for secondary sufferers to find the endurance that will allow them to be truly helpful (become caregivers) through the long haul of a mental illness. Comparing living under the influence of mental illness to a foot race, the mother of a child suffering from schizophrenia said, "Living with mental illness is a marathon, not a sprint."

Living under the influence of mental illness is not for the faint of heart. Tongue-in-cheek, one family member told me, "Families have the problems of Job, so we need the wisdom of Solomon, the strength of Hercules, and the Midas touch to pay for all the doctors." He added, "The disposition of Gandhi and the generosity of Mother Teresa helps, too." Therefore, family members need an infusion of many different resources in order to survive, let alone thrive under the influence of mental illness. In fact, just as the primary sufferer has responsibilities to uphold, so, too, do family members. While some family members need only information and support, others need more intensive help. Such aid will not only allow the secondary sufferer to have a more meaningful life but also will enable the primary sufferer to progress in his or her healing. *All* family members have the responsibility to get one or more of the following twelve kinds of assistance:

1. **Information and education about mental illness, its treatment, and impact on the individual and the family.** The beginning of wisdom is to call things by their right name. Until the family knows what it is up against, it cannot mount a powerful or empowering response. Unfortunately, mental illness is still shrouded in secrecy and shame. We know much less about mental illness than physical illness, although it is now widely accepted in the professional community that serious mental illness (schizophrenia, bipolar disorder, major depression, and OCD) is physiologically based. It is a biochemical illness, not a psychological failure or defect.

2. **Support to deal with the mental illness and the distress under which all family members typically live.** It is clear that the primary sufferer needs unconditional love and support. No less is true of the loved ones! They need to be able to talk to others who will be able to understand what is happening to them. The family illness cannot be healed alone. A community of what Jungian analyst Alice Miller calls "enlightened witnesses" is essential.[96] The family must learn how to share feelings in a healing and healthy way with others who know what they are experiencing. One of life's enduring truths is that we may be able to appreciate the suffering of others only when

we have endured similar suffering ourselves. This is the premise upon which all support groups are built.

The following story shows the importance of support groups. One day, a man walks down the sidewalk, and he falls in a big hole. He starts yelling for help, when a doctor comes along. The doctor says, "I can help you by tending to your injuries once you get out of the hole." The man replies, "Thank you, but that doesn't help me get out of the hole." Then, a lawyer comes along who says, "Here's my card. As soon as you get out of there, we'll sue the guy who left the hole open." The man replies, "Thank you, but that doesn't help me get out of the hole." Soon, a priest walks by and says, "My son, it appears that you have fallen in a hole. Let me read the scriptures to you and give you some peace." The man replies, "Thank you, but that doesn't help me get out of the hole." Finally, a fellow traveler walks by and jumps in the hole next to him. "What are you doing?" the man demands. Now we are both stuck in this hole!" The friend replies, "Yes, but I've been here before, and I can show you the way out."

3. **Skills to cope with the primary sufferer as well as other family members and situations.** Once armed with the appropriate knowledge and the support of others, family members are in the position to acquire the skills necessary to deal with the mental illness, its impact on their loved one, and its impact on each other. These skills include stress management, communication training, problem solving, crisis management, assertion, dealing with the mental health system, and skills that promote strengths and self-esteem. The family needs to be trained, not blamed. Under the best of circumstances, it faces enormous challenges. Most of these challenges require new learning and new roles. It is unrealistic and self-defeating to expect the family to perform tasks for which it has not been trained.

4. **Realistic expectations.** The family must learn to accept exactly what it will, or will not, be able to have, experience, or accomplish in the presence and the intrusion of mental illness. There must be realistic expectations for your loved one, for yourself, and for the relationship(s). Many of you believe you should be able to alleviate, if not cure, your loved one's illness with kindness or support. Not only is this unrealistic, but it is what we call magical thinking. Be patient and have sensible expectations for both your loved one *as well as* yourself. For example, you can often help your loved one, but that does not make the illness disappear. By accepting the reality of the losses to your loved one *and* to yourself, you begin to develop more appropriate expectations. The old maxim, "If at first you don't succeed, lower your expectations," applies.

   There is an old Hasidic tale that I will often share with family members. It is a story that places expectations into perspective. The story is as follows: When I was young, I set out to change the world. When I grew a little older, I perceived that this was too ambitious, so I set out to change my state. This, too, I realized as I grew older, was too ambitious, so I set out to change my town. When I realized that I could not even do this, I tried to change my family. Now as an old man, I know that I should have started by changing myself. If I had started with myself, maybe then I would have succeeded in changing my family, the town, or even the state—and who knows, maybe even the world!

5. **Maintenance of routine.** It is very easy for the mental illness to occupy the central role in the family, with everybody's lives revolving around it. It is essential that family members learn to stay out of the illness' sphere of influence—one more time than they fall into it. They must have their own lives apart from the disorder.

They must maintain old friendships and develop new ones, and participate in as many of their usual activities as possible. It might seem trite but the routine of eating well, exercising, and getting a good night's sleep is one of the most important routines a family member can develop. The bottom line is that family members must make time for themselves. But routines are not enough.

6. **Creation of rituals.** Ritual affords the opportunity to share rather than merely doing what is required. In families under the influence of mental illness, ritual is typically replaced by *mindless* routines, obligatory acts of going through the motions of life. Ritual, on the other hand, is born of a celebration of family togetherness. While routine is useful for getting on with life, rituals are designed for getting "with" life and for strengthening the family bond. Routines are often done hastily and without thought, while rituals are done slowly, mindfully, and contemplatively. It is through ritual that dignity and symbolism are imparted to the simple acts of eating together, saying hello or good-bye, or commemorating special occasions. Celebrating birthdays, marking anniversaries, honoring important events, or telling nightly bedtime stories to the children are straightforward rituals that can make a significant impact on all family members.

Every family develops rituals that provide stability, meaning, and direction. The rituals help form and inform its members; they serve as initiations and introductions into the family traditions. Rituals answer questions about three core issues: our identity (Who am I?), our bearing (Where am I going?), and our purpose (Why am I going there?). They can enliven the self and others with possibility. Meaningfully shared rituals shape our stories.

The initiation rites that once marked the transition from one stage of life to the next have all but disappeared in most families.[17] Life-affirming rituals are typically absent in families under the influence of illness, addiction, and trauma. Where appropriate, I suggest that families become aware of the rituals they have implicitly formed that revolve around the four major transitions of the day: awakening, going to work, arriving home, and going to bed. Families have already developed a series of rituals, or a sequence of behaviors, around each of these transitions, which can carry meaning deeper when done with the conscious awareness of sharing.

To begin, what is it like waking up with you? What message do you send to those around you? The new ritual you choose to create, which can be as simple as a word, a phrase, even a touch, contains the message that you are projecting as you start your day. Is it a warm "hello," "leave me alone," or "get away from me"? How do you say good-bye when you leave the house (for work, or to go to the store)? What tone do you set? What is the essence that you choose to create? When you come home at night, how do you establish the atmosphere for the evening? Do you immediately bury your head behind a newspaper or go to the computer and check your e-mail or portfolio? How would you like to be greeted, even if turmoil awaits you? Last, what do you do or say before retiring for bed? What would you like to do or say, if only to yourself? The answers to these questions develop powerful new behaviors. When you become conscious of the specific behaviors involved in each, major transformations will occur in *every* family member. And they will occur quickly.

7. **Learn not to take the illness personally.** Just because you are impacted personally by your loved one's illness does not mean that it is personal, or about you. Your family member is not "doing this to you." If your loved one is terrified, depressed, unable to socialize, or even obstinate

and angry, most likely it's the illness that is speaking. Constantly remind yourself that the negative reactions you may be receiving stem from the illness and not from the person. They are about the illness; they are not about you. This is one of the most difficult and yet one of the most important ways to take care of yourself.

8. **Ask for help.** The family must be able and willing to ask for help from other family members, professionals, and other concerned potential caregivers. People under the influence of mental illness live and breathe in a complicated and difficult world. Not only is life full of stress and conflict, but also it can take a toll on your health, your emotions, your social life, your work, and every important aspect of your life, including your future. No one has all the knowledge, skills, or resources to cope single-handedly with such a complex and difficult situation. Reach out to family members and friends as well as professionals. Create a team of caregivers around you. Dare to feel, dare to share, dare to trust, even if these behaviors may seem to break the implicit or even explicit rules of the family.

9. **Take permission.** Family members need permission to take care of themselves. Family members need permission to rest and permission to venture beyond the spell of mental illness and beyond the home, where other identities and roles can give them the strength and stability they need. Family members need permission to have *all* of their feelings—the good, the bad, and the ugly. Often, family members don't feel entitled to their feelings and are embarrassed, guilty, and ashamed, especially of their anger and resentments. As one parent said, "God forgive me; I hated him [his nine-year-old son] so much while I continued to love him." Sadly, permission can be hard for many family members who feel at fault for the plight of their loved one.

10. **See the doughnut, not the hole.** With mental illness, the hole is always the illness and the doughnut is the welfare of the whole family. Extending this metaphor, the healing of a family member is maximized when he or she is able to shift attention from the external circumstance (the hole) to an internal realization of self (the doughnut). The healing family member is constantly seeking to shift his or her attention away from external trauma and misfortune to the self-created meaning and challenge of his or her own self-development. More than keeping one's perspective, seeing the doughnut is a constant and ongoing battle for the only control the family member may have—control of himself or herself.

    Dr. Viktor Frankl, in his classic book *Man's Search for Meaning,* writes, "It is not freedom from conditions but it is freedom to take a stand toward the conditions."[45] In other words, the outcome of a situation or event depends on the decisions one makes, not on the conditions of the circumstance.

    Such a shift, or transformation, usually takes time to acquire and is not something that once acquired is always present. Rather, like any muscle, it strengthens with use and weakens with disuse. Repetition is the key to mastery.

    The goal of this re-formation is to have a clear and strong vision of the person you want to be and to continue to return to this vision of yourself time and again when the inevitable circumstances of life cause you to stray. Learn to build the muscle of seeing the half full glass rather than the half empty one. Again, repetition is the key to mastery of a triumphant life.

11. **Meaning for the trauma and loss.** Perhaps the greatest antidote to despair is a sense of purpose for one's suffering and pain. When the person is able to add meaning to his or her life, all of the other skills become "supercharged."

A synergy of forces result. So while meaning certainly is not a substitute for the preceding ten, nor does it replace the others, it becomes an invaluable complement, which can fill the void created by a loss worth enduring.

Dr. Frankl, in his therapy of meaning,[45] writes that meaning can be found in three different ways: "(1) by creating a work or doing a deed; (2) by experiencing something or encountering someone [that is, through love]; and (3) by the attitude we take toward unavoidable suffering." This latter way, the attitude one has toward his or her circumstance, is critical for all of those affected by illness. Dr. Frankl time and again reminds us: "We must never forget that we may also find meaning in life even when confronted with a hopeless situation; when facing a fate that cannot be changed. For what then matters is to bear witness to the uniquely human potential at its best, which is to transform a personal tragedy into a triumph, to turn one's predicament into a human achievement. When we are no longer able to change a situation—just think of an incurable disease such as inoperable cancer—we are challenged to change ourselves."

In a different context, Dr. Frankl states this important message in yet another compelling way: "It finally turns out that even the helpless victim of a hopeless situation, facing a fate he *cannot change*, may rise above himself, may grow beyond himself, and by so doing *change himself*. He may turn a personal tragedy into a triumph." So, once again, we are reminded that *triumph's crucible is personal tragedy*, a crucible in which we learn to create a life that is worth living, while dealing with the complementary loss that is worth enduring.

Just as there is no "one" best move in the game of chess, so, too, there is no one single meaning to life. The meaning of life differs from person to person, as well as from day to day and hour to hour. What is important is not the meaning of life *in general*, but rather the *specific meaning* of a person's life at *a given moment*. Dr. Frankl provides countless examples of triumph. The following is just one:

> I then invited the mother of the handicapped son to imagine herself similarly looking back over her life. She replied: I wished to have children and this wish has been granted to me; one boy dies; the other, however, the crippled one, would have been sent to an institution if I had not taken over his care. Though he is crippled and helpless, he is after all my boy. And so I have made a fuller life possible for him; I have made a better human being out of my son. As for myself, I can look back peacefully on my life; for I can say my life was full of meaning, and I have tried hard to fulfill it; I have done my best—I have done the best for my son. My life was no failure! She found a meaning which included all of her pain.[44]

Finding, or more accurately creating, true meaning inherent in the ruins of mental illness is analogous to the phenomenon of the Phoenix rising. Living under the influence of mental illness typically results in a tumult of inner feelings that each family member must learn to tame. The most resilient members are those who realize that, regardless of their life situation, they can surmount, even defy, all external forces by mastering their fears, their emotions, and keeping a broad perspective on life.

Fortunately, shifting your thinking, refocusing your vision, and adopting meaning are skills that can be learned. Countless studies have shown that the objective conditions of life do not determine your happiness, your sense of value, or your experience of life.[98, 119]

As you can recall, relevant to this way of perceiving life is the concept of a sacred wound,[52, 71] or a wound that reveals to you the gift of who you really are, why you may be here, and what your ultimate purpose for being here may be, which has been discussed in the chapter, "The Wounds."

12. **Course correction, not perfection.** An old adage states that the road to recovery is always under construction. When a pilot flies an airplane, the plane veers away from its flight plan at least 90 percent of the time because of such factors as human error, air traffic, the weight of the plane, the wind, the temperature, the humidity, and other weather conditions. Sometimes, the flight is bumpy and the weather is turbulent, so it is not possible to be on the right path at all times. The effective pilot brings the nose of the aircraft back to the flight plan again and again, whenever it is forced away from its course.

This is a useful metaphor for the family, although the work of living under the influence of mental illness is even more difficult. Because of the inherently self-absorbing, self-referential nature of mental illness, everyone's feelings can be hurt easily. There is often aggression perpetrated by both the primary and secondary sufferer that may be unconscious or unintended, and can be denied by both the people with the illness and the family members. Such aggression can be manifested in treating others as objects and frequently invites counteraggression.

Therefore, it is critical for all family members to be gentle and loving with themselves as they inevitably get pushed, shoved, and taken off course by their circumstances. Even fully functioning families are off course 90 per cent of the time! But they have a vision, or a plan, and the ability to "course correct" and get back on track.[23]

Many of these twelve responses to living under the influence of mental illness, while relatively simple to grasp, are much more difficult to put into action. Yet, they will enable the family member and family to cope with what could appear to be impossible situations. These responses become profound instruments of healing when enacted.

As more of these behaviors become available, the individual family member is stronger, as is the family as a whole, creating a more nourishing atmosphere for *everyone's* healing—both the primary sufferer's and the secondary sufferer's. When the family can adopt enough of these healing behaviors, it will move from merely surviving the mental illness to actually triumphing over it and members may even have the chance to thrive under its influence.

Family healing is a by-product of these key responses to the situation under which the family lives. These healing factors are not innate, nor are they automatically bestowed upon family members. Fortunately, they all can be acquired, but they require action. This type of action is often in the form of a journey, not unlike our mythical counterparts who were given the call and were asked to go forward to slay dragons in order to save the realm.

CHAPTER *1 6*

Stages of Healing

Each time the person cycles through these stages of healing,
he or she becomes stronger at the broken places.

———————

A s a teacher, I have always found it helpful to think in terms of stages of development. These stages can serve as a roadmap providing signposts for the trip. While no one expects the road to be exactly like it is on the map, the map can provide enough of an approximation to give direction to the journey. It "chunks down" the process of healing in a manner that provides an overview of the whole process and simplifies it in a way that makes it easier to understand.

I cowrote a very popular book called *Recovery: A Guide for Adult Children of Alcoholics*, which describes the stages of healing from the effects of growing up in an alcoholic family, one of many traumatic environments.[65] I also wrote a book that dealt with stages of family recovery and healing from OCD, called *Obsessive Compulsive Disorder: New Help for the Family.*[61]

Although these two books deal with the stages of healing for very specific groups of sufferers, both of them have a universal nature and can apply to recovery from any serious, chronic illness, trauma, or addiction. As I have continued to learn and grow, I have refined and re-defined some of these stages of healing. Each stage has its own central tasks and principles. Each stage can also be seen as a "state of consciousness," or a way to view the world or your life.

Most important, these stages are not so much linear, as in going from stage one to two to three, etc., as they are circular and spiral. In other words, travelers will constantly circle back and forth among the different stages, reviewing what already has been learned, thus understanding each stage from a different and deeper perspective, while spiraling forward to new levels of awareness and growth. Implying far greater potential for healing than the old adage, "Two steps forward, one backward," the circular nature of stages is an acknowledgment that powerful issues require many, many visits for resolution and mastery.

The following are seven stages of healing or recovery from illness that have been most helpful to the individuals and families with whom I have worked. They can also be applied to trauma and addiction in general.

Chaos

The first stage is called Chaos. The largest numbers of sufferers fall into this stage. Healing generally begins with chaos, because chaos is the first reaction of the family to the trauma of mental illness. The hallmarks of this stage are denial and minimization along with a high tolerance for inappropriate behavior, all of which are initially adaptive, normal, and natural survival strategies. The goal of this stage of recovery is simple: it is survival.

The depth of chaos depends of the type of illness; the stage of the illness, whether early, middle, or late; the strengths or weaknesses of the person; the resources of the family; and the response by the environment, or context in which the illness occurs. The family is generally disconnected or overly involved, traumatized, grief stricken, and exhausted.

The predominant feelings of this stage are fear, shame, guilt, depression, anguish, and fatigue. The predominant behaviors of this stage, which are generally driven by the illness, often leave sufferers vulnerable to other illnesses, stress disorders, and addictions.

An old saying proclaims that injury begets injury. More psychiatric or medical diagnoses are made in this stage for all members of the family than in any other stage. However, chaos is also a time of great creativity and opportunity. As the bricks of the past crumble, there is the chance to rebuild in new and even better ways.

Chaos becomes a problem only when there is no movement to the second stage. Problems occur when the emotional, mental, physical, and spiritual energies becomes trapped in survival. When this happens, sufferers endure alone and in agony.

Diagnosis

Diagnosis is the second stage of discovery. The sufferer and the family make a remarkable awareness: "It is not me [that is causing all of these problems]; it is the illness." This new perception releases a great deal of energy that has been trapped in defensive strategies designed for survival. The stage is set for the rest of healing, because accurate diagnosis and assessment are the foundation upon which healing rests.

The proper diagnosis is the beginning of the end of denial. The shift from suffering, which is continuous and endless, to pain, which has a beginning, middle, and end, occurs. The predominant feelings of this stage are often relief at first, followed by feelings of being overwhelmed as a whirlwind of ambivalent emotions erupts. But now there is also the hope for a new beginning.

The essential tasks of this stage are to acquire new information, new skills, and validation. One of the greatest roadblocks in this stage of healing is for a family member to continue the journey alone. Another obstacle is the result of attributing anything and everything to the diagnosis, which then becomes so intertwined with the person that the family cannot separate the person from the illness. While it is certainly true that a diagnosis closes some doors, it is equally true that it also opens others.

An expert on making transitions, Dr. William Bridges[14] reminds us that "renewal comes neither by taking a rest nor changing the scenery, nor by adding something new to our lives, but by ending whatever is, and then entering a temporary state of chaos when everything is up for grabs and anything is possible." He goes on to add, "Then—but only then—can we come out of what is really a death-and-rebirth process with a new identity, a new sense of purpose, and a new store of life energy."

Core Issues

Core issues flow from diagnosis. It is a stage of problem identification, problem ownership, personal accountability, and self-responsibility—not toward the loved one but toward oneself. It is the stage in which the family member acknowledges the impact upon himself or herself. Awareness of the core issues presents the person and the family with an accurate picture of the cost of the illness and what the cost of caring for the loved one has been. I have described many core issues, which range from denial, hypervigilance, high tolerance for inappropriate behaviors, demoralization, physical symptoms, low self-esteem, and eventually the loss of self. [61]

If the family is well informed, supported, and given permission to feel their wounds, the energy that has been trapped in the wounding becomes more available in this stage. It also becomes more possible to see the wound in such a way that opens each member to his or her unique purpose for living. This stage is the beginning of self-esteem. Acknowledgment proceeds, denial recedes, and self-esteem grows. The major pitfall for family members at this stage is overestimating their abilities and underestimating the influence of the illness. Maturity and discipline are required in order to face core issues.

Moving Beyond

The fourth stage of healing occurs naturally as family members realize they have a right to their own life just as the primary sufferer does. The major task of this stage is to create a safe or healing distance from the illness. It marks the shift from a preoccupation with the illness or the loved one's behavior to other areas of life that require the family member's time, attention, and effort. It can involve a re-commitment to friendships, hobbies, business, career, and, importantly, to the family member's own health.

This stage involves the creation of boundaries. Boundaries can be as simple as making sure family members have time alone or with friends, getting a baby sitter, taking a vacation, moving out of the house, or asking a loved one to move out. In this stage, family members expect less, but also must expect enough from their ill loved one. Family members begin reporting that they feel safer and stronger—emotionally, physically, mentally, and spiritually. There is often a resurgence of guilt as family members begin to take better care of themselves. Problems can occur when family members become stuck in this stage and confuse moving away from the illness with moving away from the person.

Getting It Together

This stage is a continuation of the momentum achieved in the previous stage. One of the longest stages in duration, it occurs as the family addresses its own wounding and becomes as committed to its healing as it has been to the healing of its loved one. The goal of this stage is for family members to get themselves together; the concern is not in getting a loved one together. There are two essential tasks in this stage: dealing with chronic grief and coping with chronic stress. These are creative acts at best. They involve generating new priorities and establishing new roles, because often one of the quickest ways to change someone is to change his or her role.

A major shift occurs in the transition from the role of caretaker to caregiver in this stage. The person knows what he or she is dealing with—namely, a chronic and potentially devastating illness that can result in considerable social and economic burdens. There is an increasing proficiency in establishing good yet permeable boundaries.

There are five key shifts that family members make in this stage: the shift from shame to self-esteem; the shift from unconscious to conscious living; the shift from victim to hero; the shift from personalization to universalization; and the shift from addiction to spaciousness. These shifts result in a complete surrender and acceptance to what is and what is not. It is a bio-psycho-spiritual transformation.[55]

The central task of this stage of Getting It Together is to proceed in life with integrity. This stage typically involves concentrated and active effort, and it often requires going to conferences, workshops, and even psychotherapy in addition to directed readings and attendance at support groups. The result of this stage is genuine forgiveness of self and others. The family member is now in the position to carry out the vision of the family and truly be supportive and loving.

Refamilying

This is the sixth stage of family healing, the discovery or rediscovery of the miracle of "us." It is the affirmation of family power and a family way of coping with daily living and all the challenges it brings. It is the natural outcome of the previous stages. As family members get their lives together, they have the energy for family renewal. The possibility for a stronger and more vibrant family can now unfold. The needs of neither the primary nor the secondary sufferer no longer predominate; rather, the family becomes a place in which *all* members of the family are more able to grow and develop.

The family spends more time tending to its needs, because there is now more time available. No longer as stressed, grief stricken, and exhausted, everyone has more energy for each other. With this newfound energy, the welfare of the family takes more center stage. In the relative absence of blame and guilt, family members are now enjoying the presence of the others and are willing and able to spend time together. A sense of family pride unfolds, which is now based on mutual respect and caring.

It is in this stage that the family is rebuilt, or developed. The past is released (and grieved) as everyone focuses on building a new and more positive future. New behaviors and new roles are becoming more stable. The illness now occupies less and less time and space in the lives of family members and is no longer the central organizing principle of the family. Family members can once again, or for the first time, have the opportunity to delight in the amazing experience of growing together.

Refamilying has become a triumph and the family experiences a resurgence in pride! The family once again—or perhaps for the first time—can attend to its primary duty of preparing its members to venture forth into an uncertain world, with the knowledge that they can return home when needed for rest and restoration. Our most basic instinct may be for family, not survival. The family must be taught the skills of family growth, of Refamilying after the family is torn apart.

During this stage, families often need guidelines concerning what is appropriate to say to family members and what is not. Struggling with "the truth," they are not sure what would be helpful and harmful. While this is certainly not a simple issue, the following Sufi saying is often helpful. It says the truth must pass through three doors before it can be spoken out loud. The first door is whether it is accurate. If the truth passes through this door, it must next pass through the second door, which is whether it is necessary to be spoken. If it passes through both of these doors, the third and final door that the truth must pass through before it can be voiced is whether it is done with kindness and love.

Transcendence

The last stage of healing is called Transcendence. A process of "stepping over, going beyond, surpassing, being above and beyond," Transcendence is the "brass ring" of healing.[12] While it is available to all, few actually get to this stage. The mystics tell us that in order to get to the Temple of Enlightenment, one must pass through the pillars of confusion and paradox. No less is true of this stage. In Transcendence, illness is seen as opportunity and initiation. Appearance aside, like the character of Yoda in the Star Wars movies, illness is accepted as teacher.

As teacher, illness becomes the royal road to Self-realization. Illness, the vehicle to a sacred wound, becomes the "blessed curse." Pain is no longer seen as punishment or a random act. As the Jewish Talmud says, "When sufferings come, utter thanks to God, for suffering draws you near the Holy One." It serves to accelerate progress by shattering complacency, as in the old adage, "God gives us gifts and they are often wrapped in problems."[57]

In the stage of Transcendence, the gift is received and acknowledged, and this occurs through a process of connection—connection to self, to others, and to something above and beyond the self. Strength and guidance come from beyond the limited confines of the self. The primary feelings of this stage are love, awe, mystery, reverence, and respect. Obviously, this stage is about the development of spirit and spirituality. While infused with spirituality, this stage is not necessarily about religion.

This stage is open to all family members. The further into recovery one goes, the more conscious and the more delicious life becomes. The major pitfall of this stage is "turning it over" too quickly, that is, before the hard work of recovery is done. Problems can occur when family members are caught in the light side as well as the dark side of illness. An old expression says, "Before you seek Allah, tether your camel."

Transcendence is neither a pipe dream nor is it a state of permanent and unending bliss. And it is not a state devoid of pain. The injuries of loved ones still hurt and wound, but as family members have discovered, there becomes greater meaning in the wound. And it is in the meaning of the wound, which each family member uniquely creates, that the journey from surviving to triumphing is initiated.

There is no single pattern of healing and recovery for family members nor an invariable universal series of sequential phases, because the process of family healing is simply too complex and too varied. So while the map is not the territory, it still provides useful signposts and warnings. It bears repeating that these stages are not a linear sequence. Rather, the person (and family) keeps returning to previous stages in order to make appropriate assessments, identify core issues, move beyond them, get it together, reaffirm the power and significance of the family, and transcend the external circumstances of the illness.

Each time the person cycles through these stages of healing, he or she becomes "stronger at the broken places." The ultimate expression of healing is a life of triumph, the topic to which we now turn and explore in great detail.

CHAPTER *17*

From Surviving
to Triumphing

The concepts will prove simple, albeit not easy.

—⁓—

Movement through the stages of healing and recovery is movement from defeat to triumph, from surviving to thriving. A few people seem able to move beyond their life circumstances almost effortlessly with grace and ease. But for most of us, we need to learn how to triumph. Fortunately, it is a learned behavior. Once we do, each of us can strengthen our ability to triumph by adapting the perspectives in this book to our own unique circumstance. The concepts will prove simple, albeit not easy.

In order to learn to triumph, we need to understand its nature and the conditions that call it forth as well as maintain it, because it can easily be misunderstood. Therefore, we must define our terms carefully. Otherwise, we will trivialize and distort the experiences of all sufferers, and adopt a series of platitudes that offer an implausible goal or an unreachable destination. We also can make triumph into a pipe dream rather than a realistic way of responding to life's adversities, a way that is potentially available to everyone under the influence of mental illness.

Triumph Revisited

Recall, the *American Heritage Dictionary*[3] defines triumph as follows: "to be victorious or successful; to win; to prevail." Recall, too, just as courage is the ability to act in the face of fear, triumph is the ability to move forward in the face of our problems. No adversity, no triumph! To triumph in the presence of mental illness is to move forward in a positive manner *in the midst of* adversity.[55] Triumph unfolds as extreme conditions no longer prevent you from loving and living a full life. But you do have to change yourself.

Triumph does not imply a life free of pain. It means that joy, peace, and happiness can be found to coexist with the illness. I vividly recall a life-changing moment for Mr. Abel, whom we met in an earlier chapter, "The Power of Us." One day early in treatment, he was pondering the question, Could he ever be happy again, given the enormous losses he had incurred? He initially believed that "being happy means I can't be sad." Since he would always be sad, his understanding of joy had to expand, which it finally did. "I realized," he said, "it has to be possible to be happy and sad all at the same time. Otherwise, I am doomed."

Another family member put it this way: "To triumph, you have to wear bifocals and learn which lens to look through." People who triumph have this "dual vision." They are present for both the sorrows and the joys of life. They have surrendered to the inevitably simultaneous presence of pain and joy, happiness and sadness, as well as the good and the bad, and the light and the dark. Life is ten thousand joys and ten thousand sorrows, the Buddha reminds us.

The ability to triumph, like any worthwhile skill, is almost always developed in increments, step by step. First, there are triumphant moments. They need not be dramatic! Watching a beautiful sunset and allowing oneself to really enjoy it, especially after a disappointment with a loved one, is an example of a triumphant moment. Failing to fall under the spell of a loved one's illness by refusing to fly into a rage, even though many others would, is a triumphant moment. Taking a night off and going to a movie, or going out to dinner with a friend, is a triumphant moment. Even taking a warm bath can be a triumphant moment. There are as many moments, or opportunities, for triumph as there are adversities.

Moments of triumph soon become more frequent and begin to form the fibers of a new muscle called a triumphant life. Just as a muscle grows as its fibers break down from the strain of a heavy weight or burden, so too the muscle of the heart, mind, and spirit grow with stress, strain, and breakdown. In many ways, a triumphant life becomes a habit. As with all habits, they grow in strength with practice and repetition. Stephen Covey's classic book *The Seven Habits of Highly Effective People*[24] as well as his book *The Seven Habits of Highly Effective Families*[23] give many examples of learning to develop triumphant habits.

Triumphant Families

Triumphant families, like triumphant individuals, can accept what they cannot change and change what can be changed—and they have the wisdom to know the difference. For a triumphant family, obstacles serve as possibilities for new learning, rather than defeat. Such a family does not focus on eliminating problems; rather, it concentrates on learning to handle the problems well—or "struggling well," as one family member said. Earlier in the book, we watched a triumphant family, the Abels, grappling with this paradox, and succeeding.

To triumph, families under the influence of mental illness must face an essential choice: they can see illness either as an endless trip to doctors, hospitals, clinics, or crisis centers, or they can see illness as a journey to the self. In triumph, the mental illness becomes the latter. Family members learn that life is not about being given good circumstances. As Robert Louis Stevenson says, "Life is not about having good cards, but playing a poor hand well." Triumphant families are effective families. They are made . . . not born.

Effective Families

Effective families have a greater possibility for triumph than their less effective counterparts. It can be instructive to discover the skills, attitudes, traits, and behaviors that modern psychological studies have revealed about effective families. Awareness of these characteristics will initiate the healing and recovery process, for change starts with awareness and with awareness comes choice. When you infuse these precepts into your daily vocabulary and practices, you will strengthen the muscle of triumph. By developing awareness of how others deal with adversity, you can permanently rewire your ability to triumph so that you can perform optimally under the onslaught of the challenges of living under the influence of mental illness.

Effective families[26, 27, 41] have been shown to possess the following qualities, all of which are attainable and can be taught to virtually every willing and committed student: they engage in open and direct communication with themselves and with others. They do not keep secrets from others or from themselves.

Showing mutual tolerance and respect for all members of the family, they demonstrate ongoing caring, commitment, and affection to each other.

While expectations are held of each member in effective families, love is essentially unconditional. Members adopt age-appropriate roles and responsibilities, and each member contributes according to his or her ability and health. They develop good problem-solving skills, and they have learned basic coping abilities. They have a flexible and adaptive response to stress. They encourage individual and family growth, as there is room for each member to develop to his or her fullest capacities. They develop a sense of family satisfaction and cohesion, and they spend time with each other. They have a clear acceptance of the stressor or trauma; they know what they are up against.

There is a family-centered locus of problem; people aren't blamed in effective families. Members engage in solution-oriented problem solving. They have little tolerance for complaining and whining about their situation. Having a high tolerance for pain, they have developed sufficient skills for coping with life's adversities. There is a marked absence of physical violence, and emotional violence is also at a minimum. In addition, members have no alcohol and no other drug abuse.

As Good as It Gets

The results of these attitudes and skills become a life "as good as it gets." As good as it gets may be the ritual Sunday barbecue with a loved one. As good as it gets may be as simple as taking pleasure in children playing happily, even in the midst of some family turmoil, or enjoying with realistic expectations the role of a loved one as she or he accomplishes some important goal or commitment. As good as it gets means seeing the glass as half full one more time than seeing it as half empty. As good as it gets is a muscle born of constantly refocusing on what is really important in your life.

As good as it gets is no less than a triumph in life. It is an affirmation of life's gifts in all of their forms. And it is within the grasp of virtually every family member. But it does require effort and learning to distinguish between positive and negative attitudes toward life's problems. It can become a form of artistic mastery, even a meditation. Such mastery, however, comes at a high price. As one family member said: "Life gives us these moments [of as good as it gets], and for these moments we give our lives."

As we have seen, triumph has little to do with the presence or absence of fear. To the contrary, triumph may require it. While the French poet André Lourdes does not use the word "triumph," he easily could have, when he wrote: "When I dare to be powerful, to use my strength in the service of my vision, it becomes less and less important whether I am afraid."[57] Triumphant individuals and families claim their victories even in the midst of fears, disappointments, and hurts.

—*m*—

CHAPTER *18*

The Key to Triumph

Just as courage is the ability to act in the face of fear,
triumph is the ability to proceed in the face of our problems.

—〰—

Because triumph and adversity always coexist, the key to triumph lies in understanding the nature of trauma.[136] Because the family under the influence of mental illness is exposed to a catastrophic stressor, the opportunity for triumph exists in each adversity and every trauma. The course begins with the reminder that wounds are inevitable. They differ only in how they are acquired and what responses they engender. Family members can lie back and utter that life is unfair, that mental illness should never have happened to them, and that they have no choice but to suffer its consequences and be miserable. Or, they can take M. Scott Peck's "road less travelled,"[108] Joseph Campbell's "hero or heroine's journey,"[18] transform their wound and make it what Ram Dass calls "fierce grace,"[111] Lynn Grabhorn's "joyful unfulfillment,"[54] or Jean Houston's "sacred wounding."[71] Family members might even find Nietzsche's "good enemy" in their traumas, addictions, and illnesses.

As mentioned earlier, if necessity can be considered the mother of invention, then trauma may well be the father of triumph. Trauma is one of those words that evoke a variety of reactions in almost everyone. For many, even its sound is threatening and its implications serious. Often, it is associated with physical injury and emergency rooms, not emotional events. We hear more about head trauma than heart trauma. Rarely perceived as a call for positive action, trauma is a term that typically elicits feelings of dread, horror, terror, and victimization. Moreover, its impact is often shrouded in denial, secrecy, and shame.

As we have noted, we live in a culture that historically has had little tolerance for trauma and even less for the family members of those who have been traumatized. Few have considered themselves victims of trauma, or even survivors of trauma. Yet, very few of us are strangers to trauma and its wake. In fact, our whole relationship to trauma is being challenged and transformed as these very words are being written. In the wake of 9/11, the massive changes in security measures have increased the awareness of trauma so that it is now a commonplace word. Many of us feel traumatized, for example, simply by going to the airport and boarding an airplane. For some, even the thought can be traumatizing.

What Is Trauma?

Unlike other psychological problems, the central issue in trauma is an overpowering life event that breaches the protective barriers of the self.[20, 29] As an event that is outside the range of normal human experience, a traumatic circumstance or incident is one that almost all people would find overwhelming. It is the truth of the unpleasant situation that forms the crux of a trauma, not a bad childhood or poor family relations (although they clearly affect the course and outcome of the problem). The word denoting "wound" comes from the Greek word *traumaticos.*

Trauma is watching a loved one tormented by his or her thoughts, thoughts that you know aren't even true or real. Trauma is being pulled into the hallucinatory or delusional world of someone you love, being perceived as the enemy, and finding yourself rejected or avoided. Trauma is frequently the outcome when you are not able to help your loved one.[40]

Trauma results from not being "seen," or being ignored because everyone is too busy dealing with the current crisis or planning for the next. Trauma is learning to have so few wants or needs that you can't possibly be disappointed. Trauma is praying every night to a god who never answers and feeling abandoned and disconnected from life's beauty and mystery. Trauma is the constantly breaking heart.

Trauma can cause symptoms on many levels, physical, emotional, and spiritual—symptoms like illness, losing sleep, eating poorly, feeling nervous almost all of the time, trembling, or feeling anger, agitation, and annoyance. Insult to injury occurs when the person feels inappropriately guilty that she or he has these feelings, because they are entirely normal. This point cannot be overstated: the plethora of feelings that family members experience are all natural, typical, appropriate to the situation, and very common. What makes them abnormal is not their appearance, but how they are expressed.

The Core of Trauma

The wound of trauma is any circumstance that jeopardizes the very survival of the person. For a life event to be traumatic, it must be considered life threatening and dangerous, invoking intense fear, helplessness, or horror. Studies of traumatized people show that it matters little whether the person actually experiences the event(s) directly or bears witness to it.[29]

Both can be substantial and lasting.

The essence of being traumatized is the inability of the person to integrate the reality of particular experiences accompanied by the incessant replaying of the injury in mental images, behaviors, feelings, physiological states, and interpersonal relationships. However, the central element that makes an event (or a diagnosis like mental illness) traumatic is its subjective assessment, or perception, by the person. Put differently, what makes an experience traumatic or not is the way we think about it.

Earl Nightingale, the twentieth-century "dean of self-development," adds to the theme of "meaning," and points to the key to opening the doors to triumph in the following way: "We become what we think about."[102] These six words were immortalized in his inspirational recording entitled *The Strangest Secret,* the first spoken word message to win a Gold Record by selling over a million copies.

Nightingale's words remind us of the choices we have surrounding *how we think about trauma* (that is, our attitude, as Dr. Frankl would say), even if we cannot control its occurrence. (It goes without saying that unlike primary sufferers, who have a neurobiological disturbance in their brain, secondary sufferers can have an easier time learning to master their thoughts and perceptions.)

While our perception of the trauma is not necessarily false, it is almost always incomplete. Because trauma tends to freeze-frame our experience, it cuts us off from seeing the greater picture and hearing whatever messages are hidden deep within the injury, blocking our feeling of connection to something larger.

Therefore, we need ways to expand, enlarge, and broaden our view of external circumstance, lifting the traumas from the depths of our more personal and individual experience and elevating them to the more general and universal heights of humankind. In the process, we learn that it is not just *my* pain, but also *the* pain, which is experienced.

The Meaning of Trauma

Although the reality of events outside the range of normal human experience is at the center of traumatic stress, we now know that *the meaning that the person attaches to these events is as fundamental as the trauma itself.* Thus, family members' beliefs about their experiences will be a major factor in determining the extent to which the illness can permeate the family and its individual members.[146] In other words, it is *not* purely the presence of the mental illness per se that defines the family's, or each member's, process of adaptation.

The modern spiritual guru Deepak Chopra, who blends Eastern wisdom with cutting-edge Western science, conveys this basic principle of subjectivity of interpretation in the following way: "The meaning that you give an event is the event."[57] Other religious, philosophical, and scientific statements leave little doubt as to the veracity as well as the perspicacity of this canon.

The ultimate freedom to make choices belongs to everyone. For example, family members may view the illness and the family situation as temporary or permanent. Recovery can sound like a hopeless endeavor or as a hopeful one. The burden of illness may appear as challenging or crushing. Loved ones can experience themselves as passive victims of their plight or as active agents in its resolution. They can see their situation as punishment or as part of life, their ability to solve problems as effective or ineffective, or their understanding of the problem as within, or not within, their control.

In choosing how they will perceive the illness and how they will act or react, family members can also influence the ill person's behavior, as modern physics has repeatedly shown. Recall that the concept of "observer participancy" expressed by quantum physics illustrates that the observer is always part of the observed. What this can mean in terms of family systems is that when the family can see its loved one in a particular light, it is more likely that the loved one will show up in that light. More than a self-fulfilling prophecy, perception and expectation can set an entire sequence of behavior and emotion into effect.

In a complementary vein, the philosopher Aldous Huxley states, "Experience is not what happens to a man; it is what a man does with what happens to him." Family response follows interpretation! Perception is a vital element in the family experience. And while events themselves cannot be changed, your change in perception of those events will inevitably enrich their meaning for you. When you change the way you look at something, *you change the meaning it has for you, as well as its impact on you.* Pain can be eased when the family views the illness and its impact from a less anguished perspective.

The questions of the meaning of life are granted a distinct bent by the great existential psychiatrist and Holocaust survivor, Dr. Viktor Frankl, whose family, including his father, mother, brother, and wife, were killed in concentration camps and gas chambers. While confronting his own likely death in Auschwitz, he faced a dilemma with a man and a woman who were contemplating suicide, because they no longer expected anything worthwhile from life.[44]

Inquiring whether the question was really what we expected from life, Dr. Frankl answers, "Was it not, rather, what life was expecting from us?" He then goes on to say: "Man should not ask what he may expect from life, but should rather understand that life expects something from him. It may be put this way: in the last resort, man should not ask, 'What is the meaning of my life?' but should realize that he himself is being questioned." Dr. Frankl pursues his reasoning: "It is life itself that asks questions of man . . . it is not up to man to question; rather, he should recognize that he is questioned, questioned by life; he has to respond by being responsible; and he can answer *to* life only by answering *for* his life."[45]

Stories as the Gateway to Triumph

Making use of this simple, yet fundamental principle regarding the nature of experience is a crucial key to unlocking the doors to triumph. I share this principle with family members in as many different ways as I can and as often as I can. I have a number of favorite stories that I typically tell family members to illustrate this profound principle and its application to families under the influence of mental illness.

The first is about the value of *dis*satisfaction, and it comes from Robert Thomsen's biography of Bill Wilson, the cofounder of AA. As Thomsen tells the story,[133] it was the winter of 1940, and Bill Wilson was in the midst of a major depression. A critical article on AA was about to appear in *Reader's Digest* and everyone close to Bill was worried that he was about to ruin this golden opportunity for AA.

One night, a Jesuit priest named Father Ed Dowling came to visit Bill in order to discuss the similarities between AA and the exercises of St. Ignatius, the spiritual discipline of his order. The two men talked for hours, and, as Thomsen recounts, Bill felt so close to Father Ed that night that he took his Fifth Step (one of the twelve steps that members of AA take in which they admit to another human being "the exact nature of our wrongs"). He told Father Ed about his anger, his impatience, and especially his mounting dissatisfaction with life.

In response, Father Ed quoted *The Gospel According to St. Matthew* 5:6: "Blessed are they which do hunger and thirst." Then, he told Bill that it is the yearnings, restlessness, and thirst that have always distinguished the saints. Bill then asked the priest if he would ever experience any satisfaction in life. The old priest snapped back, "Never. Never any." Thomsen goes on to write, "There was only a kind of *divine dissatisfaction* [italics added] that would keep Bill going, reaching out always."[133]

In that moment, Bill surrendered to his chronic and ongoing dissatisfaction and got the gift in trauma's other hand. His lack of satisfaction could now also be a blessing, bringing him closer to God. Bill's life and the course of AA were changed forever by that one sentence, which Bill W. embraced. As we shall soon see, Bill's ordinary dissatisfaction became transformed from a common or "profane wound" to a holy or "sacred wound."

Like the story above, the most powerful teaching tales are those about people we know or have heard of. The real-life story of Baba Ram Dass, one of the wisest and most respected teachers of our time who left his teaching position at Harvard University to blaze a new spiritual trail and shape the consciousness of a whole generation, continues to inspire us in its extraordinary lessons for life. In his most recent book, *Still Here,* he takes us once again on a quest, this time to share the gifts he received from the stroke that left him paralyzed, unable to speak, as well as full of love, gratitude, and peace. Writing of this experience, he says:

Shortly thereafter, I began to leave my former identity, my Richard Alpert-ness, behind to embark upon a journey of becoming Ram Dass, or Servant of God—a journey which continues to this day. Looking back it is clear to me that the despair I experienced [from the stroke that had essentially crippled his body] was a prerequisite to what came next. The negative thing, the depression, pushed me to find something. The positive thing, the spiritual growth, pulled me out of the depression. I have witnessed similar cycles among friends on the path to consciousness, when the spiral into deep depressions that proves, in time, to be preparation for something else.[111]

When I told this story to one family member, she humorously reminded me of the words of the late Winston Churchill: "If this is a blessing, it is certainly very well disguised." Laughter can take away some of the sting and clean the wound. Our sense of humor gives us the opportunity to laugh, and make a friend of what was once a fierce enemy. Remember the late comedian Jimmy Durante, who constantly poked fun at his long nose. Laughter in the face of adversity has a healing effect. In fact, neuroscience documents the release of a cascade of key neurotransmitters during laughter.

Knowing how the brain literally uses stories to build and rebuild neuronal networks, I will tell a different story to reveal how profound the significance of our own interpretation on an event can be. It is a story told by Viktor Frankl. He was describing a severely depressed woman whom he had treated to a group of psychiatric residents. She had recently lost her child and was in utter despair, unable to understand why such a tragedy happened to her. "I proceeded," he recounts, "with the question whether an ape which was being used to develop poliomyelitis serum, and for this reason punctured again and again, would ever be able to grasp the meaning of its suffering?" (The obvious answer, of course, is that with its limited intelligence, the ape couldn't comprehend why it was being subjected to such treatment.)

"Then," Dr. Frankl continues, "I pushed forward with the following question: 'And what about man? Are you sure that the human world is a terminal point in the evolution of the cosmos? Is it not conceivable that there is still another dimension, a world beyond man's world; a world in which the question of an ultimate meaning of human suffering would find an answer?'"[44] Meaning is possible even in spite of suffering. The woman's profound depression lifted. While she still felt great sadness at the loss of her child, she now had a way to interpret her loss.

Another universal teaching tale that I often tell families with whom I work is called "The Prince and the Squire." There was once a prince who cut his foot while hunting with his faithful companion. His friend, a sage, looked at the cut as the prince sat moaning and said, "All is for the good." The prince, enraged at his friend's callousness, pushed him into a nearby well. From the bottom of the well, the friend hollered, "All is for the good." The exasperated prince rode toward home, but was shortly caught by enemies who planned to offer the prince to their gods as a sacrifice.

At just that moment before the prince was to be killed, their leader noticed the hunting wound and immediately ordered the prince to be released, saying, "This man is unfit for our gods; he is not perfect!" The prince remorsefully returned to his loyal friend who was still in the well. As he pulled him out of the well, the prince told his friend everything that had happened to him. The prince concluded by saying, "You were right; my accident was for the good." But then, seeing his friend damp and dirty said, "But what about you? I pushed you into this horrible well! Everything isn't for the good after all." "Ah," said the friend, "you are wrong. Everything is for the good. If you had not pushed me in the well, surely I would have ridden back with you. Then, I, too, would have been captured and, having no cut, I would have been sacrificed!" Yes, "All is for the good."

By sharing stories like these, as well as many of the others that appear throughout the book and from disciplines of study such as religion, philosophy, literature, physics, health, even entrepreneurialism, I seek to awaken in the family members the seeker within them (who is almost always an angel of triumph) and ask if it is possible—at least on some level—that their misfortune can be cast in a light that offers hope and solace?

Other Words That Heal

The depth and breadth of the path to triumph through wounding can be gleaned in religious writings, the words of philosophers, mythologists, poets, mental health practitioners, scientists, even business leaders.[57] Each illustration attests to triumph as a journey that leads through struggle and adversity.

Christian religion reminds us of the Phoenix, who lived one thousand years ago. "And at the end of those thousand years, its nest is engulfed in flames, and consumes it. But the germ of its essence survives and renews itself and lives (*Midrash Rabbah, Genesis, 19:5).*"

The great Greek philosopher Epictetis said: "Every difficulty in life presents us with an opportunity to turn inward and to invoke our own submerged inner resources. The trials we endure can and should introduce us to our strengths. Prudent people look beyond the incident itself and seek to form the habit of putting it to good use."

Myths, fairy tales, and the great works of literature abound with cripples, hunchbacks, one-eyed monsters, and big-nosed loves. They suggest that these abnormalities are not only normal, but necessary in the scheme of life. They shape our character and unleash our destiny. They forge our greatness. They entertain and they educate all at the same time.

Dr. Larry Dossey, who many believe is one of the leading proponents of the new medicine, writes:

> Lying deep in the depths of the human psyche is the sure knowledge that adversity is an essential component of any existence, if that existence is to be complete. The steel must be hardened, and the trial must be by fire if it is to be a trial at all. The mythic archetypes of all cultures represent this idea, enduring enormous physical onslaughts, pains, tortures, woundings—finally coming through, emerging greater and more complete than before—as the examples of Achilles, Prometheus, and Oedipus demonstrate in Western mythology.

Dr. Margaret Wheatley, who combines modern science with principles of organizational development, states: "But the science is helping me understand, among many things, the uses of chaos and its role in self-organization. I think I not only expect chaos now, but I've grown more trusting of it as a necessary stage to greater organization."[141]

Even preeminent leaders in the business and entrepreneurial world point to the importance of adversity as the fundamental building block of triumph. For example, Sumner Redstone, the Chairman of the Board of Viacom, Inc., believes, "Big success is not built on success. It's built on adversity, failure, and frustration, sometimes catastrophe, and the way we deal with it and turn it around." Napoleon Hill, the great twentieth-century entrepreneur and chronicler of success who wrote the classic book *Think and Grow Rich*, says it this way: "In every negative event is the seed of an equal or greater benefit."[69]

The bottom line in all of these stories and words by ancient and modern wisdom keepers is that we rarely know what anything ultimately means—that is, until we create a meaning for it! One family member summarized this core tenet of triumph in the following way. "Survivors make sense out of whatever happens to them," she stated. To the limited nature of our ego, calamity is never good. But for the soul and spirit, adversity prompts our growth. The essential relationship between triumph and trauma is a universal theme in ancient and modern writings and in all aspects of life.[55]

Two Kinds of Justice

These kinds of stories open the door to distinguishing between divine justice and human justice, a distinction I find critical in my work with family members under the influence of illness, addiction, or trauma. Human justice, or what happens on the human plane when there is adversity, can encompass holocausts, famines, disease, crime, and a host of other problems. Innocent people get killed, bad people profit, and, of course, the good often die young. Occurring on planet Earth, there can be little apparent rhyme or reason to human justice. From this viewpoint, human justice is often seen as punishment or evidence of a cold, harsh, indifferent, and meaningless world. Divine justice, on the other hand, is birthed on a higher plane. It is not punitive, but rather loving. It is intended to teach us the core principles of life and help us see the errors of our ways so that we can strive toward a higher standard. Divine justice can rarely be understood on the human level.

The great theologian Martin Luther illustrates this distinction in the following way: "If God's justice could be recognized as just by human comprehension, it would not be divine." When distinctions such as the above are incorporated into one's cosmology, or worldview, then one is forever changed. Such distinctions become a healing salve for virtually any wound. Herein lies the opportunity to triumph.

Most important, these stories of triumph over great odds—of grasping victory from the hands of defeat—and the lessons that they carry foster a sense of meaning, purpose, and comprehensibility for life. Empowering others, they add to the essential ingredients of a triumphant life by conveying a sense of morality and responsibility. They suggest that the most basic of all human motivations is the will to meaning. In the words of Dr. Frankl, one of the most articulate and passionate proponents of a science of meaning: "Man's search for meaning is the primary motivation in his life and not a 'secondary rationalization' of instinctual drives. This meaning is unique and specific in that it must and can be fulfilled by him alone; only then does it achieve a significance which will satisfy his own *will* to meaning."[45] In order to survive "the most unfavorable conditions," you must evoke a person's will to meaning.

The place of individual freedom in this context of the will to meaning is critical to our discussion of the impact of illness. Freedom is by no means the last word; it is only part of the story and half of the truth. As Dr. Frankl asserts: "Freedom is but the negative aspect of the whole phenomenon whose positive aspect is responsibleness. In fact, freedom is in danger of degenerating into mere arbitrariness unless it is lived in terms of responsibleness. That is why *I recommend that the Statue of Liberty on the East Coast be supplemented by a Statue of Responsibility on the West Coast.*"[44]

The key to triumph ultimately suggests that to triumph in life is to assume the responsibility to discover your own answers to life's many complex problems, including and especially your loved one's serious mental illness, and to fulfill these tasks in as most a life-affirming manner as possible. This leads you directly to the next leg of your odyssey toward triumph.

—∿—

CHAPTER *19*

Becoming a Triumphant Family

No day will be meaningless.

—⚋—

More and more families are transforming their profane wounds into sacred wounds and, in the process, are experiencing triumph through creating a life worth living and a loss worth enduring. The Abels, the family that we first met in the chapter "The Power of Us," illustrate the metamorphosis from despair to triumph. Because this transformation can be such a rich as well as complex phenomenon, I have found it critical to go outside the usual confines of the fields of psychology and psychiatry and bring in the findings from other relevant disciplines. Almost every family with whom I have worked has commented repeatedly on the usefulness of downloading the information from these key disciplines.

Chapter 24, "My Path to the Work," presents the core disciplines of study that I have found invaluable in my work with families under the influence of illness, addiction, and other traumas. Because this unholy trinity frequently strikes the same family, a multidisciplined approach is needed. The ten fields of study presented in this chapter are those that I use again and again with virtually every family with whom I work. This chapter illustrates many of these different lenses, or ways of looking at what happens to the family, and provides examples of how they can be used to triumph over virtually any of life's major problems.

The Abel Family

The Abels, as you may recall, are a pseudonym for a real family with whom I worked. Even now, stigma continues to prevent them from disclosing their identity. Both Mr. and Mrs. Abel believe that some of their neighbors and co-workers would find fault with them, because the Abels have heard them express harsh judgments about other families impacted by mental illness or drug abuse.

However, the extended family and closest friends of the Abels know what is happening, so they are not alone in their struggle. There are no more secrets, especially from each other. The secrets they kept from each other might have been the most damaging of all. As we have seen, these secrets were an unwitting outcome of their lack of coping skills, limited intimacy and trust, and their inability to face and accept their situation.

Actually, the Abels had been through a previous experience that had helped to prepare them for Joe's hospitalization. Their eldest son, John, had been hospitalized three years earlier with a severe mental illness. *In fact, the Abels were once the Unabels before they began the journey that transformed every member of their family!* At that time, the family was totally unprepared. When John had a psychotic break, the family was unable to cope effectively. They were understandably confused and afraid, shamed and isolated by the stigma of the illness.

But when their youngest son Joe was hospitalized three years later, the Abels knew what to expect and how to cope, even though they were indeed traumatized by this latest adversity. They have now learned to share their pain, and their burden has become lighter. They meet monthly with other families who have weathered similar situations, and they no longer feel as isolated. At first, they hadn't known what to insist on from their sons; now, they have learned the art of knowing what to overlook.

The Abels have a family plan for emergencies, so future threats are less terrifying. Now, they have the information they need for dealing with their very complex *and* surmountable situation. They have developed their emotional IQ to deal with the many hurdles they will surely encounter. More important, they have developed what the leading expert on human and organization and performance, Dr. Paul Stoltz, calls their "AQ," or Adversity Quotient, in his book about turning obstacles into opportunities.

Although the pain of their sons' illnesses remains, the Abel family is now strong enough to move forward against great odds, a sure indication that this is a family who has learned to triumph. Every member now has a better chance to heal. While the Abels become upset and afraid at times, they demonstrate their courage daily. They have learned that courage doesn't always roar. Sometimes it is the quiet voice at the end of the day, which whispers, "Tomorrow is a new day, and I will try again." They now look forward to a shared life of love and hope. Life may not be easy, as they have discovered, and more importantly, they have learned the principles that govern a life of triumph. Every day may not be a happy one, but every day can offer some joy. No day will be meaningless.

The mother and the father of the Abel family were at the vanguard of their family transformation. They have learned to accept and embrace the prospect that the decisions they are making today will influence their children, and will influence their children's children tomorrow. They have learned to welcome the responsibility of being parents and willingly take this role of leadership in the family. Mother and father stand firmly as matriarch and patriarch of the Abel family. Rather than alienating other members of the family, their stand of authority, which at first may seem paradoxical, gives them the freedom to be fully present, accepting themselves in the present, holding the vision of a positive future, and surrendering to the fate of their sons.

By looking more closely at the Abels, we can discern the principles that created their transformation to triumph. What is the structure of this transformation? What is its anatomy? Answers to these questions teach us how to use some of the patterns as healing agents in our own families, regardless of whether our family is under the siege of mental illness or some other illness, addiction, or trauma. Principles are highly transferable, and they are available to almost everyone who is willing to expend the effort.

When I first met the parents, it was a year after the hospitalization of their first son, John. Despairing and defeated by the illness and by the very health system designed to protect and help them, they believed the remainder of their life would always revolve around suffering the agony of a seriously mentally ill child. They sought my help solely because of John's most recent problems, when he was in danger of being hospitalized again. They suffered a great deal, but they did not acknowledge the depth of their pain to themselves or to anyone else. Their grief was borne in silence. The avoidance of their feelings (what is often called "denial" or "minimizing") hindered their progress of the acceptance of the pain brought by the illness and the natural corollary that the pain would pass if it wasn't subverted into suffering.

In the early stages of the work, I met with only the father and mother. The children, especially John, were not interested in counseling. They had their own lives and wanted little to do with any "head shrinkers." When both boys eventually became a part of the treatment, they liked the new idea of "head expanders." In those early sessions, my primary purpose was to awaken their sense of hope, inviting them to move from what I called "the suffering," which I distinguished as that which could never be healed, to "the pain," which could be healed. I resisted talking about "their" suffering and "their" pain in the effort to make it less personal and more manageable.

In those early sessions I actively searched for the family's strengths, and I regularly mirrored and reflected their strengths back to them. When they thought that *their* problems (as opposed to *the* problems) were unsolvable, when they thought there could be no hope, when everything seemed useless, I would tell them stories, some of which follow.

Tales of Transformation

The first story concerns a situation that appears to be overwhelming. I haven't met a family yet that didn't smile when they heard it. It is about a farmer who seeks a guru's counsel because his wife perpetually nags him, his children always fight, and his surroundings are in constant chaos. After listening to the man's tale of woe, the guru tells him to go home and move all of his chickens from the barn into the house. The farmer cries out, "What good will that do?" Nevertheless, he agrees.

Two days later, he returns more frantic than before. "Now my wife nags me, the children fight, and the chickens are everywhere, laying eggs, dropping feathers, and eating our food. What am I to do?" The guru tells him to go home and bring his two cows into the house. "The cows?" cries the distraught man. "That can only make everything worse!" But the guru insists. Again the man complies.

He returns a few days later more stressed than ever. "The chickens are into everything, and the cows are knocking over the furniture. You have made things worse!" The guru once again sends the frantic man home, this time telling the farmer to bring his two horses into his home. The next day the man returns in utter despair. "Everything is knocked over. There is no room for my family. Our lives are in shambles. What shall we do?"

Now the guru tells him, "Go home and take out the two horses, the two cows, and all the chickens." The man happily complies and returns the next day, smiling. "Our lives are now so calm and peaceful. With the animals gone, we are a family again. How can I thank you?"

The second story, about an old man and a horse, is a wonderful Sufi teaching tale. It is a reminder of the adage that people plan and God laughs. It goes as follows: A long, long time ago, in a faraway place, there was an old villager who had a beautiful white stallion that was his pride and joy. His envious neighbors said, "Old man, see how lucky you are." The old man simply replied, "We'll see."

One day his prize stallion was stolen. When his neighbors heard, they came by and said, "Old man, see how unlucky you are." The old man simply replied, "We'll see." Soon, the great stallion escaped his captor and returned, bringing five other beautiful horses with him. Envious, his neighbors said, "Old man, see how lucky you are." The old man simply replied, "We'll see."

Soon, the old man's only son was breaking in the new horses when he had a bad fall and broke his leg. When his neighbors heard, they came by and said, "Old man, see how unlucky you are." The old man simply replied, "We'll see."

Soon, war broke out in a neighboring province. The soldiers came and took every able-bodied young man in the village. Envious, his neighbors said, "Old man, see how lucky you are." The old man simply replied, "We'll see."

When John's parents thought that they could never move beyond their burdens, I told them the story of the donkey and the well. One day a farmer's donkey fell into a deep well. The animal cried piteously for hours as the farmer tried to figure out what to do. Finally, he decided the animal was old and the well needed to be covered up anyway; it just wasn't worth the effort to retrieve the donkey. He invited all his neighbors to come over and help him. They grabbed a shovel and began to shovel dirt into the well.

At first, when the donkey realized what was happening, he cried even more horribly. Then, to everyone's surprise, he quieted down. After quite a few rounds of shoveling, the farmer finally looked down the well and was astonished by what he saw. With every shovel of dirt that hit his back, the donkey was doing something amazing. He would shake it off and take a step up. As the farmer's neighbors continued to shovel dirt on top of the animal, he would shake it off and take a step up. Eventually, the donkey was able to climb up over the edge of the well and he trotted off.

Life is always going to shovel dirt on you, all kinds of dirt. The trick to getting out of the hole you're in is to shake it off and take a step up. Each of your troubles becomes a stepping-stone. Never stopping, never giving up, you can get out of life's deepest wells by shaking off the dirt and taking a step up!

While different people relate to some stories more than others do, both of John's parents especially liked this story. We expanded this metaphor to include the idea that there are more unexpected twists and turns in life than anyone could possibly predict. While one day may appear to be a disaster, the next day can clearly be seen as an opportunity.

That day came sooner than we had thought. One winter eve was especially trying for the Unabels. Exhausted after coping with a suicide attempt by John, they felt betrayed by their son, convinced that he was going to be a lifelong albatross, draining the energy of the whole family. Once again, I shared another of my favorite stories about betrayal, one that I adapted from Neal Donald Walsch, whose "conversations with God" have become modern classics.

Why Bad Things Can Happen

The story I chose to tell them is called the "Little Soul and the Sun."[138] Once upon a time, there was a Little Soul in heaven who wanted *to experience* what it was like to be the Light. He knew he was the Light, but he wanted to *be* who he was. When he approached God with his request, God responded by telling the Little Soul that the only way to experience his Light would be to experience the dark. He explained that to experience anything at all, the exact opposite of it must appear. God added that this "experience of opposites" is a great gift, because you couldn't know what anything is like without it.

Satisfied for only a short time, the Little Soul again came to God, this time wanting to experience *forgiveness*. Looking upon the Little Soul with great love, God told him that it would be much more challenging to feel forgiveness, because there is no one to forgive in heaven: there, everything is perfect.

Many other souls gathered from all over the Kingdom as the word spread that the Little Soul was having an extraordinary conversation with God. Seeing that the others were indeed perfect and that there was no one to forgive, the Little Soul despaired.

But just then, a Friendly Soul stepped forward from the crowd, and told him he would help by coming into his next lifetime and doing something for which the Little Soul would have to forgive him. In his next lifetime, the Friendly Soul explained, he would be the "bad one" and carry out something "really terrible," so the Little Soul could experience himself as the "One Who Forgives."

The Friendly Soul further explained that in order to be something so terrible in his next lifetime, he would have to slow down his vibrations to a point that would not be at all pleasant. "I will have to pretend to be something very unlike myself," he added, "so I have one favor to ask of you in return."

The Little Soul was now very excited and told the Friendly Soul that he would do anything, because he was such an angel to be willing to do this terrible act for him. God interrupted at this point, and said, of course, this Friendly Soul is an angel, but everyone is. "I have sent you nothing but angels," He repeated.

So the Little Soul, more than ever, wanted to grant the friendly angel's only request and asked again what the Friendly Soul would need in return. "In that moment that I strike you and smite you," the Friendly Soul answered, "in the moment that I do the worst to you that you could possibly imagine—in that very moment . . . Remember Who I Really Am."

And the Little Soul agreed. "Good," said the Friendly Soul, "because, you see, I will have been pretending so hard, I will have forgotten myself. And if you do not remember me as I really am, I may not be able to remember for a very long time. And if I forget Who I Am, you may even forget Who You Are, and we will both be lost." "I won't!" promised the Little Soul.

The point of this story is that whenever someone visits a terrible circumstance upon you, one way to be able to triumph, to keep your perspective, is to cast it in the lesson that God has sent you "nothing but angels." In other words, a bad situation can be cast in the light that it has been selected or destined so that you will have the opportunity to experience forgiveness or whatever other state is necessary. While some people may find this explanation hard to believe, can you imagine how you would feel if you were to embrace this belief? True acceptance is based on the belief that whatever is happening is exactly what needs to be happening in order for you to move forward in your purpose for being here. Obviously, believing in this story, and stories like it, is predicated on a belief in something greater and beyond you, and this story, too, illustrates the difference between divine justice and human justice. What on the human plane seems like a curse is on the divine plane a gift that needs only to be unwrapped.

Throughout this book, I have described many ways to unlock the door to your own personal triumph, regardless of your situation. The employment of story is one of the most powerful means to find your way through the dangerous dance between freedom and responsibility that is experienced by everyone who lives under the influence of illness, addiction, and trauma.

We have seen that there is even a neurological basis underlying the importance of the powerful stories by which we can choose to live, because such stories can literally alter the structure and increase the number of neural networks in your brain.[25, 112, 125, 147] Most important, virtually any ordinary person can learn these stories; they are keys that unlock the doors to triumph. The trouble, however, is that so many of us do not even know they exist. It may take effort to find them, as they are often hidden in obscure places. Then, we must give ourselves the time to remember these keys, to make the effort to live our lives in concordance with the new neural pathways we have built in our brains.

Changing Identities

As you begin to appreciate the process that transformed every member of the Unabel family to the Abel family, you can discover the keys to your triumph. How many of the keys can you find in the following stories that show how this family triumphed?

About six months into therapy, the Unabels developed a family mission, which was the real beginning of their transformation to the Abels. A family mission is a vision statement that extends beyond the youngest member, who was now John, Jr., and their one-year-old grandson. It can even reach beyond John, Jr. to their great-grandchildren, who have not yet been born. They have a family vision about "what" they want their family to stand for, "who" they want their family to be, and "how" they want to act, all of which we carefully worked out in our family counseling sessions.

Family expert Dr. Stephen Covey writes: "A family mission statement is a combined, unified expression from all family members of what your family is all about and the principles you choose to govern your family life." He adds that a family vision is "greater than baggage," meaning that the family's potent and positive vision for the future will prevail over whatever horrors have accumulated from the past, or may seem to exist in the present.[23]

I remember when the Unabel family was in the midst of their re-formation into the Abels. They were learning the power that the future holds, a future that they actively chose, one that would serve as a magnet (or flight plan) that could pull them forward. They ultimately grasped the concept of a family vision once both parents realized that they wanted to create a legacy greater than the inheritance of mental illness to pass on to their children. This transition may have actually marked the beginning of the Unabels transformation to the Abels.

The Creative Use of the Future

Another exercise I taught family members is what I call "My ninety-year-old self." It is quite simple. Whenever members—both primary or secondary sufferers—found themselves in a difficult situation and were not sure how to respond, I suggested that they go into the future (age progress) and imagine themselves at ninety, sitting on their porch, rocking back and forth, looking back at this particular situation.

I further suggested that they see themselves smiling and feeling proud, because they had just triumphed over the situation and accomplished exactly what they wanted to accomplish. I then asked them to describe in great deal exactly *what* they did and did not do and *how* they went about doing or not doing it. This relatively easy exercise is surprisingly helpful when people are caught with no perspective in a present-time situation, wondering what they should and what they should not do.

I suggested additional ways to stimulate parts of their brains (and develop new neural networks) that words alone might be unable to do. I recommended that they spend several weeks looking at magazines and papers, cutting out pictures, symbols, and words that had special significance for them. We gathered for an extended session, which lasted several hours. Everyone was present. I first asked each member to sort through all the materials they had collected and make a collage representing how they saw the family *now*. They spent the next thirty minutes putting together their pictures of the family.

As one might imagine, the pictures were full of dark colors, images of despair and destruction, and pictures of people crying. Each family member also found symbolic representations of the mental illness. For the father, it was a huge octopus. For the mother, it was a devastating tornado. Both boys used images of snakes, huge pits, and even pictures of damaged body tissues. An overall sense of chaos permeated each family member's collage.

Next, I invited them to journey into the future and make a collage of how they wanted their family to be. (In the language of clinical hypnosis,[149] I asked them to engage in a powerful process called "age progression.") When each member made a collage of the future, they used brighter colors, found words and phrases of hope, and their pictures contained lots of smiling faces. A visual representation of the family experience, such as this collage, can be much more compelling, as new possibilities can emerge more clearly when we are not limited by spoken language.

In a subsequent session, I asked each member to create a third collage to represent ways they would move into the future that they wanted. While more challenging, these future-oriented collages showed pictures of people hard at work, often with brows of sweat. Their collages showed pictures that symbolized determination, resolve, steadfastness of mind, boldness, faith, and conviction. Several family members had pictures of schools. Every member had a representation of God, or a higher power. Mr. Abel had a staircase, which had twelve steps leading to sunshine. Mrs. Abel had a picture of a woman climbing a mountain leading to a pot of gold. Both boys had pictures of medications. Almost every member had words like *patience, effort, compassion,* and *love* pasted throughout their collage. I asked each family member to frame his or her collages, and put them in a very prominent place, one that each person would see every day.

Chaos as a Creative Experience

Because mental illness and its impact are such complicated and complex issues, I have found it helpful to teach families many of the principles that I have learned from fields of study other than psychology or psychiatry. For example, many of the stories that I share with families, such as the tale of the old man and the horse, demonstrate the principle that one can never tell what any given event can mean, even if it appears to point to the utter chaos and senselessness inherent in many of life's calamities.

In this regard, I have found that many families take comfort in the discoveries of modern science that can apply to their situation. An illustration is the findings from the field of chaology, or the scientific study of chaos. While the findings of this new and burgeoning field are beyond the scope of this book, its basic tenet is that order can be found in the most disordered system. The mere fact that science is discovering a deeper coherence in what appears to be the most unpredictable of situations offers a type of hope and reassurance to many families that traditional mental health science frequently cannot.

For example, Mrs. Abel especially enjoyed it whenever I mentioned the physical sciences, perhaps because she earned a degree in science while she was in college. One of the most helpful principles for her came from the work of the Nobel Prize-winning Belgian physicist, Dr. Ilya Prigogine. He said that when instability results, a new order always emerges.[51, 106, 141] What is more, Dr. Prigogine showed that the falling apart of systems is one way in which order is achieved. Dissipation, then, actually may be seen as the driving energy toward coherence.

I have discovered that different family members find different metaphors and stories effective. Unlike Mrs. Abel, Mr. Abel preferred stories from mythology. Interestingly, the boys especially liked my references to the principles from the fields of success, peak performance, and personal excellence. They found concepts like mission and the idea of consciously constructing compelling futures especially valuable. They also discovered that viewing their illness as an altered state of consciousness helped reduce their shame and led to better ways of managing and understanding their illness. All members of the family found the findings from the field of traumatic stress helpful. And they soon realized the comfort from feeling part of a larger order and purpose.

Everything Is Already There

An important outcome of these exercises for Mr. and Mrs. Abel was an increasing ability to separate their sons from their sons' illnesses. They found that they were now able to step back and reflect on the situation. This process of "externalizing the problem," as it is called in psychotherapy, is essential for every family member's health and welfare.[105] It enables each family member to rally more quickly around the ill member against his or her common opponent, the mental illness. By knowing the real adversary, family members learn to respect the power of the illness while also keeping it in its proper perspective.

Finding the resources in these stories and exercises, and accenting their usefulness to each *individual and to the family,* sets the stage for the next level of the work, while simultaneously providing a foundation upon which to build adaptive, life-enhancing responses. These stories were constantly referenced throughout the Abels' treatment. They were then able to serve as powerful reminders, or in the language of neurolinguistics (often called NLP), they become anchors, or strong connections, to feelings of triumph.[67] Whenever these stories were mentioned (that is, the anchor is "fired" in NLP terms), there was an instantaneous reminder that awaiting them (and us) are choices and freedom from suffering—if we are willing to work for them and undertake "the hero's journey."

After acknowledgment, the next key to transforming wounds is to create meaning. Validation frees the energy to be creative. I continued to tell stories, this time about wounding. Both parents especially enjoyed the works of Baba Ram Dass and they loved hearing about "fierce grace"—the new "gift" that came with Ram Dass' stroke and propelled him forward on his path. Because the father had used alcohol excessively as his medication, he loved to hear about the "divine dissatisfaction" of Bill W., the cofounder of AA.

Weaving the Strands of Triumph

Both Mr. and Mrs. Abel became admirers of Joseph Campbell and embraced "the hero's journey." They bought several of his books and devoured them. The father went to several workshops just for men that were given by poet and mythologist Robert Bly to develop "the inner warrior." He even learned to beat drums at one of these gatherings, not unlike his great ancestors, with whom he began to identify and take comfort. Once he brought me a drum as a present and told me that whenever he felt alone, he would go into his room and pound on his drum as a reminder of the connection he felt with his ancestors.

The family members, especially the father, were now ready to look at *their* trauma and *their* loss—traumas and losses, as we have seen, that society very often ignores and disenfranchises. They found no rituals or ceremonies to mark the passage of their wounds. More fortunate than many, though, one of their sons had a child, and there was the possibility of future generations of Abels. Now well armed with the knowledge, skills, and support needed to triumph, there was the possibility not only of illness, but also of health.

The father was a creative man who loved to learn. In a way, he had to be: if he was to triumph over mental illness, he would have to find new ways to contain all the pain that it can bring. His wife, his two sons, and his own mother were all sufferers of one form of mental illness or another. He had learned enough at workshops and through readings on his own to know that the family would never be cured. At first, when he wasn't feeling guilty for surviving, he was terrified by what the future might bring. He was the person who originally told me that his family members had the problems of Job. He also loved to play games, especially mind games.

With his imagination, he learned to create a "great story" in the mythic sense, one from which he could live a full and rich life regardless of external circumstance. An avid reader, he read a number of books on the legends of historical characters. He learned their stories. Like the wounded healers of old, he predicated his healing on his wounds. He was here on Earth to take his next step in *his* cosmic development as a human being this lifetime. Like many, he found the metaphor of being in "soul" school very comforting, and he was a student. Actually, he was more than a student. In his story, he pictured himself as a "cosmic gladiator," a phrase he often used. His home became the coliseum, and the lions and tigers were the illness. Each day he would fight the lions and tigers. "Cosmic couriers," as he came to call these inner guides, were constantly bringing him messages, many of which he did not like.

I presented the concepts of sacred and profane wounding, pain and suffering, spaciousness and addiction, conscious and unconscious, victim and hero, and a host of other distinctions that are presented in the appendices. Mr. Abel was like a sponge that filled with enough water not only for himself but also for everyone in the family—at least on a good day.

Mr. Abel especially liked the distinction of divine justice and human justice. Whenever he couldn't explain an event, or something happened that defied his logic, he construed it in terms of divine justice. Divine justice was never handed out as punishment. It was a test. Like most tests, each one was very difficult. He often referred to his "lesser" self when describing situations with which he dealt poorly and to his "greater" self for those situations in which he felt he was who he really wanted to be.

He learned to become stronger and stronger, and he was becoming more and more able to hold (or not react as much to) the trauma and loss inherent in mental illness. He still felt the loss, the pain, and even at times the betrayal at the hands of an "unfair" universe. He felt all of this and he felt *more*. He also felt joy, connection, satisfaction, fulfillment, and even peace. In fact, one day he told me that he thought he might be in denial of what was happening. When Joe was hospitalized, a psychiatrist had even told him he was in denial. Worse, he thought he was going crazy himself because he was not in great agony. He said he loved life—even though his wife and sons were suffering, sometimes terribly. "How could this be?" he asked. Was he refusing to accept "reality"? Did it mean he was insensitive? Was he callous? Was he heartless?

It was a great paradox: the unfathomable anguish brought with it immeasurable love. One day, Mr. Abel said, "I just have to figure out how to live in these two realities." I reminded him that the famous Swiss psychiatrist Dr. Carl Jung defined maturity as "the increasing ability to reconcile opposites." Soon, he began to say, "I have to figure out how to incorporate the person I am becoming with who I used to be." He thought it would be especially helpful if he could have a statement or a mantra to remind him of, and focus him on, what he was really here on earth to do.

On another occasion, Mr. Abel and his wife saw the movie *Out of Africa*. He found one scene particularly meaningful for him. The actress Meryl Streep was with her houseboy when the coffee factory for which she had worked so hard burned down. "God plays with us," he said. For a while, that became his mantra, a sentence to which he constantly returned. Soon, his motto was "friction polishes," a phrase he saw on a bumper sticker. He finally settled on the mantra "struggle builds muscle." He told me that when life got rough, he repeated these words to himself over and over. While it did not take the pain away, he said, it provided another very real and tangible way for him to deal with his extraordinary situation. Like the previous stories, these mantras were one more tool in his arsenal for triumph, tools he would use regularly.

It can certainly be argued that these "inner constructions," or what mythologists might call "Great Story,"[71] were fantasies that have validity in few minds other than his. And this could be true. Equally true, however, are his statements that since he began to look at his life in terms of his having incurred a sacred wound and embarking on a sacred journey, he was able to restore a sense of predictability and stability. His world became much safer, and he no longer felt like he was a bad person. He was building the inner scaffolding he needed to triumph over the circumstances in which he found himself.

In the process, Mr. Abel learned that there is no absolute answer to why bad things happen. There is only the meaning we can make out of our suffering. In Rabbi Harold Kushner's book *When Bad Things Happen to Good People*, he quotes the German theologian Dorothee Soelle: "The question is not where does the tragedy come from, but where does it lead?" What good can come, what are its lessons, and how can the world be made a better place? These are the questions addressed by sacred wounding and the hero's journey.

Mr. Abel's sense of personal empowerment enabled him to be available to other members of his family. He had learned the hard way that his cup couldn't run over until he filled it. He took his own needs seriously and developed appropriate self-focus, or what is sometimes called healthy narcissism. He loved hearing the reminder that a chain is as strong as its weakest link, but a family is as strong as its strongest member.

Without resentment, Mr. Abel took on the task of being the strongest member, not from the point of view of the ego, but from the point of view of the soul. In other words, he decided to use his wound as the entry point to his own healing, not only from the mental illness of his loved ones but to develop his full self. And in the process, other members of his family began to heal, too. Like Melvin in the movie *As Good as It Gets*, his behaviors had such powerful effects that others in the family developed their own healing journeys.

The end of this story is still being written. When I last saw the family, I was told that Mr. Abel was just diagnosed with serious cancer. The whole family had worked so hard to achieve the triumph they had. I was shocked, angry, and disappointed. Seeing my upset, they both looked at me with what seemed like a twinkle in their eyes. Reminding *me* of the old man and the horse, they simply said: "We'll see." And then, as if to really make the point, they said everyone has their share of life's dirt. Everyone in the room, including the boys and, if I take a certain poetic license, maybe even the grandson—all three generations—smiled.

Mr. Abel's parting words to me that day were, "People sacrifice a lot more for a lot less." I can still remember one of Mrs. Abel's last comments to me as she left. She said, "There is no magic, no tricks to not being defeated—only hard work. You can either do the work and make something of your life, or you can make yourself a victim, hoping circumstance will treat you kinder." "The choice," she said, "is for each of us to make. It's pretty simple, just not at all easy," she said with a smile. The Abels, all of them, have become my heroes.

The Abels realize that their "before and after" shift is dramatic, but they no longer *live* in drama. They want their story shared. More than once, they have said to me, "Someday we hope we will be able to use our real name with no fear. We want to share the pride and joy we feel." More than once, they said, "If we can do it, any family can do it." While they were certainly blessed in many ways, their statement, I believe, is essentially accurate.

This family's odyssey—*your family's voyage*—through mental illness is a modern day heroic journey.[18] It is no less fraught with danger than that of our ancestors; it is no less hazardous; it is no less rewarding. The transformation of the triumphant Abels, who were once the downtrodden Unabels, is a story of triumph as worthy as any of the great mythological tales where dragons threaten to destroy the kingdom. It brings hope to many other families.

A Letter of Triumph

Not long ago, I heard from the Abels. Mrs. Abel called to tell me that a new member, Mitchell, had just joined the family. Probably to no one's surprise, Mr. Abel continues to enjoy a meaningful and productive life, she reported. "Nothing has really changed on the outside. Our two sons still struggle with mental illness and so do I," she added. "But with the recent advances in medical science, all three of us are taking medication." Because of the genetic component of serious mental illness, they are concerned for the next generation. However, it is clear that everyone in the family has a life worth living.

In that telephone call, I asked Mrs. Abel what she thought the ingredients of her family's triumph were. She paused and said she would like to think about that question and ask the other family members. Two weeks later, I received the following letter:

Dear Dr. Gravitz,

We all thought about your question together.

One night we sat around the kitchen table and came up with a number of points that we keep coming back to again and again. I guess they are our anchor points. They are like the mantras we learned in our work.

First, we believe that there really is a meaning to life. Nothing happens without a purpose. No encounter occurs by chance on the divine plane. It only seems that way on the human level. We recognize that the great spiritual traditions all teach that we live in a loving universe. We are learning to feel this truth daily. Some days we actually forget to remember, but we each have learned the good days will follow if we are patient.

Second, because we think that all of our difficulties have a deeper purpose, we know it is up to each of us to find that purpose. This is God's challenge to us. Adversity, while never pleasant or fun, is our teacher, pushing and at times demanding us to extend our limits, just like building body muscles requires stress and strain. We remember, "Struggle builds muscle."

Third, if this doesn't sound like a contradiction, we really believe that everything is meaningless until we give it a meaning. There is no one truth, just each person's truth. Each person has a different take on even the most obvious and simple events, and each is convinced that her or his view is right. We all remember when you asked us as a family to see the classic Japanese film Rashomon, *which showed a crime over and over, each time from the view of one of the witnesses. Each person saw the same crime in totally different ways. That made such an impression on us. Truth was never the same again.*

Fourth, we now really believe that transforming hurt and hatred and completing our own *[italics not added] unfinished business are probably the single most important skill in life. We are learning to accept the fact that getting someone else to change may not be a realistic goal. Besides, we would now rather be happy than right.*

Fifth, we now fully know that when we each do our own inner work and fight our own inner demons and monsters, we can't help but to transform our outer relationships as well. You of all people know that I can't control my feelings. Slowly, I am learning to do the right thing anyway.

Last but not least, we are no longer in a hurry. We know that this type of healing is a lifelong process. It is the hardest work we will ever do, because it demands that we face our deepest hurts and greatest fears.

We know that no other experiences bring as much pain and joy as our relationships with each other. And at the moment of death, it is our loved ones, not our other accomplishments, that we most likely will be thinking of.

We all realize that everyone does not share our beliefs. We know that some even might consider us foolish. We have as much been told that we are weird. We have even been called delusional, because we live in our own made-up world.

Nevertheless, these thoughts make our lives more significant; we feel safer living in the world, and we feel good about ourselves. In a sense, they have become the virtual reality of our minds. So, we guess that the bottom line is they work!

I know this letter is a bit long. It just kind of wrote itself once I got started. I guess that is how it is when you have learned something well. Thank you for helping us to make these beliefs become clearer. We have all of these points posted on our refrigerator door right next to our family vision.

All of us send our love and blessings to you and your family.

The Abels

The Abel family is a living demonstration of the power of us. Their triumph and healing stemmed first of all from their willingness to engage in the hard work that is required. However, it is likely that the regenerative powers of the family would not have been harnessed if only one member had chosen to make the journey alone.

Sometimes, the family needs the help of competent professionals to point the way. If you are fortunate—or if you accept the grace that always accompanies life's great wounds—you will find someone or something to guide you through. Luke, the hero of the movie *Star Wars*, had Yoda. Like Luke, you may find that your guide can come in many forms—a teacher, a friend, a word, or words that inspire.

—w—

CHAPTER 20

The Price of Triumph

Triumphing . . . is arduous
and can often be very discouraging work.

———⚹———

Triumph in the face of serious mental illness exacts a price that most people are unaware of having to pay. Once aware of this, though, many are willing, even eager, to surrender to the losses incurred along the way, and persevere through many difficult situations. Triumphing over the profound personal, moral, and ethical responsibilities and issues, as well as other questions ignited by mental illness, is arduous and can often be very discouraging work.

Some sufferers feel victimized by their circumstance. Others become disoriented and lose touch with the divine inspiration that originally set them on the path to triumph. Still others cannot continue with their forward momentum without professional help. You can expect to be left in the lurch on occasion; you can expect to get lost at times—perhaps, in fact, many times.

Working through, or perhaps more accurately living through, feelings of victimization and confusion are an integral part of the quest toward triumph.

The Role of Surrender

To move forward on the path toward triumph requires the conscious decision to accept, even embrace, adversity. Ours is a culture that has little tolerance for the effects of trauma (despite the outpouring of post-9/11 sentiment, which itself seemed too short-lived), and even appreciation for what we have come to understand as "the gifts in trauma's other hand." Our culture imposes subtle limitations upon the growth of our consciousness, and our creative capacities can be restricted by such persistent, insidious conditioning in more ways than many of us realize.

To triumph is to free yourself from these cultural limitations and to overcome the limitations effected by the illness itself. To triumph is to form a productive, creative, and positive relationship with wounding, adversity, and loss, and an understanding that, in addition to the limitations imposed by our cultural conditioning and by the illness itself, you may unwittingly generate additional restrictions upon yourself. It is important to be alert to the self-incarceration that you will create if you make negative judgments about yourself, the mental illness, your loved one, or the experience of adversity itself. Triumph requires that you accept adversity's constant presence and, with vigilance and discernment, reject its potential to subjugate.[55]

Balance

To pay the price of triumph, to open the doors to triumph, you need to give to adversity and trauma the attention they deserve, *while at the same time refusing* to allow them to become the defining circumstance in your life. Adversity and trauma cannot be ignored, nor can you permit the wounding to determine who you are, what you believe, how you respond (in contrast to react) to situations, or how you relate to others. To triumph, you learn to become less dependent on what is happening in the outer circumstances of your life and to become more connected to what is occurring deeply inside of you.

Most important, understanding the price of triumph means that you understand at the core of your being that there is not anything wrong with you. It means that you, whether "you" are the person with the illness or the loved ones of the person with the illness, know at the level of your "essence" that you are not a bad person because you are facing mental illness. And it means that you aren't being chastised because you are wounded and facing mental illness. Mental illness is not a punishment given to you or a family member. It just "is."

Effort and Discipline

Adversity, while necessary for triumph, is not sufficient for triumph, however. In addition to the price of adversity, triumphs asks still more of you. A triumphant life for the most part is not an effortless life. A prize not easily won, triumph demands no less than all of what you can become. It calls you to form a life of purpose, meaning, and direction. It asserts that *it is never too late to* claim the rightful custody of yourself and to be the person you want to be. Summed up in the words of Joseph Campbell, "The privilege of a lifetime is being who you are."

A highly subjective experience, triumph calls us to be flexible in thought, act, and deed. Triumph is less about *doing* and more about *being*. It involves an active, meaningful, and engaging interchange with others *and* ourselves. The Abels, for example, needed to learn how to be different with each other, in addition to doing things differently. They learned to match the love in their hearts with the actions in their deeds. They learned to let their love develop, reach, and heal one another.

Triumph closes its eye to no events, no diagnoses, and no relationships, no matter how dark, how ill, or how shameful they may appear. To the contrary, triumph is inclusive, not exclusive: it incorporates all elements of our personal story and gives them significance, meaning, and value. In so doing, it gives us the courage, the wisdom, and the energy to move forward.

While independent of gender, ethnicity, intelligence, wealth, and position in life, triumph is dependent upon proactive and creative endeavors to form new connections, new understandings, new perspectives, and new stories. And as we have seen from our knowledge of neuroscience, the brain grows through experiences of innovation and interpersonal connection, both of which create fresh neural pathways that access our highest potentials.

By drawing from the disciplines of knowledge presented throughout this book,[56] you can find the materials to craft your own sacred and heroic stories. The common elements that these empowering approaches encourage include:

- a sense of control over the problem, or more accurately a sense of control over your response to the problem

- a sense of ownership of your role in the problem, even if you are not responsible for its occurrence or origin

- a sense of a problem's limited reach, or how far into your life you allow the problem to extend

- a sense of how long you think the problem will last, or the belief that the problem's horrors, which can *seem* never ending, may actually be brief in duration, even if the illness is not.

There are many real and powerful obstacles that you will surmount on the road to triumph. Ignorance, not educating yourself about the nature of your situation, thwarts triumph. Denial can create severe impediments. Some forms of denial can be primary symptoms of the more serious mental illnesses and may be physical in origin. Recall the warning of football coach Vince Lombardi: "Fatigue makes cowards of us all." The isolation, so frequent in families who live under the influence of all illnesses, addictions, and traumas, must give way to social interaction and support that nurture the soul *and* the brain. The journey to triumph is a personal voyage *and* an interpersonal journey; triumph may be manifested when the brain is engaged in certain activities, such as tapping into the deep meaning of the great stories that have been passed from one generation to the next.

Triumph requires your time, attention, and effort. For most, this includes learning about the influences and impact of your behaviors, as well as the behaviors of your loved one through such activities as reading appropriate books, going to lectures, attending workshops, and other educational programs. You may need to seek the services of a health professional, perhaps your physician, psychologist, or a social worker, as well as a member of the clergy, a spiritual counselor, or a healer. For still others, what may be needed is participation in such programs as twelve-step groups or other anonymous fellowships, the National Alliance for the Mentally Ill (NAMI), Family-to-Family groups, the National Depressive and Manic-Depressive Association, or the National Family Caregivers Association (NFCA).

These organizations and the host of other invaluable support groups, many of whose web sites can be found on the web site www.HealTheFamily.com, complement the healing process.

They are essential in helping you to remain connected to yourself and to something greater than they are. You often need to be reminded that you are much better than you know.

CHAPTER 21

The Long Voyage Home

The path is thoroughly known,
a reflection of the spirit that lives within us all.

—⦙⦙⦙—

I've been describing the many different pathways, whether via the mind, the body, the brain, the soul, or the spirit, that lead to triumph. It is most important to remember that triumph can be learned, and requires the development and cultivation of attitudes and beliefs that foster meaning, purpose, and connection. Triumph necessitates conscious choice and determined, will-directed effort. It must be nurtured in much the same way as a gardener tends to all budding plants. Sometimes, triumph needs careful coaxing and deliberate persuasion in order to unfold.

The manifesting of triumph begins with the acquisition of information. When we become educated about mental illness, its treatment, and its impact on the individual and the family, we open the doors to triumph. Triumph is nourished as all members of a family, both primary and secondary sufferers, find the support

needed to deal successfully with mental illness. Triumph material-
izes as we develop the skills necessary to address the illness and
its many impacts. We find the importance of making realistic expectations, learning to ask for help, and taking care of ourselves.
Triumph manifests when we actively engage in thinking, talking,
reflecting, therapy, grief work, and a host of other behaviors ori-
enting us toward a life worth living and a loss worth enduring.

With the aid of the knowledge from the fields of study described and illustrated throughout this book, you can create a life
worth living and a loss worth enduring. Triumph requires both,
and both require effort. These are the prices you must pay to triumph and to reap a full, meaningful, and complete life.

To come home to triumph is, ultimately, to come home to
your full nature. It is one of the reasons that you are here.

Taking the Next Step

Triumph is not a single act, or even a series of acts. It is not a
sprint; it is a marathon. Rather than a destination, it is a journey.
It is a lifetime of applying again and again the principles described
and illustrated in this book to unlock the doors to your triumph.
Triumph is clearly not for wimps, sissies, or cowards. The perennial philosophy tells us that all the great stories of triumph begin
in a wasteland of wounds, while all narrow and limited stories
end there. To journey from the narrowness of one's circumstance
to the fullness of the situation is no easy feat. Such a journey can
require no less than all that we are. The false paths are many and
the illusions proliferate.

Dan is a good example of someone who functions poorly in
life, because he gets caught in the outcome of situations rather
than appreciating the many steps along the way, especially his
own steps. His thinking is all or none, black or white. Either he

saves the day, or he is a failure. He has not learned to appreciate that there are some things over which he has little or no control, particularly how other people behave.

A warm and caring social worker in a small community, Dan also happens to have a mother who has suffered from schizophrenia for virtually all of his life. Assuming the role of the typical responsible child when he grew up, he learned from an early age that the "safest way in life is to be in control." However, what he is less aware of is how much energy that control requires, and he is left in a constant state of exhaustion, which he doesn't realize is connected to his rigid need for control.

Because of Dan's profession as a helper, his family places the expectation on him that he, "being a professional," should be able "to fix his mother's illness," or at least gracefully manage all of her psychotic episodes. Because Dan is a professional helper, he, too, expects that he should be able to handle whatever crisis his mother's illness creates. His all-or-none functioning precludes any feelings of success and accomplishment, even on those occasions when he is able to be helpful.

Whenever a crisis occurs, it is Dan and Dan alone who rallies the other family members, even when they don't want to participate. He believes that he should be able to mobilize the forces of the family to serve as healing agents for his mother, who he still loves and cares for. So he is constantly on the phone, monitoring her whereabouts and her medications. He runs himself ragged calling his mother, his brothers and sisters, the hospital, and sometimes the police.

The pain of his mother's psychosis is too much for him to bear without his trying to control her behaviors. Unfortunately, what worked so well for him when he was a child and was so responsible no longer works for him as an adult. He is not responsible for another person's, even his mother's, well-being. His guilt and other wounds are become more indelible by his isolation and lack of support.

The result is a sad, depressing story: he hasn't learned to embrace his own personal journey because he cannot let go of hers. Because he has not been able to control her behavior, he has judged himself a failure. Only when he discovers that he is the only one whom he has any real chance of controlling will he move beyond the influence of the illness. Only when he faces his pain, not just hers, will he move forward, even in the midst of all his mother's chaos. Only when he dares to take the journey the heroes of all time have taken will he have the opportunity to be free. So far, he has fooled himself into thinking that his journey is about her and in the process he has lost who he is. Unfortunately, not every family member is able or willing to take the arduous journey that healing and triumph require.

The Journey to the Self

The study of mythology teaches us that every wound, including the trauma of mental illness, can be the occasion for a journey, an odyssey no less dangerous or important than those our ancestors undertook to save the realm.[55] The journey is seldom easy or short, and is always fraught with both danger and opportunity. In fact, the occasion for the journey is typically a *crisis*, a word that is expressed in Chinese symbols, one for danger and the other for opportunity. Crises are indeed the juncture of danger and opportunity.

All members of the family under the influence of one of life's major wounds are exposed to this crossroads. They go forth on the journey described by the sages from all of time. Called the hero's (or heroine's) journey[18] by modern mythologists, it is universal and has been described as consisting of three main stages.

The first stage is *Separation*. We leave that which has been familiar and comfortable. In mythological terms, the realm is under siege and a call is made for someone to leave home to do battle. For families under the influence of mental illness, the monster or dragon is the illness. Oftentimes, the beast is a secondary illness such as alcohol and other drug problems, which can attack both the primary and secondary sufferer. For all family members, the stage of separation starts with the onset of the illness and its attendant symptoms.

This launches the second stage or *Initiation*. In this stage we endure major trials that test our strength and courage. We are usually thrust into the darkness where we must do battle with our demons, face our monsters, and dispel the falsehoods and misunderstandings. A frightening time, often scarcely imaginable, it is full of doubt and confusion and wonder. For family members, this stage involves learning about the illness, dealing with the false beliefs surrounding mental illness, as well as dealing with their own feelings of fear and shame. All members of the family face this stage. Like the primary sufferer, secondary sufferers have their own issues[62, 64, 65] as well as their own descent and initiation into another life.

If we survive this part of the crossing, we enter the third stage of the hero's journey, or the *Return*. Having left the familiar, having fought our devils from within and without, we return home with the gifts of our new learning, and we share them with others. For family members, this usually involves a process of "refamilying,"[62] a critical concept that we explored in greater depth in an earlier chapter, in which there is a "return home."

Unfortunately, like the mythical heroes of old, we may be tempted and attacked on the way home, as so often is the case. The process of reestablishing our position in the family home is in itself an important, and seldom easy, part of the journey. For example, armed with new understandings about the nature of the illness and its impact, we may alter our previous reactions to family members. Both the primary and secondary sufferer may be asked to assume more responsibility (for example, be in treatment or recovery), and secondary sufferers may no longer participate in some of the unhealthy behaviors of the primary sufferer.

The Journey of a Lifetime

In this book, you are invited to take an extraordinary journey, a journey no less profound or difficult than the one taken by our ancestors hundreds and even thousand of years ago.[18] The path is thoroughly known,[18] a reflection of the spirit that lives within us all. It is a story as old as time, a story of danger and opportunity, a momentous tale of the kingdom besieged. Usually, the health and well-being of the whole kingdom are at stake in these great stories. A person is summoned (or presented with the call) and asked to face the forces that threaten the realm. Although the person is given an extraordinary feat to accomplish, he or she is typically quite ordinary. This person is usually reluctant to accept the assignment, and may not believe that it can even be accomplished.

Our hero or heroine, as the person comes to be known in these tales, nevertheless goes forth, albeit with fear and trepidation, to fight the forces that threaten the realm, facing great, often extraordinary, adversities and overcoming enormous odds. Along the way, there are trials or tests that the person must pass in order to save the kingdom. At times, there are magicians, sorcerers, and guides along the way who may help in charting the territory, or who may try to block the path. After successfully confronting dragons and demons or whatever other mythical dilemmas, our hero now turns toward home. The process of returning home is a unique part of the hero or heroine's journey, itself also fraught with danger and intrigue.

The American existential psychiatrist Rollo May[92] summarizes the universality of this journey, which applies to all of us: "All through history it is true that only by going through hell does one have any chance of reaching heaven. The voyage through hell is a part of the journey that cannot be omitted—indeed, what one learns in hell is prerequisite to arriving at any good value thereafter." He adds, "The agony, the horror, the sadness, are a necessary prelude to self-realization and self-fulfillment."

Passed from one generation to the next, such great and noble journeys are called epics. These uncommon tales involve a pursuit for salvation, a quest for values, a triumph of the sacred, and a homecoming. These stories have lived for thousands of years because they tell our story. And even as each of our journeys is unique and individual, our life stories express universal themes, experiences, and feelings. The messages in these stories have transcended time. Although the form, content, and context differ, their compelling essence overrides cultural and religious beliefs.

One such tale is the story of Ulysses,[15] whose Roman name is Odysseus, the hero who helped win the Trojan War in Homer's three-thousand-year-old epic poem, the *Iliad*. He was the cunning Greek warrior who conceived the idea of the Trojan horse, a mighty wooden horse, filled with soldiers, that the unsuspecting and unprepared Trojans brought into their city. While everyone slept, the huge structure released its cargo of soldiers, and they were now able to capture the once-impregnable city of Troy.

But the fall of Troy didn't end this story. It was just the beginning of another one. Ulysses had to return home to his beloved family in Ithaca to fulfill his heroic mission. The ten-year voyage home became the subject of Homer's next epic, the *Odyssey*, which is the story of Ulysses' return to his loved ones after the wearying siege of Troy and a succession of intense encounters with himself. Along this part of the odyssey, he encountered new and different adversities. Prepared by decades of defeats and victories, Ulysses was equipped to deal with any new set of problems. All of his trials and tribulations proved necessary for his triumphant return.

When Ulysses returned home to his wife and son, he found his family impoverished and the kingdom in disarray. Despite his heroism in the war, he wasn't welcomed or even recognized by many. Rather, a band of ill-willed suitors sought to take his wife, and laid waste to his kingdom. They were also a danger to the safety of his only son. After another series of trials, in which he once again summoned his well-tested courage, he triumphed over those who had tried to take away his family and steal his realm. Order was eventually restored and the *Odyssey* has become the classic story of the final stage of the hero's journey, aptly called "The Return." This final stage, the return to home, is fraught with no less danger than any other stage, and requires unwavering discernment and persistence.[18]

Having been forced to engage with his demons in the long odyssey home, Ulysses' awareness and understanding had been further broadened. He was able to apply and refine the skills that he had acquired during the war. Had our hero not fought in the Trojan War, learning to hone and sharpen his skills in the face of adversity, he might not have survived on the dangerous trek home. Moreover, Ulysses had successfully reintegrated into his family, once again using his skills for survival over great odds. Rising skillfully above the many dangers of the war *and* the journey homeward, he had given himself the opportunity to live a full and meaningful life.

Ulysses had survived the siege of Troy, he had survived the surprisingly dangerous return from the war, he had crafted the rebuilding of his family and his realm, and he had integrated the many new aspects of himself into his new life with his family. This is a life that reaches beyond survival, which is difficult in and of itself, a life that continues upward into the realms of triumph, a life lived fully.

Daring to engage fully in the crisis, showing true courage in the face of danger, persevering with skill and wisdom, one passes through the danger. The opportunities inherent in the nature of crisis are unveiled. The expansion of our humanity flows naturally from overcoming our fears. Repeating this cycle many times throughout our lives, we continue in a state of grace, finding our "true" nature, becoming who we are. This is the privilege of a lifetime.

Modern Heroes

Like the ancient heroes of old, the children of alcoholics with whom I have worked were wounded by the wake of the disease of alcoholism, and traveled their own journeys of recovery (the modern-day hero's journey) that led them beyond the family's denial, secrecy, silence, and shame.[65] They read books to acquire new information, attended workshops, participated in counseling, and then returned home to their families to share with their loved ones what they had learned. Often, they were greeted with disdain and the refrain, "There is no alcoholism in this family, and don't you dare tell anybody!"

How often do the family members of the mentally ill make a comparable voyage to encounter their fears, their demons and monsters, and return to their home with new skills, only to hear a similar refrain? Without the knowledge they have gathered, those under the influence of mental illness, too, might not overcome the difficulties that are a part of their homecoming.

In fact, those under the influence of *any* major sustained illness, trauma, or addiction are fighting their own battles and might have a similar fate. They are the contemporary heroes or heroines of classical mythology. Christopher Reeve, the star of the Superman movies, tells how he completely redefined his concept of a hero. After his horrific accident, in which he became totally paralyzed, he no longer believed that a hero is someone who commits a courageous action without considering the consequences. Rather, he came to deem that a hero is an ordinary individual who finds the strength to persevere and endure in spite of overwhelming obstacles. He gives the examples of a fifteen-year-old boy who landed on his head while wrestling with his brother, leaving him barely able to swallow or speak, or Travis Roy, who was paralyzed in the first thirty seconds of a hockey game in his freshman year at college. These are real heroes, he writes, for they went on to develop lives worth having and losses worth enduring. Reeve adds that so are the families and friends who have stood by them.

Perhaps the person who lives next door, thrust into an overwhelming and catastrophic situation by one of life's extreme mishaps, is combating a monster no less scary, or dangerous, than the menacing dragons faced by our mythical hero. In the case of mental illness, however, the person frequently does not have the support of his or her homeland. In addition, his or her battle may be shrouded in secrecy, shame, and stigma so great that terror, fear, and danger may ensue.

Like his or her mythic counterpart, everyone who lives under the influence of mental illness is on a journey of triumph. Rather than one climactic journey, however, it is a subtle and extended journey, one that unfolds on a daily basis. On this voyage, rather than the kingdom, it is the realm of the family that is often at stake. On this odyssey, body and mind, soul and spirit, are in jeopardy. The outcome of the trials and tribulations of the journey can affect the welfare of every member of the family, as well as its future generations.

—m—

CHAPTER 22

Coping Strategies

Last and perhaps most important:
Never give up—ever.

—⁓—

To get the most from reading this book, there are some simple and powerful coping strategies that may make your life easier and more productive. Do not feel patronized or be deceived by their simplicity. They can be very helpful, and they may remain useful to you long after you have finished this book. They may ease your pain, as the passage of time allows you to view events from a more balanced perspective.

While there are an abundance of strategies such as be flexible, focus on the positive, avoid blaming others, don't judge, don't panic, or do one nice act for yourself every day, many are difficult to implement. The twelve coping approaches that follow can put you in a state of consciousness that will enable you to do the more obvious ones such as those listed above.

If you have difficulty following some of these strategies without guidance or extraordinary effort, be patient with yourself.
They require time, effort, and attention. In addition, some of
you may have a serious mental illness that involves faulty brain
chemistry and faulty brain functioning, which may necessitate
even more consideration. Nevertheless, you can learn more than
you've ever thought possible, regardless of any biological and
physiological impediments:

1. **Check in to discover what is happening and what you
    are experiencing.**

    "Checking in," a term borrowed from energy medicine
    and energy psychology,[88] is the master, or overarching,
    strategy. First, however, it may prove helpful to "check in"
    on the concept of energy itself, which is likely to be the
    most controversial and speculative of all the perspectives
    presented. The energy "therapies" are the oldest and new-
    est healing methods. In ancient times, the idea that we exist
    in both matter and energy states was commonplace, while
    cutting-edge technologies today are often energy-based,
    providing extensions of Einstein's famous equation, $E=mc^2$,
    meaning that ENERGY is the product, or result, of accel-
    erated MATTER by the speed of light squared; hence, that
    matter and energy are interchangeable.[88]

    This perspective asserts that we not only have physi-
    cal bodies, but we are also energy bodies. Modern science
    shows that we live in electromagnetic fields that support
    and contain the body.[16, 32, 47, 48, 49, 88] These electromagnetic
    fields move charged particles that neutralize unbalanced
    charges within ourselves. At times, we can take on a
    charge so intense that we "shut down" electromagnetical-
    ly. When this occurs, our consciousness becomes narrow
    and limited, we are no longer in present time, and we re-
    act to situations instead of responding to them, thus

becoming less capable of effective action.[88] In short, we can become disabled by these out-of-sight influences.

The words that we speak and use for communicating possess their own energy, which significantly influence our energy field. Words in the form of language, whether through story, poetry, or prose, have a major impact on our thoughts, attitudes, beliefs, feelings, and ultimately our behaviors. Consider, for example, some of the following words: you can't, you won't, no, yes, never, maybe, absolutely, love, anger, hate. Do they not have a clear and distinct resonance? One can only imagine the power of carefully crafted words made into sentences that convey meaning and purpose.

In fact, the companion book to this one, *Words That Heal,*[57] dynamically illustrates this relationship among energy, language, and the person by presenting example after example of words that inspire, words that move, and words that heal. Almost all of them are from the perennial philosophy, or the wisdom of the ages, including modern perennial philosophy.

When a person receives any strong emotional message, such as a diagnosis of a family member with mental illness, he or she can experience a "short" in the electromagnetic energy field that supports the person. As with an overloaded electrical circuit, the protective circuit breaker opens, causing a temporary state of darkness— that is, a disruption in the energy flow—until the circuit can be restored. Being overwhelmed by a thought or feeling can disconnect the person from his or her resources and wisdom. The person may dissociate, and experience a "broken or impaired circuit" to other abilities. The result will be a person who functions below his or her capability until the connection is fully reestablished. The technique referred to as checking in alerts the microcircuitry of your brain to "turn on your lights again" so that you will be able to process your experiences more effectively. This process can be invoked by using one or more of the strategies described below.

2. Ask questions that lead to empowering answers.

Each of you is a composite of many different personalities, often called sub-personalities, although you may fail to recognize them. When stuck, you may be caught in one or more of our sub-personalities. For example, when you are stumped, it may be hard to separate the "child" part of you from the "adult" part, and you may fuse the "child" and the "adult," or you may become entangled within your "child." When this happens, your lack of perspective can make it difficult to decipher which part of you is in control. It can be difficult to tell whether the child part of you or the adult part is in control. This is called "age regression," a term borrowed from the language of hypnosis and altered states of consciousness.

In situations like the above, it can be helpful to ask questions of yourself that draw you toward powerful inquiries, such as: Through whose eyes am I looking at this situation? With whose ears am I listening? Whose opinion is this? Is this the mental illness speaking? Who in my family would feel like this or have similar beliefs? If you see a vision of hope and optimism, or hear the call of your destiny, ask if it is your adult self that is bringing forth this vision. If you are feeling as if you will never be able to succeed, is it your child self who feels overwhelmed? Or, might it be a "critical parent self"?

Curiosity is one of your most valuable instincts. Rely on it to lead you forward. Give free rein to your curiosity. Let spontaneity lead you beyond such limiting conceptions as blame, which too often merely confuses the situation, or guilt, which is often just more about you. Both blame and guilt can cloud understanding and blind you to solutions. Be curious about who is in your "control tower." As one of my clients says, "Check in to see who is driving the bus." Is it your fearful child, is it your mature adult who is thinking rationally, or is it your out-of-date parental voice?

Illness begs for answers, the answers to life's most difficult questions, the questions that examine life itself. "There are questions," as author Gregg Levoy[86] writes, "to which you need to respond, expose yourself, and kneel before." These are questions invariably brought on by the wake of illness, addiction, and trauma. These are questions such as, "Who am I?" "Does this situation define who I am?" "Do I deserve what is happening?" "Why me?"

Levoy continues, "You want a question that will become a chariot to carry you across the breadth of your life, a question that will offer you a lifetime of pondering, that will lead you toward what you need to know for your integrity, draw you to what you need for your journey, help you understand what it means to burst at the seams."

3. Get the problem out of your head.

Externalize the problem. Separate the problem from you. Give it a voice. It is very empowering to give it a name. For example, many children with whom I have worked have learned to give their disorder or illness a name. One little boy who suffered from OCD would speak of "the worry monster," which was always around during the constant negative thoughts he suffered. He learned to become much less afraid of the worry monster. One family member called her constant worry about her loved one "Ms. Worry Wart." "Ms. Worry Wart" was a signal that the problem was being overdramatized, further obscuring the issue and the possibility of resolution.

Fear and shame thrive in secrecy, silence, and darkness. So, if you or a loved one has an illness, addiction, or trauma, speak to someone trustworthy, someone in whom you have complete confidence, and with whom you might feel very safe. Use the words "mental illness." As Al-Anon so frequently reminds us, "Mentionable is manageable."

Rather than being overwhelmed by fear, tell yourself that fear (out there) is invading you (in here). Look at the problem through your eyes rather than through the eyes of fear; listen through your ears, not the ears of fear. Separate your feelings from the feelings that fear has. Learn to relate "to it," rather than "from it." (These and other useful distinctions can be found in Appendix B.)

4. "Snap" yourself into a more resourceful state.

We can get mired in a negative state of mind. An easy and surprisingly helpful strategy called the "rubber band tactic" will sometimes help you snap out of a negative mind-set, particularly if it's not a major one. Professional athletes, like former basketball great Charles Barkley, use this approach to help them stay focused and present. The procedure is simple. Place a rubber band around your wrist. Whenever you want to be reminded of a certain thought, or wish to snap out of a particular state, simply pull the rubber band back several inches and let it go. It needn't be far. Some people can pull that rubber band out ten inches!

Realize that the rubber band tactic can be a short-term solution, even for a long-term problem. Interrupting a negative pattern in which you may find yourself, it will work especially well with situational issues, such as being irritable, controlling, aggressive, compliant, or over-indulging, any of which can be mindless states that need not last long. Use this strategy to snap out of a more fleeting fear or restraint. This tool is not appropriate for interrupting the deeper, more firmly entrenched habit patterns. Don't use this tool to stop a hallucination or an obsession. Be gentle with yourself as you use it.

5. Change your physiology.

A change in your physiology or your body state also shifts your psychological state. A powerful way to eliminate a negative psychological state is to move your body. Breathe consciously and deeply during difficult moments evoked by this book. If one is frightened, one tends to take only shallow breaths, leaving the brain in need of more oxygen. Breathing deeply and consciously feeds your brain with energy. If you feel emotionally bogged down, you may be holding your body in a rigid position when you are stymied or baffled, so change your posture. "Checking in" with yourself invariably involves a change in your body.

6. Create "anchors."

Anchors, a term derived from the field of neurolinguistic programming[67] (see the Glossary for definition), are external objects that will often connect you to a more powerful and resourceful mindset. They are useful and effective. Whenever you feel immobile or frightened, for example, reach for your key. A car key (house key, apartment key, or office key) can be a powerful reminder, or anchor, of our freedom. A key can be a strong point of focus. When I did my clinical internship training, I asked my supervisor what was the real difference between the patients and us. (Some looked and even seemed to act just like I did.) He simply said, "You have the keys!" Keys have never meant the same thing for me again.

Other anchors that you might use could be a special stone, a particular song, or a favorite passage in a book. Be gentle with yourself and don't expect the anchors to solve major problems. They are valuable opportunities for you to pause and reflect. Anchors provide breathing room for you to do the work.

7. Know your allies.

Connect with someone else as often as possible. Get outside of yourself. Reach out to others whom you can trust. There is strength in numbers. In the parlance of AA, "When under siege, reach for the phone and not the bottle." Mental illness should never be fought alone. The noted mythologist Sam Keen aptly noted, "The first rule of war: know your enemy." When I told one family member this, she said, "And the second rule is to know your allies." So, last but not least, reach out. Connect with a family member, a friend, your therapist, your doctor, and your clergyman or clergywoman. Connect especially with those who are on the same journey.

8. Identify actions that you can use to keep you moving forward.

Before anyone knew about the benefits of therapy and medication, people throughout the millennia found comfort and support in the immediate obligations and habits of their ordinary, daily life. Sometimes, the greatest incentive for coping lies in your relationships with other people, especially those who depend upon you. Sometimes, the simplest act can have profound implications. Bob would always shed tears of gratitude (and relief) when his wife, who suffered from bipolar disorder, acknowledged *his* plight. He knew that as long as she could empathize with him, she was not entering a manic phase of the illness. When she was unable to express compassion, he knew that she was perched on the threshold of a manic episode.

Hope follows action. Procrastination is often the archenemy of effective crisis management. At times, a situation escalates to a crisis level because someone has failed to initiate. People can become so afraid (to fail) that they can shut down and do nothing. Failure is part of the learning cycle. Try something and if it doesn't work, try something else.

Discovering what *you must do* can provide, at times, a type of psycho-spiritual scaffolding for the construction of more positive states. Becoming aware of what you are actually doing—even if it's "just surviving" or "just managing"—can be the first step toward rebuilding your sense of personal agency and control. Clarity is the beginning of effective action.

Therefore, ask yourself specific questions about your immediate circumstance and future, such as "What do I need to do tomorrow? What do I need to get done in the next hour/day/week? Who needs what from me? Am I capable of giving at this moment?" Writing down practical, immediate plans can provide you with a specific focus during the chaos of the moment.

Then imagine someone who loves you telling you exactly what you have been doing right. Write down the person's words or speak them into a tape recorder. Review them—often. Many who do this simple exercise find, to their delight, that they are already (or are becoming) the person they need to be to deal with the situation.

9. Find ways to become inspired.

The word "inspire" is derived from the Latin *inspirare*, meaning to breathe into. On the long journey of living under the influence of mental illness, or any other serious adversity, it is absolutely essential to have an ongoing source of support that can breathe the life back into you. There are many ways to become inspired: through friendships, through the arts, through athletics, and through the words and actions of others.

Create reminders for yourself of intentions that you choose to birth. One of my favorites is the Serenity Prayer. Discover your own words that take you back to a place of safety, healing, and triumph, especially after a difficult day.

Words That Heal: More Help for the Family is a treasure-house of the accumulated wisdom of the ages. Written as a readily available source of inspiration, it is organized around the stages of recovery from any of life's major adversities, it parallels all of the important concepts and principles that are presented in this book, and is a wonderful companion and supplement to this book as well as my previous ones.[61, 65] It can enable you to find your own special reminders to complete the difficult task of finding a life worth living and a loss worth enduring.

10. When all else fails, do something safe and radical.

Sometimes, you need to take effective action that will change you or remove you from a situation. One of the simplest is to take a break, go for a walk, take a shower, or make love in any of a dozen ways—physically, verbally, or spiritually. One man with whom I worked said that if all else fails to shift your feeling state, stand on your head. It is rather drastic, but it's also highly effective. I have never known this strategy to fail to change a person's state of mind, or consciousness. The effect may not last long. Repeating it can help.

11. Ask for help when you feel lost or overwhelmed.

It is a consistent research finding that people who can ask for help when they need it are those who not only survive difficulties but also actually thrive in difficult situations. Some situations, such as active chemical abuse, suicidal behaviors, and other out-of-control behaviors, virtually demand it. Often, merely reaching out to others is the first step to restoring balance and instituting calm. While this strategy has been given in other contexts of the

book, its importance cannot be overestimated and it cannot be repeated enough.

12. **Last and perhaps most important: Never give up—ever—
for the next moment can bring order and relief from even
the most chaotic situations.**

Life doesn't proceed the way we think that it is sup-
posed to. We get off the path, we fail, we miss important
opportunities; it can even look like we are just moving
in circles. But those who triumph persist anyway. They
hang on to hope even when the situation looks hopeless.
To them, the belief that where there is life, there is hope is
not an old cliché. They just don't quit! Don't you either.
Each day, each hour, indeed each moment, is another beginning, another opportunity to re-create yourself anew.
There is no reason to stop trying! Ignorance is not bliss.

A number of other useful and powerful tools have been
described to help you to create a triumphant life. In the
process, they can also help you to move from one stage of
healing to another. Just as the map is not the territory, or
the menu is not the food, the tools are not the house. But
they can be very powerful. Each one actually builds on the
previous. Actually, all of them are a variation of the very
first one, checking in. It is through checking in that you realize where you are and who you are.

The tools presented throughout the entire book can
help you forge a container strong enough to hold all of
your feelings and thoughts. They can guide you in directions that call you forth as a person and as a family. Use
the tools to help you build the house of your aspirations.
Remember, do not be misled by their apparent simplicity; they may be simple but they are not easy. Become the
architect of a triumphant family, a person who will build
the future, not re-create the past.

—ᴠᴠᴠ—

CHAPTER 23

The Role of
the Professional

Honoring the family.

—⁊⁊⁊—

Historically, most professionals have not understood the challenges facing secondary sufferers, nor have they recognized the value that the family offers in the process of triumph.[89, 90] In the process, they have missed the many opportunities that the family provides. Rather than giving comfort and understanding to the family members who are traumatized, professionals have minimized their plight to the extent that they have avoided family members. Consequently, they have excluded the family from their loved one's treatment, while at the same time holding them responsible.

Exclusion often breeds fear, and professionals have sometimes been harsh, unkind, and inaccurate in their judgment of the family. Rather than including the family as the invaluable resource they can be, too many professionals have ignored, discounted, and marginalized the family.[62] I know that I engaged in all of the above behaviors until I realized just how crucial the family is to our well-being.

Learning what seems to be a self-evident truth—two or more people facing adversity can bond together and be of invaluable assistance to each other—has revolutionized my clinical practice, and it has made me become more effective as teacher, coach, cheerleader, comforter, and healer, as well as the many other roles, such as "holder of the healing vision," when the family is too stressed, too overwhelmed, too grieved, and too exhausted.

Difficult Beliefs to Grasp

Even well-intentioned family practitioners can make important mistakes in assessing family members if they do not understand the subtleties of the impact of the illness on those under its influence. Many of these errors stem from the paradoxical nature inherent in working with those who experience the wake of serious mental illness.

The following ten paradoxes are taken from the work of Rex Dickens,[31] whose work on identifying the impact of mental illness on the individual family members is a seminal contribution to the field. Each statement is more often true than not, although each one can seem counterintuitive and appear to defy common sense. When practitioners do not take into account the soundness of each point, they can make significant errors in judgment.

1. **Those who appear least affected in the family can be the most affected.** Like other family members of disenfranchised groups, such as the children of alcoholics, those under the influence of mental illness do not like to stand out. Adopting roles that result in their looking good on the outside, they often suffer profoundly on the inside.

Further, as trauma becomes more severe, the sufferer's affect, or feeling state, may become less noticeable, because the person learns to dissociate or disconnect with his or her emotional state.

2. **The most healthy-looking family members may be the most vulnerable.** The cost of a high-functioning outer life can be an inner life of turmoil and isolation. In addition, the "healthier" members can be those who are more like "human doings" than "human beings." Neglecting their own needs, they focus on others and become codependents. Because they appear nonsymptomatic, they are often ignored. As we have discovered, the price of caring can be very high. Also, the less healthy family members, in some ways, may be partially immunized against the impact of the illness, because they may have less emotional range and receptivity.

3. **The less severe forms of mental illness in the long run may be more disorienting and conflict producing than the more severe forms.** This paradox stems from the fact that those with more severe illnesses are less able to function and thus the illness becomes obvious to all. Consequently, they are more likely to receive early treatment. The less severe illnesses are less obvious, and those who suffer from them are often more prone to denial. It is only after a long period of uncertainty that treatment is solicited, if at all. Without a psychotic break, years and even decades of confusion may await the family members.

4. **Offspring who appear responsible and mature in younger years may fail to develop in adulthood and may become increasingly immature with age.** Childhood wounds often become resurrected and appear in later life when new challenges and traumas are experienced. As we have discovered, early trauma predisposes us to later vulnerability

if a healing or recovery process has not been initiated. Lost childhoods exact a heavy price.

5. **Rather than making siblings closer, as one might think, mental illness can fragment and separate them, which can result in little closeness among siblings, especially as they grow older.** While common experiences can be bonding, what often happens in families is that the "well" children can become neglected. While the squeaky wheel may get the attention, those whose needs constantly get ignored can feel resentful of the burdens placed upon them. Perceived favoritism can occur, which creates hard feelings. In adulthood, they may want little to do with their ill brothers or sisters.

6. **Family members may be told to "get on with their own lives," disregarding their reality that they, too, have experienced major trauma.** As one family member shared, "Not only am I ignored, but I am not even allowed to have my pain. This is insult to injury." It is crucial to acknowledge the pain and suffering of all members of the family. Few escape what can be lifelong wounds and the denial of these wounds only fosters further injury. Ironically, attention to the wounds maximizes the likelihood that the damage will be minimized.

7. **Family members are told to "treat the afflicted like everyone else," but the reality is that the ill member has an altered mental/emotional reality.** Messages like these only reinforce the sense of denial that can be so pervasive in families under the influence. They further isolate the sufferer from his or her true experiences and from others as well.

8. **There is the mistaken belief that children are minimally affected by mental illness in the home, because they are too young to understand what is happening.** In reality, they may have been significantly affected, because they

are more vulnerable. It may be easier to believe that the children are too young to notice what is happening, but the earlier the trauma, the more damaging it tends to be—psychologically, neurologically, and spiritually.

9. **Family members may later undertake a healing journey in adulthood that they were unable to take as children.** Ironically, as they move beyond the influence of the mental illness, they become too healthy to remain unhealthy. It is often only when these family members have the added resources and maturity of adulthood that they may recognize that something has not been right and seek help.

10. **Therapists' abilities to identify ordinary trauma can preclude their ability to recognize severe trauma.** Therapists commonly identify trauma by a person's anguish. In severe trauma, there can be few feelings, many of which are muted. There may be little overt anguish because the dissociation is so profound. The result can be that severe trauma is often overlooked.

The mistaken belief that mental illness is on a continuum with mental health rather than an abject break with reality, combined with an inability to recognize the various forms of trauma, can create a situation that allows the family practitioner to do as much harm as good to these family members. Effective practitioners must be willing to undertake fresh understandings.

A Full Life Revisited

There is another paradox that may be the most insidious of all. Working to achieve better relationships upfront often backfires. This is not the most fruitful place to start. The effective helper knows that family interaction isn't always fun in any family. Family healing does not *begin* with correcting the communication and interaction patterns of the family so that the primary sufferer can recover. Focusing on family interaction too early in the healing process is too reminiscent for many families of the turbulent era of the 1950s and 1960, when families went through the horror of being called "schizophrenigenic."

Too many parents, especially mothers, have been stigmatized this way. The blaming of the family did much harm to the valiant struggle of many families. Therefore, the healing capacity of the family is often reduced and the healing resources that are inherent within the family remain hidden when the family is approached in this manner.

Rather, only when each person feels that his or her struggle is validated and understood can that person then interact in more adaptive and healthy ways. The healing of the family is an outgrowth from and result of each individual family member's triumph. Producing a healthy family, let alone a happy family, more likely becomes a natural by-product of the healing of each family member. It cannot be said often enough that triumph is facilitated when the plight of each family member is honored. Only then does the person have the greatest chance to create a life worth living and a loss worth enduring.

Remember that a "full life" is one that goes beyond a pleasant life, a good life, and even a meaningful life. It encompasses all three.[119] A full life is a triumphant life, one in which all experiences are accepted by the individual, whether good or bad. The value of life goes beyond sensory pleasure, which is always circumstantial and temporary. A full life is independent of circumstance. Stated differently, one family member put it this way: "Just as there are people who starve in the midst of plenty, there are others who thrive in the midst of anything!"

In the final analysis, triumph, family healing, and a full life do not depend on the progress of any one family member, but the long overdue attention to all family sufferers. Too often, however, by the time families receive help in these tasks—if they do at all—there has been so much injury and hurt that some families believe family healing is impossible.

Some may argue that happiness or a happy family is an oversimplified, oxymoronic idea. When considering the idea of a full life, the following Sufi teaching provides yet another illuminating glimpse that offers all family members additional ways to place their circumstance in context: The goal of man is Truth. Truth is more than happiness. The man who has Truth can have whatever mood he wishes, or none. We have pretended that Truth is happiness and happiness Truth, and people have believed us. Therefore you, too, have until now imagined that happiness must be the same as Truth. But happiness makes you its prisoner, as does woe.

Life's constant play of opposites, victory and defeat, sickness and health, pleasure and pain, the best of times and the worst of times, are part and parcel of a life fully lived, a source of richness and depth rather than an obstacle or impediment *when approached with compassion, understanding, and support.*

It is in this sense that a full life and a complete life is virtually always possible, regardless of circumstance. As such luminaries as Victor Frankl remind us, we have choices. Yet, our ability to deceive ourselves seems never-ending. I have discovered the process of remembering this is less an end in and of itself than an ongoing challenge every day. For the helping professional, let alone the family, this is something we not only must teach but also live ourselves.

New Challenges

To birth the great challenge and potential posed by mental illness, professionals must reach out proactively to this neglected population; they must validate and support the plight of the whole family; they must provide concrete and practical expertise on becoming more effective communicators, negotiators, and navigators through what can be a very complicated and frightening experience; and they must understand, appreciate, and convey the interpersonal and systemic nature of trauma so that everyone in the family can begin to make sense of what is happening to them. What is more, professionals must recognize the contributions and expertise of the family, as well as acknowledging the legitimate rights and needs of family caregivers. They must normalize the family experience, empower its members, respect their plight, and offer realistic hope. They must forge a collaborative spirit—a three-way alliance with the person who has the mental illness, the family members, and themselves.

There are ten essential characteristics that the family-helping agent or consultant must have. They transcend disciplines. In other words, they are more important than whether the health provider is a psychiatrist, a psychologist, or a social worker. They include the following:

1. **Knowledge of the specific kinds of mental illness, other illnesses that are concurrent or are associated with them, and the impacts of both on the individual and the family.** Helping professionals should be adept in identifying mental illness and its many effects, especially compassion fatigue. They must be able to distinguish problems of living from the problems caused by mental illness, as well as being able to identify the harmful effects of alcohol and other drug addictions on the treatment process. Consultants, therefore, must be good diagnosticians. They must be able to make moment-to-moment assessments of whether the family is moving in a healthy direction or not, and they must have the ability to act and

intervene quickly when the family or one of its members is off course and moving away from health. Families need respectful direction.

2. **An extensive referral network.** The good diagnostician knows when, how, and to whom to refer her or his clients. The capable professional, like the capable family member, does not make the journey alone. He or she should have a thorough knowledge of the kinds of support groups available, be they face-to-face groups like NAMI and Family-to-Family, or twelve-step groups like Al-Anon and AA. With the advent of the Internet, the clinician can also direct the family to more impersonal but nevertheless effective avenues, such as chat rooms, listservs, or other computer services for a new generation of "netizens."

3. **The ability to identify, acknowledge, and utilize capacities and competencies that the family already possesses.** The family almost always has sufficient resources for the task when they are properly accessed. The effective family consultant must repeatedly point out strengths and focus minimal attention on the more apparent weaknesses. The consultant constantly uses what the family is doing that is right, or what is already working in the family, to fix what is wrong, or not working. Research shows that more can be accomplished when strengths are maximized than when weaknesses are emphasized.[37, 38] For example, the commitment, love, and the caring of family members are used to build family alliances and to secure agreements among members. Other resources that can be utilized in the family include a strong sense of family, friends, values, desire, motivation, the ability to cooperate, life skills, hobbies, freedom from drugs and violence, the absence of other physical or mental illnesses, money, intelligence, rituals, and religious or spiritual practices.

Each one of these has the potential to be a therapeutic lever to higher functioning.

4. **The ability to remain calm in the face of the family's overwhelming sense of chaos, confusion, and wounding.** Helping agents must be able to hold the heat and construct a crucible of triumph and healing. This ability cannot be underestimated. The family under the influence of mental illness is a family under siege. It is stressed, strained, traumatized, and conflicted. Effective consultants must be able metaphorically to hold up the rafters of the ceiling so that family members can do the work they need to do instead of letting the rafters of injury and hurt fall on everyone. They must not fall prey to over-pathologizing what is actually normal behavior, given the abnormal nature of the situation. They must be able to put family problems into the proper context where they can be solved. Like skillful chefs, they know that too much heat will burn the food, but too little will not break it down into something nourishing.

5. **Allegiance to the family unit.** Rather than any one member, the family is the unit of treatment. Unless there is the danger of harm, it is critical for the practitioner to remain neutral and loyal to the family as a whole. Very importantly, the consultant must be able to find, see, and articulate a family vision—ideas and goals that virtually every member of the family can identify with and agree upon. A general rule of thumb is that the clinician is never more than two thoughts away from the family's goals, because it is these goals that will keep the family moving forward. A critical part of this allegiance to the family unit is to maintain a multigenerational perspective of the family and present this perspective to the family repeatedly. Family members, exhausted by discouragement or disillusionment, can often see no further than their

own generation, thereby missing the powerful resources inherent in making the connection to their futures. A new source of hope can await each new family generation.

6. **The willingness to initiate and to reach out to all members of the family.** Few families understand mental illness when it first occurs, particularly its impact on every member. Practitioners need to make special efforts *whenever possible* to engage the family, and they should routinely inquire whether there are other members of the family who could become part of the therapeutic team. Without understanding, support, and skill building, the family can fall prey to the illness as easily as their loved one can. We no longer have to wait for proof to support the importance of family interventions.

7. **The commitment to help all family members, both the primary and the secondary sufferers, not only to survive their plight, not only to manage their plight, but to actively create meaning and make sense of their world so that they can achieve their purpose for living.** In this sense, working with family members is not just about treatment, not just about healing, but encouraging and engaging their curiosity about their own beliefs and reasons for living. There is always something useful that the practitioner and the family member can create together. Every encounter can be like a fresh canvas on which the meaning of the family's existence can be painted. Each member is offered an invitation to step outside his or her limited life story long enough to discover anew that it is indeed only a story that was created, and that stories can always be rewritten. Part of this commitment by the professional is to refuse to be overwhelmed by the family member's current situation or story, and constantly to establish a context in which new possibilities can emerge. Family members know a great deal. Ask them about themselves

and their dreams. They know much more than you think. If you show them respect, if you acknowledge their plight, and if you ask politely, they will more often than not tell you what they know.

8. **The ability to braid a fabric of intervention by synthesizing the healing ingredients of listening, empathizing, inviting the family to examine the consequences of its behaviors, finding agreement, and building partnership, all of which enable the family to reach compromises, resolve problems, and implement agreements.** The effective practitioner does not preach, and is an expert in establishing collaboration. By weaving back and forth among the five core tasks above, the practitioner remains connected to the family vision. It is the family vision—whether it is one of peace and quiet, keeping a loved one out of the hospital, or getting the primary sufferer a job—that is the thread with which recovery is woven.

9. **An attitude of optimism and faith in the power of the family.** Perhaps no attitude is more important than this one. Families under the influence of mental illness are typically discouraged, disillusioned, and dispirited. They live not only under a repressive atmosphere generated by the mental illness, but they also have to contend with society's all too frequent condemnation. By the time they have seen a professional, they are often exhausted and burned out. They have lost direction and have often lost hope. Family members need someone to hold forth a vision of what can be possible, a vision that is realistic and judiciously optimistic. Many family members need at least one unrelenting voice that spurs them to take the hero's journey described by mythologists such as Joseph Campbell. The bottom line is that any family member can recover *and* even triumph, regardless of what any other family member does or does not do.

10. **The willingness to assume responsibility for enrolling the family into a healing vision and to be accountable to the family for its progress.** This may be the most controversial characteristic, because many professionals are reluctant to assume "too much" responsibility. Initially, most families are unable to articulate a vision, and the professional often is unable to deliver a vision, or to hold the emotional space to keep the vision clearly in view. Capable professionals are never far from validating the family's needs, desires, and goals. Initiative and boldness are key qualities of the helping professional.

While there are clearly other desirable qualities that the consultant or family helper must have (e.g., positive regard for family members, genuineness, flexibility, the ability to deal with confrontation), the above ten behaviors of the helping professional are those that I have seen to be essential to ensure a positive family outcome. While not all consultants will have all of these qualities, the more they possess, the greater the possibility their effective participation in the healing process will be.

Honoring the Family

One of the founding mothers of family therapy, Virginia Satir, aptly and simply stated the importance of the professional: "If you did nothing more when you have a family together than to make it possible for them to really look at each other, really touch each other, and listen to each other, you would have already swung the pendulum in the direction of a new start."

It is important for family members, *and* the professionals who treat them, to remember that families must be included in the treatment and healing process, not because they are ill or dysfunctional or because they caused the illness. Rather, *the family must be included so that it can become a positive force* in the healing of its loved one. Inducing positive health, rather than reducing negative symptoms, is the ultimate goal. Families triumph by connecting with themselves, others, and through the peculiarly human longing to connect with a presence beyond their everyday experience.

Every family can improve when family members accept the illness, the impact, the nature of treatment, the nature of the illness, and the opportunities that are being offered for transformation and triumph. Every family can build a future, a much more worthwhile endeavor than trying to save a past or constantly repeating it. Every family must learn to apply the age-old wisdom from the alcoholism and addiction fields, which reminds everyone under the influence of the four Cs of Al-Anon. These cardinal beliefs that have changed the lives of millions of people are as follows:

- You didn't *c*ause the mental illness.

- You can't *c*ure it.

- You can't *c*ontrol it.

- You can *c*ope with it.

When you add the other three Cs listed by the NACoA,[100] you help take even better *c*are of yourself by:

- Communicating your feelings.

- Making healthy *c*hoices.

- And *c*elebrating being yourself.

We now know that these beliefs can alter both the structure and the functioning of the brain, awakening and extending the number of its neural pathways, creating new circuitry—and thus a new future.

CHAPTER *24*

My Path to the Work

Passion meets practicality.

—⟋⟋⟍—

Throughout this book, I have made an effort to describe the nature and structure of triumph, just as I do when I work with the families in my consultation room. I have shifted back and forth among a number of different knowledge bases or disciplines, just as I do with families in my office, actively teaching and illustrating in as many ways as I can the essential principles and concepts that will help you to create a life worth living and a loss worth enduring. If you apply them with intention, you can discover for yourself that it is never too late to have a full life yourself and even a happy family.

Whenever I sit with a family that is under the influence of illness, addiction, and trauma (and as I have mentioned, they often co-occur in the same family), I am humbled by the knowledge that is needed to serve the many different needs of its members. We've mentioned the importance of the wisdom of Solomon and the patience of Gandhi, as well as other notable traits and personalities.

It is too much to expect traditional psychology and psychiatry, both of which have focused primarily on understanding and treating abnormal behaviors, to be sufficient to address the incredibly complicated and complex needs of wounded family members. Rather, family members require a variety of different methods through which their problems, their behaviors, their beliefs, and their feelings can be seen and addressed.

In this chapter, I would like to share the strands that weave the fabric of triumph that I have uncovered. Making them explicit can be as much help to you, the reader, as to the many family members with whom I have been privileged to work.

An understanding of how I got started on this path might be a good place to start. More important, it will demarcate the important steps on the path—at least the ones I have found most helpful to all sufferers who live under the influence of illness, addiction, and other traumas. My professional work began in the late 1960s, as the section in the book "About the Author" shows. But my personal journey really began with my birth into a Holocaust family: both of my parents lost many family members during the Nazi persecution. My mother's mother was taken outside her house and shot. Her father starved to death. My father, too, incurred wounds that I cannot even imagine. Most of my aunts, uncles, and cousins also were murdered. These events made an indelible impression on me and set the tone for much of my professional and personal life.

Passion Meets Practicality

For much of the last two decades, my *passion* as a professional psychologist has been the study of success, peak performance, achievement, self-actualization, and other states of excellence, all of which involve triumph.

I began to read more and more about health and well-being and less and less about sickness and "psychopathology."

I became increasingly drawn to what happened to ordinary people who are exposed to extraordinarily distressful circumstances. How did they survive, and actually thrive in the midst of exceptional adversity? I examined everything I could find on thriving under difficult circumstances, which is not too surprising given my personal background.

At the same time that I was discovering the literature on success and well-being, my clinical practice was being driven by my work with the sufferers of many types of severe trauma, including the more serious mental disorders (as defined in the *DSM-IV*[29]).

One of my earliest consultation relationships was with an alternative treatment center for the seriously mentally ill called Sanctuary House. Living in a home-like setting, seven "residents," all of whom suffered one or more major mental illnesses, lived in a comprehensive, twenty-four-hour, seven-day-a-week therapeutic environment. I was the "psychological consultant." I worked with the staff as well as with the residents, conducted the first group therapy treatment program for residents, and I consulted with the family members.

I was asked to confer with the Santa Barbara Psychiatric Emergency Team, conducting staff training and development. In addition, I had an active private practice. In my role as a Founding Board of Director of the National Association for Children of Alcoholics, I had the opportunity to work with thousands of family members of those who suffered from alcoholism and other addictions. Working with this group of clients quickly led me to my work with people who had experienced many sorts of other trauma and abuse. I noticed that a huge proportion of those individuals were living with mental illness in their home; frequently, there had been mental illness in previous generations of their families, as well.

Different types of disorders can cause severely wounding experiences for everyone in the family. I could see that almost all of my clients bore the mark of some form of mental illness, addiction, or trauma in their family. In fact, these problems have touched the lives of the vast majority of people. It is the rare family that has not been touched. It may also be the rare family that is helped.

I wondered about the strange combination of the following seemingly dissimilar domains: triumph and disorder, health and illness, victory and defeat. What do the most severe forms of disorders and illnesses have in common with the greatest successes, with the people who perform at peak levels, and with the people who pursue self-actualization? Carl Jung recognized maturity as the increasing ability to reconcile opposites.

As I matured in my clinical practice, as well as my own personal journey in life, I began to transfer and apply the knowledge and skills from my passion and personal interests to the clients that I was treating in my office. The results of this translation were astounding. I began to see that when people were exposed to the concepts of wellness while enduring horrific circumstances, they began to reach far beyond mere survival, to a life in which they thrived. I soon became a witness to triumph on a regular basis. I saw firsthand how triumphs accumulate and become the building blocks of healing.

A Novel Synthesis

This book captures what I have found to be so helpful to those under the influence of any major, chronic wound. Ten core fields of study in particular have provided me new perspectives for helping those impacted by illness, addiction, and other trauma. Over the last thirty-five years, I have consistently found that these ten areas are common paths pointing toward triumph. I found that when I listened for what was most helpful to family members, when the family member and I were at the interface of the healing edge, we were drawn again and again to these teachings and principles.

The sources of study rich in direction for those who pursue triumphant lives are as follows:

- traumatic stress
- loss and grief
- altered states of consciousness
- addiction and recovery
- classical and modern mythology
- healing from physical illness
- success, personal achievement, and excellence
- the contemporary sciences—especially recent advances in neuroscience, or the scientific study of the brain, developments in quantum physics, as well as chaos theory
- what are loosely referred to as "energy therapies"
- spirituality

They form the core curriculum for mastering the art of triumph, regardless of the circumstance.

Dealing with a wound such as mental illness requires that you examine it through many different perspectives and see it through many different angles in order to *move beyond* its impact. You will find that every life circumstance can be seen through these ten viewpoints. I invite you to view the issues that all family members face through one or more of these lenses. Each contains information to unlock another door to triumph.

Each of these ten disciplines, or fields, can provide additional ways to understand mental illness, its impact on *every* member of the family, and its relationship to triumph. Each serves as a different lens, allowing you to see new principles and transform your beliefs. By having the freedom to change "lenses," you can examine which beliefs serve you and which do not. Discovering, for example, that serious mental illness is a physical illness can open the door to empowering beliefs, beliefs that can free you from unnecessary guilt.

When the father of a boy suffering from schizophrenia learned that this disorder is a biochemical illness, he stopped blaming himself *and* his wife for the difficult childhood that their son had endured. Free of this burden of guilt, they were able to let go of their resentment, and it became easier to love their son. Their marriage improved, and he and his wife felt a comfort and sense of peace that they had not experienced in years.

As new observations and possibilities for triumph and healing are opened with each lens, you are led to different discoveries, conclusions, and interventions, each providing you with fresh ways of thinking about the world and how it operates. If you are like many of the people with whom I have consulted, these lenses and the new opportunities that they reveal can change your life.

Systemic Traumatology

The field of traumatic stress, particularly "systemic traumatology," or the study of the impact of trauma on the individual and the family, is at the core of our understanding of mental illness and its impact. It is not surprising that mental health professionals view mental illness as a catastrophic stressor.[28] By shedding light on the nature and quality of the wound that *all* family members sustain from mental illness, we learn that when we are subjected to an extraordinary or overwhelming negative experience, which is called a "trauma," we often freeze-frame the experience, as described in the chapter called "The Wounds."

The wound becomes especially severe if another person inflicts the trauma, and can be particularly devastating when it is at the hands of a loved one or family member.[29] In addition, traumatic environments create a setting that allows messages, especially negative ones, to become more easily imprinted upon our minds, bodies, and souls.

In a traumatic environment, we are more vulnerable, and we are less alert to guarding ourselves from these negative messages or suggestions. They can more easily bypass our normal screening processes, becoming an integral part of our inner world, from which they are so often automatically evoked, especially in stressful situations. This cycle perpetuates reactions that are again traumatic. Our vulnerability leads us through this predictable landscape, its outstanding feature our unmindfulness and its countless repercussions.

We learn, too, that the effects of watching or witnessing trauma,[40] often called "secondary traumatization, or secondary victimization," are profound as well, and can create all the signs and symptoms of the original trauma. This finding is especially relevant for family members. When they see a loved one in the midst of an acute symptom or shocking episode, for example, they can become frightened, even terrified.

One family member described the experience of witnessing trauma in the following way: "When I see my child lost in a delusion, oblivious to anything but the terror of her own experience, not only does my heart ache, but my heart breaks. I start to sweat and I feel like my stomach is going to come out of my mouth. Sometimes I can't even eat or sleep!"

Imagine the terror of parents who know that their son is wandering the streets, suicidal, and hearing voices. They have seen this exact scene played out many times before. Their horror is compounded when they don't even know which street or town their loved one is restlessly (and agitatedly) roaming.

Commenting on what it is like to watch her husband engulfed in a manic high, another family member recounted: "I feel terrorized. I know the scenario. Soon the yelling and screaming will start and that's only the beginning. I feel so helpless and out of control. I know it's happening to him, but it feels like I am being swallowed by it, too. I just can't get his screaming out of my mind. It just keeps going around and around in my mind." This woman's trauma can be as frightening as her husband's trauma; in fact, it can be even more so.

The field of traumatic stress also indicates that family members who witness their loved one's illness can suffer a special type of burnout and exhaustion called compassion fatigue.[39, 40] Compassion fatigue creates a condition called learned helplessness, a state of feeling utterly impotent, which stems from family members' beliefs that they are unable to make any real difference in the life of their loved one. As one family member said: "Why bother? I just want to give up. No matter what I do, it doesn't make any difference!"

Loss and Grief

Trauma by definition involves loss.[76, 136] Consequently, what we have learned from the field of thanatology—the study of loss, death, and dying—becomes a critical ingredient in dealing with mental illness. Loss and grief are at the heart of the family experience, burdens central to the impact of mental illness. Something important is taken from us, whether it is the possibility of a relationship, freedom, privacy, peace, money, or opportunity. As one family member described the plight of her son diagnosed with paranoid schizophrenia, "It's as if my son has died. I no longer recognize him. He is no longer the boy I knew."

To complicate matters, these tremendous losses to which the family is subjected are generally not seen by the larger society, or even acknowledged by the sufferer. The sufferer's family members, too, often get lost in the pain of their loved one's illness. As the losses accumulate, grief, particularly grief that is unresolved, overwhelms the person as well as other family members, and becomes a constant companion. One well-spoken family member expressed the loss this way: "I am surrounded by the continual presence of unrelenting absence." Grief takes it own toll.

When the grief is also traumatic, there is loss, and additionally, there is a shattering in the coherence of the self. Very different feelings and beliefs result from the natural death of a ninety-year-old grandmother than from the violent death of a thirty-two-year-old mother who is also raped. Traumatic grief, illustrated by the latter example, is especially difficult to come to terms with, and causes far more severe damage.

Altered States of Consciousness

Trauma and grief can throw us into an altered state of consciousness, a harsh trance or spell. When we have the larger perspective to perceive trauma and its associated conditions as a deep, negative trance or spell, we can open the doors to the powerful understandings of modern clinical hypnosis. This field studies "high influence communications," which are the very kinds of communications that occur among family members under the influence of trauma and grief.

The distortions in our experience produced by negative trance states render us especially vulnerable to trauma's effects. If we are under the influence of trauma and grief, for example, everything, especially negative events, can be magnified out of proportion, and we can feel as if these distressing situations may last forever, affecting every aspect of our lives. One of my clients remarked, "Dealing with my son's illness is a hallucinatory experience that's not much different from the bad trips I had when I took LSD during my college years."

Utilizing the concepts of altered states[149] enables us to understand and de-mystify the experiences of living under the influence of illness, as well as living under the control of trauma and addiction. The notion of "under the influence" can itself provide a nonstigmatizing, nonpathologizing, and nonviolent way for all family members to describe their experience. Sufferers are able to free themselves from shame, which can be now seen as a function of their innocent lack of awareness and our culture's harsh attitudes.

For example, all family members can get stuck in situations (that is, become "anchored" to them, in the language of hypnosis) and revert to lower levels of functioning (that is, "age regress," in hypnotic language). John was married to Emma, who suffered from severe OCD. One of her compulsions was to check repeatedly that all the electrical appliances in the house were off, because she feared "the leaking radiation would contaminate everyone." When she engaged in this particular ritual, John got frightened and angry, just as he did as a child when his mother behaved in strange and irrational ways.

Instead of accepting that his wife suffered from a neurobiological disorder and resisting falling under its spell, he would throw tantrums, yell and scream, and taunt her. During these episodes, he was reacting as much to his mother as his wife: in his age-regressed state, his wife became *a psychic stunt double* for his mother. Needless to say, such behavior didn't help her and only made him feel even more helpless and out of control, just as he did in childhood. A vicious circle resulted.

Family members can also worry about the future ("age progress," in the language of modern hypnosis), and they can engage in denial by not acknowledging the illness that is present ("negatively hallucinate" or suffer from a number of other classic hypnotic phenomena). Such languaging does not negate the faulty chemistry involved in psychotic hallucinations or other biochemical dysfunctions, but rather allows additional, more positive ways to describe what happens to family members, ways that are not as damaging, critical, or judgmental.

In addition to these benefits, the art and science of hypnosis teaches us how to compose powerful communications, which are made of three core elements: pacing, leading, and future pacing.[67] Pacing is the method in which the communicator selects a portion of a person's ongoing experience and feeds it back. If I were to pace you now, I might say, *"You are sitting* (or standing*), holding this book, reading the following words, and experiencing a variety of emotions."* Pacing conveys the message, "I hear you. I see what you're saying. I grasp what you are feeling." It signals understanding, support, and acceptance. Each time a person is paced, it weaves another strand in the fabric of rapport. Once paced, people more likely feel safe; trust and rapport will often naturally occur.

Leading occurs by introducing behaviors that are different from, but consistent with, the person's present situation and, at the same time, are directed more closely to the new desired state. It is the leading statements that contain the persuasive and influential messages. An example of leading is the mother spontaneously opening her mouth as she spoon-feeds her baby. If I were to lead now, I might say, *"And as you continue to read, you can find that the words and the concepts presented in this book become more and more useful to you in your pursuit of triumph."*

Future pacing is the final step in any effective communication. Once a person feels understood (pacing), is given new direction (leading), then he or she is told what will happen when they engage in the desired behavior. One person calls future pacing "a positive dress rehearsal." Future pacing increases motivation. If I were to future pace now, I might say, *"And as these words continue to make more and more sense to you, you will find many situations in which you can apply the principles of this book, and you will be able to deal with these situations in much more satisfying ways."*

Virtually every meaningful story continuously loops through these three basic processes of pacing, leading, and future pacing. Understanding these basic communication processes as well as altered states of consciousness can allow you to be a more skilled caregiver, as opposed to caretaker, with your loved one. The principles of *powerful languaging* are very important in creating highly influential communications, communications that are so needed when speaking with families impacted by illness, addiction, and other trauma,[34] whether you are a primary sufferer, a secondary sufferer, a professional, or any combination of the three.

Addiction and Recovery

The study of addiction offers valuable guidance to the families of the mentally ill. Like mental illness, alcoholism was once considered a sign of defectiveness, degeneration, poor willpower, and immorality. Only recently has it "come out of the closet." Not long ago, the stigma surrounding the disease of alcoholism blocked necessary attention to the family. Members suffered in isolation, feeling ashamed and responsible for the chaos in the family. Moreover, the knowledge from the field of addiction tells us of the impact of the drug or substance not only on the person, but also on the whole family.[10, 65, 140] We also learned that when the whole family is involved in treatment, the prognosis for healing is significantly more favorable.[127] The social movement called Children of Alcoholics showed the need for education, compassion, and mutual support, demonstrating the effectiveness and necessity of these resources for triumph over the impact of alcoholism.

The notion of an addict as a frustrated mystic, one who keeps knocking on the wrong spiritual door, is one of the gifts from the founder of modern psychology, Dr. William James.[72] This insight has proven to be an important one for the loved one's family members, many of whom become addicted to a variety of substances like alcohol or Valium in their effort to find a semblance of peace and comfort. They can also become addicted to activities like shopping, working, gambling, or even other people, in their attempt to come to terms with their loved one's illness. They can seek resolution to their suffering through drugs or other addictions, rather than creating meaning for their adversity. But when they learn they might really be frustrated mystics, looking to connect with a presence beyond them, their entire demeanor can change and another door to triumph may have just opened.

What is more, the field of addiction reminds us of the intimate connections between trauma, addiction, and loss.[33] Trauma creates dissociation, which is a type of separation or disconnection. Feelings of disconnection are the fuel for addictions. This is why so many addicts, and sufferers of mental illness, report feeling "spaced out," "zoned out," or out of their body.

Classical and Modern Mythology

The study of mythology[17, 72] sheds new light on the nature and meaning of wounding as well as the losses incurred by mental illness, and can also provide a map to triumph for all those under the influence of mental illness. In mythological terms, trauma and its compatriots—wounds, altered states, losses, and addictions—threaten the kingdom of the personal self and the family self. They become the beasts and demons, which must be dispelled to save the realm. And we know from the tales of old that a special person, characteristically reluctant, is needed to rescue the larger family. This person is the "hero" or "heroine." Interestingly, the word "hero" is derived from the Greek, meaning one who protects and serves. Along the way, this person becomes separated from the familiar, battles negative forces, and returns home bearing the gifts of the journey. Such a path is similar to the one family members must travel. How much more useful it is for family members to see themselves through this lens, as opposed to one which shows them to be bad, sick, crazy, and dumb.

Mythology suggests that if the person or family member refuses "the call," or the message, meaning, or purpose for the trauma, then a profane wounding will occur. The result can be a life devoid of hope, wonder, and joy. The person becomes engulfed in his or her personal experience, disconnected, separated, or dissociated from the inherent awareness of something greater than the senses can perceive. In such a state, the person becomes a victim, spinning out of control in negative states of consciousness, broken off from the present and connected to a frightening past and feared future.

Mythology opens the doors to the wisdom of our ancestors,[17] allowing us to partake of their valuable wisdom in our own odyssey toward triumph. Just as our ancient hero had to reach consciously for the light, while escaping the darkness, the modern hero must move in a direction that promotes positive effects, consciously avoiding any negative outcome. Family members who focus their attention on what is wrong fail to realize that "the highest success in living and the deepest emotional satisfaction comes from building and using your signature strengths." Bob and Sally Jonahs, who have two children with bipolar disorder, decided that they would learn to highlight what was working in their family, rather than emphasize what was not. While this certainly didn't eliminate their pain, it greatly reduced their suffering. Suffering is a never-ending cycle, while pain offers the possibility of a beginning, middle, and end.

Physical Healing

The science of physical healing brings to light the great mysteries of life, reminding us that science alone does not provide us with the deep understanding of how healing occurs. It points to the miraculous and reveals the very traits, characteristics, and attitudes possessed by those who triumph over physical disorders.[22, 84, 85] It provides countless examples of people recovering from illnesses that were diagnosed as incurable or terminal.[123, 124] It reminds us that there is always hope, and that science never has all the answers.

Research[22, 43, 70, 123, 124] demonstrates that some people, for example, come through major illness better than others; some endure surgery better than others, and still others remain healthy well into old age, while some become ill at a much younger age. Studying those who display such wide differences in dealing with adverse physical conditions can offer clues to understanding how triumph can develop. Feelings of helplessness and the perception of a loss of control over one's life play a crucial role in one's emotional and physical health. The ongoing stress, grief, loss, and exhaustion that plague so many family members of the mentally ill contribute to a host of concurrent illnesses and disorders.

Psychologist Dr. Lawrence LeShan, who has worked with cancer patients for over three decades, found that his patients had often suffered a major loss, which was accompanied by a loss of control, shortly before being diagnosed.[83] What was most important, however, was that their reaction to that loss (that is, trauma!) was more important than the adversity itself. A wide variety of studies confirm the importance of attitude as a more accurate predictor of survival than many other medical factors.

The *I Ching,* one of the world's oldest and most profound divinatory tools, reminds us, "The event is not important, but the response to the event is everything." Such guides suggest how triumph can develop. Family members who can find a reason for the adversity simply do better than those who cannot.[5, 19, 32, 41, 42, 45, 52, 71, 83, 86, 106, 111, 113, 128, 146] The Smith family believes that their daughter's major depression is punishment from God, while the Joneses believe that their daughter, who also suffers from depression, has a biochemical disorder.

In addition, the literature on healing clarifies the difference between healing and curing, a distinction essential to those under the influence of all illnesses, addictions, and other traumas. Being returned to an earlier nonsymptomatic state cures a person.

Healing, on the other hand, brings the person into a realm of peacefulness and harmony that is independent of any physical, mental, or emotional conditions. Illness is not a failure, and pain is not a punishment. How many family members would not benefit from hearing this message over and over? Can it be said too many times?

Lessons from physical healing open the door to the importance of the heart as well as the brain, showing us how indispensable are both our spirit and our soul. Healers throughout time, especially modern healers, stress that healing is accomplished through love and is love. Dr. Bernie Siegel, the author of the best-selling *Love, Medicine and Miracles,* whose work is based on his experience as a surgeon with exceptional patients, or those who have miraculous cures, reminds us, "Love, hope, and piece of mind have physiological consequences, just as depression and despair do."[137]

While love cannot cure serious mental illness, it is an indispensable ingredient in the journey through life and the core element in Refamilying. Because dealing with the impact of mental illness is a lifelong process, because it is a marathon, not a sprint, love is the lubricant through which the entire family can make the journey more livable.

The Principles of Success

The person in his or her quest must reach for the light, not just escape the dark. He or she must move in a direction that promotes positive results, not just avoid negative outcomes. The study of personal success, whether called the pursuit of excellence, healthy behavior, or optimum functioning, offers constructive models as well as fundamental beliefs for the person to follow. Based on triumphant luminaries in such diverse arenas of life as the arts, the sciences, athletics, and business, these concepts about successful living, with their profound lessons for personal triumph, have a long history that conveys the message that every individual can achieve lasting success by following a set of established principles.

Often referred to as the world's foremost scholar and thinker in the science of human success, Napoleon Hill, whose philosophy of achievement was the first authoritative treatise on the topic, described the principles of accomplishment in the best seller and motivational classic, *Think and Grow Rich,* which was published in 1937.[69] One of the most influential books of all time in pointing the way to personal success, this "what-to-do and how-to-do-it" manual was inspired by Andrew Carnegie, the great turn-of-the-century industrialist, who commissioned Mr. Hill to study the most famous business and political leaders of his day, including luminaries such as Henry Ford, Thomas Edison, Alexander Graham Bell, William Howard Taft, Woodrow Wilson, Harvey Firestone, John D. Rockefeller, Samuel Gompers, and F. W. Woolworth.

Modern-day success guru Stephen R. Covey pursued this tract in his inspirational book, *The Seven Habits of Highly Effective People.*[24] He presents a principle-centered approach for solving personal and professional problems for living in a complex and often chaotic world. His step-by-step approach, upon which enduring happiness and success are based, maximizes security, wisdom, and the ability to utilize the opportunities that change and adversity offer. Both books offer timeless and practical techniques for discovering the lasting and true building blocks of success.

This rapidly developing field of personal success establishes the importance of the future, stressing that triumph, like all winning endeavors, requires getting the past out of the present and building a compelling future that will pull you forward.[24, 50, 139]

It offers a different language, one based on fundamental truths that have universal applications, and includes terms such as vision, possibility, integrity, fidelity, courage, proactivity, industry, interdependence, character, values, service, accountability, and commitment. These qualities create the attitudes and behaviors that can be extraordinarily vital to us, their influence reaching far beyond our constantly shifting emotions.

In families under the influence of mental illness, these character traits and their development are essential for a life of triumph. They not only make the journey bearable, but they make the journey possible. And, as you can recall, they are all learnable.[119, 120, 125, 129]

The Science of the Brain

The science of the brain, or neuroscience, points to the biological basis of the serious mental illnesses and their treatment.[2, 4, 25, 90, 94, 104, 134] Significantly, it reveals that the brain is profoundly interpersonal in nature, which means that parts of the brain grow during the course of social experiences.[25, 125, 147] Evolution has designed our brains to be shaped by our intimate encounters. The implications of a brain amenable to change in response to experience throughout the life cycle are profound. They suggest, for example, that when young children have not gained sufficient emotional safety and stability from positive interactions with a caregiver, they suffer a corresponding physiological deficit within their brains.

With corrective experience, healing and triumph can occur anywhere in time, as the brain is capable of change *at any point in life*.[125] Any nurturing relationship stimulates biochemical reorganization in the brain, which can lead to the enhancement of new learning. A nurturing relationship establishes an emotional and neurobiological context conducive to neural reorganization[25]—which may be a precursor for triumph.

Nurturance can trigger what neuroscientists refer to as brain plasticity, or the brain's inherent ability to change. Reorganization and development occur where neural structure and growth may have been lacking. It is quite possible, then, that the caring, encouragement, and enthusiasm of the concerned professional, who assists *all* members of the family under the influence of mental illness, supports and reinforces triumph through the enhanced production of key neurotransmitters such as dopamine, serotonin, norepinephrine, and other endogenous endorphins. All of these neurotransmitters can enhance neural growth and plasticity.[122, 147]

The fact that most of us are able to learn new skills and remember new information throughout life is the clearest evidence of ongoing neural plasticity. Stem cells, the basic structure for many types of cells, have been found to renew themselves indefinitely. A variety of findings in brain research indicate that the notion of a dwindling brain is a complete myth. Even an elderly brain has the capacity to generate new brain cells. According to Dr. Fred Gage, a neuroscientist at the world-renowned Salk Institute: "The actual structure of our brain is modified by our experiences. In other words, how you respond to life's events literally shapes your brain."[147] Put plainly, the quality of relationship among family members can alter the physical structure and chemical functioning for each person's brain. There are more reasons than one for loving kindness, respect, and caring among family members under the influence. These traits are good for the brain!

That social connections between people can influence the physical structure of the brain was an idea unheard of only five short years ago. Conventional wisdom held that everything originating in our brain—emotions, thoughts, and dreams—was genetically programmed at birth, and we became products of a particular genetic history. We believed that we were born with all the brain cells, or neurons, that we would ever have, and that any imprinting during sensitive or "critical" periods would become permanently and indelibly etched into our neural architecture.

This neural fatalism has been declining since the advent of state-of-the-art brain scans. Such scans include the following:

- electroencephalogram, or the EEG

- computerized tomography, or the CT scan

- positron emission tomography, or the PET scan

- single photon emission computed tomography, or the SPECT scan

- magnetic resonance imaging, or MRI

- functional magnetic resonance imaging, or the fMRI

- magneto-encephalography, or the MEG

- quantitative electroencephalography, or the QEEG scan

All of these have been providing many different and exciting windows to the brain *in action*. These sophisticated tests can be used to measure the activity in the different regions of the brain while a person is performing a wide range of cognitive, emotional, and behavioral tasks. Each procedure in its own unique way is suggesting that our brain is constantly changing, producing new neural circuits and maps in response to our experiences and perceptions.[25, 116, 125]

The eminent neuroscientist Dr. Daniel Siegel states that experience "directly shapes gene expression and leads to the maintenance, creation, and strengthening of the connections that form the neural substrate of the mind."[125] Even our genes are affected by our experience, which determines which genes become expressed, how, and when. Far from being locked into predetermined patterns by our DNA—the genetic material within the nucleus of the cells that defines who the person is—the brain literally grows in response to challenge and new learning, both of which foster neural development and integration. Neural networks, or clusters of neurons that are the basic microscopic units that make up all parts of the nervous system, encode and organize our behaviors. More to the point, they can be built and rebuilt.

Words can actually alter biological functioning. Language, particularly carefully crafted stories that empower rather than disempower the person, can become a powerful tool in the integration of fresh neural networks. Compelling stories can literally harmonize the communication between the left and right hemispheres of the brain, as well as our processing in the higher brain and the lower brain. Can you take a moment . . . breathe . . . deeply and allow yourself the opportunity to take in the full import of what this can mean in helping you to create a life of triumph?

The Physics of Behavior

Contemporary physics describes the physical world and the events that occur within it. Through our beliefs and perceptions, we assign meaning to these circumstances by the ways in which we speak about them. According to the arcane science of quantum physics, the remarkable branch of science that studies the laws of the universe at the subatomic level, we really don't "know" anything until we have observed or declared it. This reminds me of an old joke: Three umpires are sitting around, and one says, "There's balls and there's strikes, and I call 'em the way they are." Another says, "There's balls and there's strikes, and I call 'em the way I see 'em. The third says, "There's balls and there's strikes, and they ain't nothing until I call 'em."

From quantum physics, we discover a key principle called observer participancy, which can help us understand the impact of our beliefs and behaviors on our loved ones.[106] Simply stated, this important tenet asserts that the act of observing actually changes what is being observed. This means that the observer (that is, the family member) is a participant in *and* partial creator of what is observed. This in no way suggests that family members cause mental illness. Rather, it suggests that our beliefs and our perceptions of our ill family member and the meanings we attribute to the illness are critical to both triumph and healing. By changing our perceptions, we not only change our behavior, but we also influence how our loved ones can respond.

The Leonard family illustrates the principle of observer participancy and the underlying order inherent in every circumstance. Both teachers, Mr. and Mrs. Leonard are hard-working professionals who have devoted most of their lives to educating others. They have one daughter, nineteen-year-old Samantha, upon whom they have lavished their attention. At first, they could not understand the changes in their daughter's behavior. They believed that her strange behaviors, which included losing her job when she suddenly became agitated and aggressive, her marked impulsivity, her unkemptness, and her promiscuity were all acts of defiance toward their established values.

The Leonards reacted accordingly and attempted to use their parental authority to get her to "behave like a lady, and get her act together." When her behavior continued to deteriorate, they became even more authoritative, controlling, and domineering. When none of these tactics helped, they were wise enough to seek professional guidance, and discovered that their daughter was suffering a bipolar disorder and was in a manic state. Further, they learned that bipolar disorder is primarily a medical illness that needs to be treated with medication.

With the aid of a trained professional, the Leonard family was able to look at their daughter as someone suffering a mental illness, rather than a rebellious teenager. Instead of continuing to react antagonistically toward their daughter, they responded with understanding and compassion. Their daughter, in turn, became less combative and was willing to try medication, which rapidly curtailed her aggressive behaviors.

What followed was a "virtuous cycle" of more appropriate, loving behaviors by everyone in the family, as opposed to the "vicious cycle" in which the whole family had been unconsciously engaged. Their new understanding allowed them to interrupt the patterns of their daughter's illness, opening the door to overcoming the possible devastation of the entire family. As they bore witness to the end of the life with their daughter as they had always envisioned it, a new life began to emerge, like the Phoenix rising. As Mrs. Leonard said, "One door closed and another door opened." In the process, they learned to become less afraid of her disordered behavior and were able to use it as a signal for a needed intervention on their part. Their new attitude became a key element in the family's triumph. As they began to see the half full glass, as opposed to the half empty glass, their lives became more and more full of love, happiness—and triumph.

Quantum physics also confirms what the mystics have been saying all along. We are all a part of a richly patterned cosmos of interconnection in which disintegration and chaos are necessary ingredients for regeneration and rebirth. Ilya Prigogine offers a clear explanation of the necessity for disharmony. Dr. Prigogine's pioneering research has been so influential that he won a Nobel Prize. His theory of "dissipative structures" proves that energy passing through a system drives that system far away from a state of balance. Stated differently, his theory suggests that disintegration, the falling apart of systems, is a necessary precursor for the order that follows. When family members can embrace falling apart as both an opportunity as well as a danger, they can open the door to a triumphant possibility, as did the Leonard family above.

Chaos Theory

Bridging many different fields, futurist J. Orlin Grabbe writes: "Somewhere between the ancient and modern definitions of chaos is the place you find creativity. Chaos is a useful concept in many areas. Piaget [the great Swiss psychologist] saw chaos as the starting point of education. Scientists are using it as a new way to describe certain forms of systems in nature, and business people are learning to ride the wave of chaos into exciting new patterns of commerce."

Best-selling author Dr. Paul Pearsall, who survived almost certain death three times from multiple cancers, describes his miraculous healing in the inspiring book, *Making Miracles.*[106] In a nontechnical and straightforward way, he introduces his reader to another one of the new fields of science—namely, chaology, or the scientific study of chaos. Dr. Pearsall writes, "I came to see the extraordinary order of chaos as the ultimate health, embracing the pain of falling apart as well as the wonder of being able to know and feel the divine dissipation surging through time." He goes on to assert: "To assume that going wrong is evidence that the universe [family] is moving toward an ultimate 'wrongness' or disastrous end is to ignore the chaology finding that the small anomalies, quirks, and coincidences of life are the necessary sparks and evidence of movement to new order." As foreign as it may sound, like other scientists, Dr. Pearsall is suggesting that "going wrong" is the ultimate means for "setting things right."

The modern study of chaos theory, writes Dr. James Gleick,[51] one of its most articulate pioneers, "has become the century's third great revolution in the physical sciences" along with relativity and quantum physics. He goes on to say, "Within the most disorderly realms of data lived an unexpected kind of order." In other words, in the midst of incredible complexity, or family turmoil, one finds underlying cycles of stability, meaning, and coherency.

Almost every family with whom I've been involved in treatment has found reassurance and hope that, *when it is actively sought*, an inherent order or underlying meaning can be found within the chaos. A cornerstone of the transformation of many families is the development of a new attitude toward the turmoil and pandemonium in the family.

The Peters are a good example. When their daughter was first hospitalized with an acute episode of paranoid schizophrenia, the trauma of the emergency and its aftermath shattered any resemblance to their previous way of life. Recurring catastrophes fed their belief that life would never get better. As I continued to share the latest state-of-the-art work of eminent scientists, such as Dr. Gleick, both of the parents began to experience less and less fear of the symptomatic behaviors of their daughter. They also learned to fear less and less their own problems.

Both were orphaned at a young age, and this wound severely impacted their ability to sustain long-term meaningful relationships. The Peters discovered that their daughter's illness led them to a new group of friends and relationships with others that they had never dreamed was possible. Their prior reclusive life, which was unsatisfying to both of them, transformed into a life of caring for others and being cared for by others. With each episode of their daughter's illness, they found more and more comfort from a NAMI support group that was becoming like a second family to them. Incidents that were once isolating with their daughter's frequent hospitalizations became surprising occasions for connecting with others. Soon, they began to look for the unexpected order and relief that resulted from their child's underlying problem behaviors. The Peters' *active* search for meaning in their experiences yielded triumph for them as well as their daughter, who became enveloped in her own cadre of support.

Energy

The ninth, and most speculative, field of inquiry that might offer help to those under the influence of mental illness is the "energy therapies." This is a generic term for therapies that recognize human beings as electromagnetic fields of vibration, or energy.

According to the 2003 Fifth Annual International Energy Psychology Conference, energy psychology is "positioned on the shared frontier of Psychology, Biophysics, and Spirituality, . . . a family of mind/body interventions that have been consistently clinically observed to help with a wide range of psychological concerns through directly and methodically treating the human vibrational matrix." This matrix includes the biofield that envelops the body, the energy centers (chakras), and the energy pathways (meridians and related acupoints).

Based on concepts acknowledged five thousand years ago, the premise of these "modern" therapies is that illness and dysfunction are physical manifestations of imbalances within and among our energy system.[47, 48, 49, 88] Emphasizing different aspects of our energy systems, some concentrate on the energy fields *within the body,* while others stress the greater energy fields in which the body and mind are embedded and are but a small part.

For example, Drs. Peter Lambrou and George Pratt, two of the leaders in the emerging field of energy psychology, write: "Energy managed well is productive; energy out of balance is a source of stress, for ourselves and for those around us."[80] The return to balance consists of unblocking the trapped fields of energy by tapping specific points along twelve major pathways *within the body,* known as the meridians, "so that the flow of energy is restored and the body returns to its natural state of physical and emotional balance."

On the other hand, Dr. Mary Lynch and Debra Harrison,[88] codevelopers of Consegrity, describe a far-reaching energy model that focuses on the electromagnetic fields that extend *far beyond the body* and in which the mind and body are embedded. They state that the physical body is made up of interactive energy fields around every cell that balance and support optimum health. When this balance is disrupted by physical trauma, environmental trauma, emotional trauma, spiritual trauma, or inherited trauma, the body adapts, overloads, and eventually breaks down. The Consegrity Wellness Program[88] restores that balance and supports all biological systems. Through a process of mirroring and reflecting a person's unique energy fields, his or her DNA is "unlocked," distortions in the electromagnetic field are cleared, and healing follows. (All cells contain DNA, which is the information a person inherits that tells the cells how to repair and rebuild themselves.)

Common to approaches of energy therapy is the belief that illness results from the imbalance of electromagnetic energy created by our thoughts and the electrical and chemical changes that occur within the body. Asserting that illness occurs when energy systems are blocked or locked, energy therapies posit that energy follows thought, suggesting that what we think can directly influence the functioning of our electromagnetic fields.[16, 48, 80, 88] Thoughts can either close down our energy fields, or they can open our energy fields, making them more available for healing.

Spirituality

Triumph requires learning how to use crises and times of falling apart as vehicles to move us toward our ever-evolving human spirit, for the ultimate triumph is that of the human spirit over the human condition. Hence, the tenth field of study is spirituality, the direct experience of the undamped energy or "spirit" that is the foundation and nourishment of life. Spiritual solutions involve changing our energy field so that we can access the highest frequency (that is, the fastest vibration) of energy, which means getting closer to spirit.[88] A spiritual solution occurs when you can learn to tolerate and welcome higher energy states to become a part of your life.[32] Occurring in many diverse ways, from changing your electromagnetic field to changing your beliefs, you can turn your worst enemies into your greatest teachers. Life's greatest gifts are often preceded by life's worst occurrences.

It is our connection to the divine (whether it is called spirit or God) that can heal our trauma. Often, those under the influence of mental illness become angry with God, lose their faith, or believe that they are being punished or even cursed, much as Mrs. Abel initially thought. Such alienation from self, others, and something beyond the person further compounds the desolation of many sufferers. Similarly, as individuals recover or develop a relationship with a power greater than themselves— however this is defined and experienced—they will find it easier to triumph and to heal. The relationship between spiritual well-being and virtually every positive health factor is thoroughly documented.[5, 21, 32, 44, 57, 88, 98, 103, 123, 129, 143]

Under the influence of mental illness, on the other hand, the person becomes disconnected from self, family, friends, others, and ultimately from higher consciousness. As the person gets separated from the soul, the spirit fades into the background. Perhaps the person's greatest wound is a loss of self, which occurs when she or he engages in progressively negative behaviors of isolation, shame, and compulsion. This, in turn, can lead to a form of spiritual bankruptcy. One man described this as "looking into the mirror and seeing someone else." The American poet Henry David Thoreau described loss of self in the following way: "Ah, to come to the end of one's life and realize one has never lived."[57]

Many, if not most, sufferers under the influence of mental illness experience dissatisfaction with life until they learn to accept the illness. Healthy family members, as well as spiritual seekers, know that peace and joy are not to be found mainly in sensual pleasure or personal comfort. Authentic seekers long for more than just sensual highs. They desire the joy of living in and being transformed by spirit, while overcoming whatever separates them from connecting with something greater than the simple preoccupation with the self or ego. Joy is spiritually different from happiness, which comes from the word "happenstance," and depends on external circumstance. Ironically, traumatic events are often the required catalyst for most people to be willing to make this discovery of joy.

A spiritual approach to mental illness is reflected in the following words of Dr. Wayne Dyer,[32] one of the great contemporary mystics and spiritual gurus: "In essence, when you finally come to know and understand the world of spirit on an intimate basis, you will see clearly that all problems are illusions in that they are concocted by our minds because we have come to believe that we are separate from our source, which I call God, but you can label it any way that you prefer." Dr. Dyer adds, "These illusions are nothing more than mistakes in our *thinking* [emphasis added] and like every error they dissolve when put face to face with the truth." The recovery movement, which has grown up around the addiction field, says this in the following way: "Let go and let God."

A spiritual approach begins with eliminating ignorance or misunderstanding of our real nature. Our essential nature is grounded in the ability to foster relationship, to be connected, and to be whole, all of which are the exact opposite of the wake of trauma and mental illness. The drive to unfold oneself in relationship, spirituality involves a desire to belong to a larger body, to become a part of a relational whole and to overcome feelings of fragmentation, dissociation, and alienation, while at the same time retaining our sense of individuality and separateness. The desire for wholeness is fueled by a powerful desire to participate in something larger than the self or ego, and to follow the otherworldly intuition, existing at the core of one's being, into every facet of creation.

It is important to note that spirituality and religion are not synonymous, although they can go hand in hand. Religion refers to our man-made, organized forms of worship—churches, temples, mosques, and the rituals that surround them. The formal structures of religion, which are also businesses that have budgets, are subject to the usual human flaws. On the other hand, spirituality is the internal and deeply personal relationship one has to the universe and the divine, rather than religion's outward and organized manifestation.

All ten fields of knowledge point to the finding that severe mental illness—whether by the person who suffers from it directly or the family that endures it—can be shattering to our personal and divine significance. Beyond experiencing the inevitability of pain, we can also *suffer* as a direct result of freeze-framing the experience by falling into victimhood, or succumbing to addictions. Senseless despair becomes the tragedy, for a tragedy is a horrific circumstance that could have been averted or need not have occurred. While mental illness *will always* have an impact on the family, there are ways to move beyond its devastating impact.

Many of these ways owe their inspiration to fields other than the more traditional treatment fields of behavior therapy and medication, which characterize the treatment of serious mental illness. The insights offered by these supplementary fields of inquiry are waiting to be utilized by those under the influence of mental illness, as well as addiction and other trauma.

To think across disciplines is like scanning the horizon: it can increase your perspective and revolutionize your life. The profound truths inherent in each feature of the stunning landscape of hope presented in this book speak directly to the heart. The journey circles through many insights with a resonance so deep that you find you are holding the keys to triumph in your hands.

You might be surprised to discover how much you have already learned if you take the next few moments and go back through your life using each of these fields as a different template. For example, what have you learned about you or a loved one from the field of traumatic stress? How does it feel to realize you might be suffering from compassion fatigue, or you have incurred a profane wound, as mythology suggests, and can create a sacred wound whenever you choose—and dare? How does it feel to know that your brain continues to grow throughout life and you are capable of forming new neural connections by the ways you relate to others, think about life, and conduct your own?

Take the time . . . now. It could make the reading of this book more even more valuable. Remember, you may experience a host of different, powerful, and perhaps contradictory feelings.

Become patient with yourself as you weave your own tapestry of victory. As one family member said, "Creating a triumphant life—and it *is* an inventive undertaking—asks more of me than I first realized."

—ᴍ—

CHAPTER *25*

Moving Forward

This transformation is a choice,
and you can make it.

—⚏—

Families under the influence of mental illness are ordinary people who are given an extraordinary challenge. How they respond to their circumstance is the only part of their experience that provides the opportunity to make choices. The family that you have been reading about, the Abels, responded in an extraordinary way to a situation that is all too common. The story of this family's triumph, while real in every important detail, is not yet commonplace. Their triumph points to the possibility for every family under the influence of mental illness to achieve victory to some degree.

The majority of families, when approached in a positive and respectful way, can rise above the horror of their circumstance. While every family has the potential to triumph and heal, not every family can or will. Sometimes the blocks are too formidable, particularly without active, ongoing guidance.

It is vital to acknowledge the limitless capabilities of family and love while simultaneously realizing their limitations. There is no doubt that both qualities, potential and limitation, coexist within the family. Perhaps in the yin and yang of life, both are even necessary.

Love can hold the possibility for anything and everything, and at the same time there are circumstances in which no matter how much, or how hard, or how well we love—and continue to love—our best efforts may utterly and sadly fail. Even the most disturbed families have powerful healing potentials and enormous recuperative resources, while even the healthiest families can fall short and falter. Hope can appear in the most unlikely places, just as hopelessness can befall the best and brightest of us.

Caveats

With this in mind, let me sound some warnings. If there is active alcoholism or another addiction, for example, neither triumph nor healing has much opportunity to proceed until the addiction is addressed. If there is ongoing physical or sexual abuse, triumph and healing proceed slowly, if at all, until the abuse is addressed. Similarly, if there is ongoing child abuse, spousal abuse, or elder abuse, triumph and healing will be very difficult to achieve until these issues are addressed. Other active addictions can also interfere. *Always consult a professional immediately* if any of these conditions are present or suspected.

And occasionally, there is not just mental illness, addiction, or other trauma in a family. Sometimes there is the actual presence of evil. The word "evil" has many meanings. *The American Heritage Dictionary* defines evil as "morally bad or wrong; wicked; malevolent; sinful and causing an undesirable condition as ruin, injury, or pain."[3] This is not what I mean by evil, because this definition, as we have seen, would apply to too many family members under the spell of mental illness. Too often, mental illness has become synonymous with evil.

Evil is *live* spelled backwards, and the essence of evil is a stance that is in opposition to life. Evil is devoid of love. M. Scott Peck, in his well-known book *People of the Lie,* says the following: "Evil, then, for the moment, is that force, residing either inside or outside of human beings, that seeks to kill life or liveliness. And goodness is its opposite. Goodness is that which promotes life and liveliness."[107] People who are the embodiments of evil cause harm, have a deliberate plan of action, show no regret, and are utterly incapable of looking within. Since evil is determined to annihilate and cannot be reasoned with, it is best to avoid it. When it can't be avoided, it is best to deal with it through collective action—that is, not alone!

It is the very rare exception that families or family members are evil. In my career as a psychologist, I have come across evil only twice. The primary emotion I felt was revulsion, and I just wanted to escape. I could almost taste the danger. Each time, there was a chilling effect. The hairs on the back of my neck stood straight up. For this to happen among literally thousands of individual, couple, and family sessions seems a very small percentage, but I will always remember those two cases.

What is much more common, and what I have witnessed over and over in the vast majority of families under the influence of serious mental illness, as well as addiction and other trauma, is their inherent goodness, their love, their commitment, and their willingness to extend far beyond all limits of ordinary care. Often, I am amazed by the persistence of families and the extraordinary care that they provide their loved ones.

Because repetition is the key to mastery, I want to remind you of some remaining points. First, biology is not destiny.

The development of the person includes, but is not limited by, his or her genetics. In a similar vein, not every family under the influence of mental illness resembles a prisoner of war camp, saturated with trauma, loss, grief, guilt, and exhaustion. Thirdly, families need help not because they are bad, sick, or crazy themselves. They need help because they are traumatized, and they need help in order to harness their inherent potential for triumph and healing. A fourth point bearing reiteration is that nowhere in this book is it suggested that family members sacrifice their own well-being *on an ongoing basis* for a loved one except under extreme situations. While sacrifice is a characteristic of all love and relationship, that sacrifice does not, and should not, consistently eclipse one's own overall well-being. Some family members are so besieged by the illness of a loved one that their very survival is threatened.

Nancy's situation is a reminder that love is not enough. She was devoted to her husband, Kent, who suffered from bipolar disorder. For as long as she could remember, she picked up the pieces of her shattered marriage and was persistent in her love. Then, Kent's illness brought him and the family over the edge of danger. After rejecting treatment, Kent began to go on uncontrolled spending binges that finally forced Nancy to file for bankruptcy. To make matters worse, he had several affairs while on these sprees, engaging in indiscriminate sex with multiple partners. After one agonizing tryst, Nancy exasperatingly told him that she could no longer stay with him if he continued to spurn medication. Kent still refused. I remember the anguish in her voice when she told me, "I love him so much, but I just can't keeping doing this; it's [the illness] destroying everything; if I don't get out now, there will be nothing left of me."

Family Response

There are three responses typical of family members under the influence of serious mental illness. They are (1) enmeshment, overinvolvement, or entanglement with their loved one; (2) separation, distance, or dissociation; and (3) more commonly a combination of both. None of these responses reflect the highest form of relationship. The first form of relationship is dependence: "I need you or it." The needs of the infant or child provide the clearest example of dependence. Too, addiction is a clear form of dependence. The next developmental form of relationship is independence. The teenager in the grip of adolescence is the clearest embodiment of independence—"I can do it all by myself"—and its limitations. Independence is born in reaction to dependence, and there can be a high price to pay, namely, unnecessary aloneness and isolation.

The typical family under the influence of mental illness frequently has become trapped developmentally either in dependence or independence, two poles of an unhealthy continuum. (I believe that attributing such disproportionate power to the concept of independence, while referring to dependence as a sign of weakness, has been one of the major weaknesses of the codependence movement of the 1980s and 1990s.)

Independence and dependence are not mutually exclusive; rather, each of these qualities empowers the other, together becoming the mainstay of the highest form of relationship, or interdependence, namely, "We need each other." It is not a win-lose or lose-lose proposition centered on "you *or* me." Interdependence is essentially a win-win relationship grounded in "you *and* me," a mutually interactive blend of dependence and independence based upon ability, situation, and need. Because of ongoing trauma, loss, grief, and fatigue, however, the family often has not been able to progress to the stage of interdependence. The process of refamilying restores the family and each of its members to this highest form of relating—and healing.

The last caveat is to remember that progress is always two steps forward and one backward. It is never an even progression of upward movement. It is a jagged, rough terrain that builds hardiness. There will be times when you and your loved ones will slip back into old, unhelpful patterns. Expect them to occur. The only reasonable goal in such cases is to make the time between events longer and the time in the events shorter. Nevertheless, because family is an innate, evolutionarily and biologically driven imperative, I believe refamilying is almost always worth the effort—and effort it definitely requires. After all, the essence of family is people to love and to be loved by. *It is never too late to become a happy individual.*

Family Triumph over Mental Illness

This book has translated and synthesized critical information from a variety of fields, including traumatic stress, altered states of consciousness, systems theory, mythology, thanatology, spirituality, physical healing, and contemporary science. Spanning and merging numerous disciplines broadens your perspective, stimulates your sense of wonder, and expands your imagination. In facing life greatest challenges, you have access to countless creative possibilities.

You, the reader, have traveled a long way, learning new concepts about mental illness, its impact on *everyone* in the family, and the skills used in the many approaches to triumph. Triumph has been defined as moving forward in the crux of adversity, against great odds. Triumph opens the doors to healing, strengthening, and rebuilding the family. This book has presented the dynamics of triumph and the principles and skills that bring it forth.

You have seen that trauma and loss are interwoven in the fabric of mental illness in particular and all chronic illness in general. You have learned that serious, chronic disorders and illnesses have the potential to induce parallel dysfunctions in those in close proximity, especially family members and other loved ones. And, most important, you have discovered that like the crest and the trough of the wave, triumph and trauma are not separate and distinct from each other. They are two identifiable points in a larger ongoing and cyclical process, the inevitable rising and receding of the tides. Hence, triumph cannot exist without trauma.

And because the effects of trauma are remarkably similar across different traumas, the principles in this book can apply to all families under the influence of major illnesses, addictions, and other traumas. In fact, as you have discovered, all three are common in families that are under the influence of any negative event(s) outside the range of normal human experience.

Illness, addiction, and trauma can make an already hard life almost impossible. As has been suggested earlier, people need help now more than ever. The new national stressors are resulting in more people visiting family physicians for stress-related disorders such as sleep disturbances, digestive problems, and headaches. There is an increase in the number of people seeking help for depression and anxiety disorders. Alcohol sales are rising as more people are drinking to relieve their fears and worries. And in the midst of all of these increasing stresses, funding priorities have changed. Homeland defense has become the nation's number one priority. Mental health and addiction budgets are being cut across the country, and private reimbursements from insurance companies are getting smaller and more difficult to obtain as costs spiral.

Yet, many also believe that we are at the threshold of a new dawn of peace, hope, and optimism. We have opportunities before us that we have never had before in all of history. The stigma is becoming less as we realize that mental illness has a neurophysiological basis as well as an emotional and cultural one. We have found that it is much less rare than we ever thought, and, in fact, mental illness is much more common than we have ever believed. We have found, too, that it is more responsive to treatment, especially when the family is considered, than we have realized. But there is much work we must do. It is time to apply the extensive knowledge of the effects of trauma to an understanding and treatment of the family and loved ones of all mental illnesses. We can no longer allow these "neglected affected" to suffer.

Those afflicted with mental illness as well as those affected loved ones can stop suffering alone, in silence, and in shame. While underrecognized and undertreated by health professionals and underreported by sufferers, the majority of those who suffer the effects of mental illness can triumph. The family and loved ones have a unique opportunity themselves to grow and develop while making an invaluable contribution to their loved ones. As Mother Teresa says, "Love cannot remain by itself. It has no meaning. Love has to be put into action and that action is service."

The family may be the only remaining environment in which you cannot be replaced. Where there is love, appreciation, and respect, anything may be possible and no problem may be insurmountable. Unless all members of the family are understood and helped, most will not be able to make the transition from an ineffective to effective family.

Research[2, 5, 39, 90, 93, 95, 99, 127] has consistently demonstrated that the prognosis for individuals with mental illnesses improves *when family members are provided with the information and support they need.* By expanding the focus from medication and individual therapy as the only solution, we can unlock the doors to triumph, which opens us to new vistas revealing potential for the health of each family member.

Life is meant to be a boot camp, a basic training for growth and development, not a prisoner-of-war camp that terrorizes and deprives. Living under the influence of mental illness can be either one of these experiences. Boot camp is a process: the new recruits, who begin as self-referential individuals, transform themselves into mature members of an interdependent team. New instincts are learned, and the now mature warriors redefine the situation—no longer do they see themselves as helpless and powerless. They know that they are accountable, and are equipped with the skills necessary for responsible behavior.

This transformation is a choice, and you can make it. The only life you can live is your own, for you are the custodians of your own future. Don't wait. But be patient, very patient with yourselves. Remember Winston Churchill's famous warning: "Never, never, never, never give up." Your upsetting life situation in the present will pass if you know how to wait. If you give the experience room, not unlike the theme in the guru and the farmer story, which illustrated how relative events in your life can be, you will move through it and on to the next experience. If you are traumatized and frozen, it is difficult to move forward, and much time is wasted in recycling through the same old, dysfunctional loops, repeating pattern after pattern and making each new situation a replication of the past.

Negative experiences saturated with trauma, stress, loss, grief, and exhaustion have a strong hallucinatory quality to them. They distort the very doors of perception. The journey will always be hard. Expect to fall down. Expect to falter. Expect to be knocked off the playing court. Expect the unexpected. An old Japanese proverb says, "Fall down seven times; get up eight." You are human.

The miracle of family triumph and healing from the influence of mental illness is not unlike the miracle of the Chinese bamboo tree. For four years after the seed of this wondrous tree is planted, you see nothing but a tiny shoot. But during those four years, there is massive development occurring underground: a strong, elaborate root structure that is wide and deep is being formed. In the fifth year alone, the Chinese bamboo tree can grow to a height as great as eighty feet.

We began our journey in this book with the story of the mathematician John Nash. In 1994, he received the Nobel Prize for economics. In the movie *A Beautiful Mind,* he said the following (to his wife, Alicia) in his acceptance speech, which is a wonderful summary of many principles we have discussed:

> I've always believed in numbers and the equations and logics that lead to reason, but after a lifetime of such pursuits, I ask what truly is logic? Who decides reason? My quest has taken me through the physical, the metaphysical, the delusional and back. And I've made the most important discovery of my career ... the most important discovery of my life. It is only in the mysterious equations of love that any logical reasons can be found. I'm only here tonight because of you. You are the reason I am. You are all my reasons. Thank you.

A recurrent theme throughout this book is that it is never too late for you to create a full life and, with grace, perhaps a happy family. To have either is to be trained, not blamed; to seek out and to be actively enrolled in a vision of healing that spans, whenever possible, the generations, involving the grandparents, parents, and children; and to implement as many of the principles in this book that fit with your specialness and uniqueness as an individual.

A powerful vision, inspiring and calling forth the capacities and skills of each and every member, can connect and unite most members of the family. A powerful vision creates effective individuals who create effective families. Ineffective families can deflate the spirit, dampen the soul, and close down the heart of each and every member. They bring out the very worst in family members, while effective family members bring out the best. Effective individuals and families can "entrain" all sufferers to the irresistibly radiant energy of triumph and healing.

My wish for you at the close of this book is that you proceed quickly through the stage of Chaos, that you arrive at an appropriate and meaningful Diagnosis, that you face your Core Issues with the courage and steadfastness you will need, that you experience the delight of Moving Beyond the influence of the illness and trauma, that you have the grace to Get It Together, that you share the good fortune that can result from the hard work of Refamilying, and that you receive the blessing and the gift of Transcendence. Remember, to be graced by the gift in trauma's other hand, you must first unwrap it.

For those of you who have accepted the call and embraced the journey, I welcome you on one of life's greatest journeys. I salute your devotion. I acknowledge your fierce loyalty to your family. I honor your extraordinary acts of personal courage and your incredible toughness. You are my heroes.

Godspeed to you, my reader! The gateway to triumph lies straight ahead, and you now have many of the keys to unlocking its doors.

—⁓—

APPENDIX *A*

Self-Help
Assessment Measures

—⁓—

The following two self-help assessment measures or guides can help you understand your current situation more clearly. They can increase your ability to be proactive, and therefore less reactive, so that you will be in the best position to facilitate your loved one's healing and well-being as well as your own. They can help give you a better sense of how deeply you are under the spell—or under the influence—of your loved one's illness, addiction, or trauma.

The first is a guide to point to where your foot may be "nailed to the proverbial floor," that is, where you are stuck. It can indicate where your thinking might get you into slight, moderate, or serious trouble. The second is a measure of how much danger or trouble you may actually be in right now. Be as truthful as you can in order to give yourself the clearest picture of where *you* are functioning now.

Both assessment measures are to be answered with a simple "yes" or "no." When you are not sure or are in doubt about a particular question, the answer in my experience most likely is "yes."

Please note that these self-help assessment tools can be very useful, but they are no substitute for an evaluation by a qualified professional; they are just guidelines. They are not formal assessment procedures; rather, they are more like informal screening tests that are intended to raise awareness. *If you have any doubts whatsoever,* please consult a qualified mental health professional. And if you are dealing with violence, suicidal threats, or alcohol and other drugs, it is imperative that you do not waste any time. Consult a professional immediately. There may be little time to waste!

The Most Common Errors in Thinking by Family Members under the Influence of Mental Illness

1. I am responsible for all the problems in this relationship/family.

2. The actions of the person with any serious, chronic, and recurrent illness, addiction, or trauma are about me.

3. It's my responsibility to solve this person's problems.

4. If I can't help, no one else can.

5. If I can convince the person with a serious, chronic, and recurrent illness, addiction, or trauma that I am right, his or her problems will disappear.

6. If you really love someone, you should take his or her physical or emotional abuse.

7. Your loved one can't help having a serious, chronic, and recurrent illness, addiction, or trauma, so I should not hold the person accountable for her or his behavior.

8. Setting limits hurts the person with any serious, chronic, and recurrent illness, addiction, or trauma and is wrong.

9. No matter what the person under the influence of illness, addiction, or trauma does, I should offer them my love, understanding, support, and unconditional acceptance.

10. If I ignore the warning signs, everything will be all right.

11. If I just work hard enough, try enough, am smart enough, am pretty/handsome enough, etc., ad nauseum, then my ill family member will be okay.

12. No one can really understand what I/we am/are going through.

13. I am alone.

14. No help is available.

15. Any serious, chronic, and recurrent illness, addiction, or trauma is untreatable.

16. A serious, chronic, and recurrent illness, addiction, or trauma is a character flaw.

17. If I am good enough, the person with a serious, chronic, and recurrent illness, addiction, or trauma will be okay.

18. Effective treatment for the person with any serious, chronic, and recurrent illness, addiction, or trauma consists of having the person understand how irrational and illogical his or her thoughts, feelings, and behaviors are.

19. Medication is for weaklings.

20. I don't have a problem; it is just my family member or other loved one who does.

21. My loved one is just lazy.

22. I can't ever burden my loved one with my problems because his or hers are so much more serious.

23. Life is a drag and then you die.

24. There are no escaping life's burdens and responsibilities.

25. There is no one I can really trust or depend on.

26. My loved one can/will never learn to be different.

27. If people really knew what was happening, they would reject me/my loved one.

28. I have to sacrifice my life if my loved one is to recover.

29. Others will always understand my situation if I explain it clearly.

30. People with a serious, chronic, and recurrent illness, addiction, or trauma shouldn't work or be employed or be responsible.

31. Others will like me if I always say positive things.

32. Others always have my best interests at heart.

33. I need to do things I don't like to do so others will like me.

34. It is selfish to put my needs ahead of satisfying another's needs or desires some of the time.

35. I must be agreeable for others to like me.

36. It is not possible to love if I voice a different perspective or opinion.

37. A good parent/spouse, sibling, etc., is responsible for the emotional and physical health of others.

38. I can feel worthwhile only if I have someone to love me.

39. I must stay alert to ensure that I do not say something that might upset my loved one.

40. I must avoid conflict at all costs.

Answer Key:

If you answered two or more questions with a yes, YOU may have a problem.

If you answered three or more questions with a yes, YOU probably do have a problem and YOU need help.

If you answered four or more questions with a yes, YOU have a problem.

If you answered more than five questions with a yes, get help immediately.

Danger Signs for Family Members under the Influence of Mental Illness

1. Do others like family, friends, or other significant others tell you they don't understand why you are putting up with your loved one's behavior?

2. Do you try to avoid contact with these people?

3. Do you feel the need to hide or cover up some of your family member's or loved one's behavior?

4. Does the thought of spending time with the person give you unpleasant physical sensations?

5. Are you becoming clinically depressed? Many do not even realize they are depressed. The two most common symptoms are that you are tired most of the time and have trouble sleeping. Also, you experience less interest in normal activities or have less pleasure; gain or lose weight; have thoughts of suicide or feel worthless; have trouble concentrating; experience mood swings. *(Count each yes as one point)*

6. Have you acted in ways that go against your fundamental values and beliefs?

7. Are you no longer able to take a stand for what you believe?

8. Are you concerned about the effects of your loved one's behavior on the children?

9. Have you ever had to intercede on behalf of a family member?

10. Have you ever felt or have actually been in physical danger with a loved one? *(Count each yes as one point)*

11. Is there violence by *any* family member?

12. Are you making decisions mainly out of fear, obligation, and guilt?

13. Are you taking nonprescription drugs to cope or ward off depression or anxiety?

14. Do you regularly read self-help books about (or for) your loved ones?

15. Do you think about/worry about your loved one more than one hour per day?

16. Are you putting your life on hold?

17. Are you participating in your loved one's serious, chronic, and recurrent illness, addiction, or trauma?

18. Do you think you might be participating in your loved one's illness, addiction, or trauma? *(Subtract one for a yes response)*

19. Do you believe your loved one has a character flaw, is weak-willed, or is malingering? *(Count one for each yes)*

20. Do you not have someone you can call any time of the day or night for any reason?

21. Do you not have something to be very passionate about?

22. Do you not have individual and family rituals that give some stability to life, no matter how little—e.g., are birthdays celebrated?

23. Do you feel unloved? Unappreciated? Unneeded? *(Count each yes as one point)*

24. Do you have difficulty falling or staying asleep?

25. Do you startle easily?

26. Have you thought that you need more friends?

27. Do you feel trapped?

28. Are you too sensitive a person?

29. Have you suddenly and involuntarily recalled a frightening experience of your loved one while doing something else?

30. Do you think that you work too hard for your own good?

31. Do you get thoughts in your head that you neither want nor can control?

32. Do you see or hear things others don't?

33. Have you ever thought of suicide?

34. Had a plan? *(Count having a plan as three yes answers)*

35. Have you become a cynic?

36. If you have answered any of the above questions with a yes, are you not getting help?

37. If you disagree with your loved one, do you think you will lose your relationship?

38. Do you think triumph and adversity have little in common?

39. Do you think fear and courage have little in common?

Answer Key:

If you answered one or more questions with a yes, YOU might have a problem.

If you answered two or more questions with a yes, YOU probably do have a problem and YOU need help. Get help.

If you answered three or more questions with a yes, you may have a major problem and YOU should get professional help immediately. Do it now.

—m—

APPENDIX *B*

Useful Distinctions

—⚹—

A basic principle in physics is called "the principle of comple-mentarity." This crucial rule states that for any concept to have meaning, a second and additional concept is needed, one that serves as a logical complement. Thus, to understand the concept of wellness, we must contrast it with, or distinguish it from, the concept of illness. As the famous anthropologist Gregory Bateson[7] noted many years ago, truly meaningful information is com-municated by accentuating distinctions: contrasts and apparent opposites, as well as discrete (perhaps even subtle) differences.

Useful distinctions are the very features that make a difference! The skillful use of language fosters deeper levels of understand-ing that lead to more effective actions. With our increasing abil-ity to recognize disparity, we generate the very heart of insight and awareness, the fundamental building blocks of life.

In my work with individuals and families, I have found the following distinctions particularly helpful in unlocking the doors to family healing and change. Each set of distinctions creates new possibilities for taking actions that lead to triumph. Important distinctions are often easy to grasp in concept, but these distinctions are much harder to put into action. When we are mindful that every one of life's challenges calls for us to bring into play these "new muscles" of discernment, they gradually become reliable, strong enough to override our old habits, or "stories."

Accountability/Blame

Family members often confuse the distinction between these two concepts. Accountability is the opportunity to be fully "a-count-on-able." It is the building block of relationship and the foundation of trust. It is inviting and attractive. It is a positive and necessary action in human relationships. Blame, on the other hand, is a judgment and indictment of the person or self. A negative and harmful act, it destroys relationships and creates resentments on the part of the "blamee" as well as the "blamer." Even worse, blame obscures the chance to be effective. Effective families cannot exist on blame; they require accountability. Accountability (count-on-able) is also distinguished from responsibility (response-able). Responsibility refers to the commitments and promises you make, whereas accountability means that you deliver what you promised.

Advice/Support

Advice is suggestions, strategies, or opinions given to another. Sometimes advice is needed and sought. However, advice in this context is based on the advice giver's resources and talents—not upon those of the other person. That is why advice often is unhelpful—it is about what *you* would do, and you are different from anyone else. What is good for you may not be good for another. With intimate relationships, advice, while often offered, is often not being sought unless it is explicitly asked for. Rather, the person just wants to be heard and understood. Support is geared and oriented toward the other. It is "from you" rather than "about you."

Affect/Feeling/Emotion

Many people do not distinguish between these, but it is important to do so. An *affect* is a purely physiological and unconscious state—the biological component of an emotion. An *emotion* is a complex conscious experience that is based on an affect. It involves a sense of physiological arousal, an impulse or urge toward action, along with a degree of discernible feelings. A *feeling* is a more subtle quality of awareness that can be introspectively distilled from the physiological urgency of the emotion. While emotions impel action, feelings do not impel one toward action. Emotions tend to manipulate and control, while feelings tend to communicate and negotiate.

It is possible to have an affect without experiencing the emotion that goes with it, like tears coming to the eyes with no accompanying sense of feeling moved by sadness; or when there are palpitations, dizziness, and sweating but no awareness of being anxious or alarmed. It is likewise possible to have an emotion without experiencing the feeling that should go with it, as when a person is aware of being impelled to act but cannot identify the feeling that is implicit and unconscious in the action. Thus, one can notice the physiological arousal and urge to action that are part of an emotion, but not the feeling that would have allowed the person accurately to characterize what kind of an emotion it will be. Finally, it is possible to experience a feeling by itself, independent of any of the physiological indicators and impulses of emotion.

The poet Wordsworth's comment that poetry "takes its origin from emotion recollected in tranquillity" suggests the kind of calm, centered, highly subtle awareness that such pure feeling involves. It is only through such a subtle awareness of feeling-tone that we are able to distinguish our own motives and values, and understand the meaning of our emotional experience.

This kind of distilled self-awareness is the goal of therapy, but the early stages of the process typically happen primarily at the level of affect and emotion. Once you fully experience emotions, you are no longer under their control. Most of the pain of feelings comes from having to fight to control them, and when you actually let yourself feel the feelings, they will not be as scary or painful as you imagine and you will actually feel more in control.

Compassion/Pity

Compassion is a feeling that stems from understanding and makes us want to move closer to the person. It is a rich and highly textured experience of being with someone. Pity, on the other hand, stems from fear and survival and makes us want to move further away. Compassion restores and renews both persons, while pity drains both.

Content/Process

This is a fundamental distinction in the communication process. Content refers to the "what" of the communication or conversation, while process refers to the "how." Comparing this distinction to a song, the content can be understood as the words and the process can be seen as the music. Content presents the story of what happened—the event(s) that unfolded, who said what to whom, and who did what and to whom. Process evokes feelings. Process is at the heart of the impact of the story on others. Content generally relates more to the "surface" of the situation, while process relates more to the underlying nature of the situation.

While content often invites advice and perhaps sympathy, process invites exploration, understanding, and real insight into the nature of how you communicate. Often, people are unaware of their process. To be unaware of your process is to invite suffering, because you will enact the same behaviors again and again. You engage in hundreds of different contents in a single day; yet, there may be just a few underlying threads of process throughout all of the content. It is critical to be facile with both expressions and know on what occasions which one is most important.

Too much of an emphasis on content (especially to the exclusion of process) can be self-referential. In other words, too much focus on content, for example, can exclude or ignore others. As an illustration, if one drones on and on with content, others might start to drift and space out. If one's content overwhelms others and monopolizes the conversation, then the other person will get lost and disengage—and often get angry.

Content often opens the doors to process (just as feelings open the door to meaning); but it cannot keep them open. Content is great for downloading information. Process is essential for intimacy. In fact, process, or "me-you talk," is at the heart of connecting with others. If you do not feel connected or engaged, check your process. Process is virtually always a more dicey conversation. That's why it is more intimate. Content is most effective either when one needs a brief reality check, when one needs advice, when one just wants to get a situation off his or her chest. Content is one of the powerful gateways to process, and process is the domain where healing takes place.

Enrolling/Selling

Enrollment is the process of offering someone something, the having of which will benefit him or her and move the person toward the very intentions and goals he or she wants. It is based on attraction. It is the presentation of a compelling possibility. Selling is offering someone something she or he doesn't need or really want. Enrolling is a function of genuineness, while selling is a function of survival. The family needs to be enrolled in the vision and very real possibility of something greater than merely surviving or even managing the mental illness; the family does not need to be sold a pipe dream of platitudes that tell members "everything happens for the best."

Freedom/Slavery

"Freedom is what we do with what has been done to us," as the French philosopher Jean-Paul Sartre once said. Slavery is living out of what has been done to us. Freedom invites discipline, while suffering thrives in unacknowledged chaos. Freedom is the very source of caregiving, while slavery is the basis of caretaking. Freedom is mindful; slavery is mindless. Freedom and denial are the antithesis of each other. I often say that in the early stages of recovery, there are very few choices for family members. In the middle stages of recovery there are many choices. Then, in the end stages of recovery, there are again very few choices again.

Perhaps the following will clarify this apparent irony: in early recovery the lack of choice stems from slavery and bondage to false beliefs, mistaken notions, and fear of being oneself. On the other hand, in late stage recovery, there are few options. At this stage, the integrity of your decision to be the person you've always wanted to be graces you with few choices. In your quest to be authentic, you find few alternatives.

Healing/Curing

These two terms are often misunderstood. The literature on physical illness distinguishes these two terms most clearly. Healing is the end of war inside; it is the peaceful coexistence of all thought, feeling, and behavior. It is under one's control, and is independent of symptoms. Thus, one could actually die of an illness, yet experience the illness as a healing (usually of deep, old wounds from formative periods in our life).

A cure, on the other hand, is the return to a previous level of functioning with no evidence of the illness, addiction, or trauma. It is generally accepted that there is no cure for serious mental illness, although there is healing—for each and every member of the family.

Hero/Victim

There are few distinctions as important as this one. To really understand the meaning of this distinction, it is necessary to look to the field of classical mythology, which is full of references to heroes and victims. As referenced before, the work of Joseph Campbell is seminal to any discussion about heroes. Campbell studied the heroes from all cultures and from all times and noted the common denominators and described the journey through which all heroes go.

In the context of a family member who has been under the influence of illness, addiction, or trauma, a hero is someone, whether male or female, who rises above the chaos and confusion of the illness. The hero (note the distinction between the family role called "hero" versus being heroic) explains his or her ability to cope *because* of the family situation, while a victim explains his or her *inability* to cope with the family situation because of that situation. The victim asks, "Why me?" The hero asks, "Why not me?"

Heroes embrace their feelings—whether anger, fear, or doubt—and know feelings are a portal to finding meaning. Heroes are proactive; victims are reactive. The victim gains his or her power through reaction rather than positive action. Heroes feel self-esteem; victims feel shame. Heroes embrace what is; victims deny what is. Heroes seek to live a conscious life; victims live unconsciously. Heroes see the universality of their experience; victims see their experience as a personal assault. Heroes experience pain; victims suffer.

Human Justice/Divine Justice

Human justice is what occurs on planet Earth. There can be little apparent rhyme or reason to it. Holocausts, famines, disease, crime, and a host of other problems appear to be unjust. Innocent people get killed, bad people seem to profit, and, of course, the good die young. It is the breeding ground of profane wounding. It is often couched in terms of punishment. Divine justice, on the other hand, is birthed from Above. It is not punitive; rather, it is loving. It is intended to help us see the errors of our ways so that we can strive toward a higher standard. Divine justice can rarely be understood on the human level. When it can be appreciated and when the person can surrender into it, it is the perfect salve for any wound. Viktor Frankl's story of the woman and the ape is an excellent example. The great theologian Martin Luther said it differently: "If God's justice could be recognized as just by human comprehension, it would not be divine."

Impact/Intention

The impact of your message can be very different from your intent. The impact is how your message "lands." It is how it is received. It is purely subjective and can have little to do with your intent, which is what you want to say. What you intend to say and what is actually heard too frequently do not resemble each other.

Mind/Brain

This distinction is often a blurry one; yet, it can be useful at times. The brain is a collection of physical structures that process sensory, cognitive, and emotional information. On the other hand, within the human head there is an inner, personal awareness, or observant self. This self, with its emotions, sensation, and cognitions, is called the mind. It arises from the perceptual processes of the brain. Because the relationship between the two is so intimately connected, they can be considered as two different aspects of the same thing.

Old Story/New Story

Old story is the story of life we are told by others. It is inherited and based on someone else's opinion, not yours. It is also generational, coming from relatives one has often never even heard of. It is usually based on untruths, half-truths, and unspoken truths. It lacks any creativity or generativity and is full of rigid rules and roles for all its characters. It is full not just of trauma, but also of great drama. An ounce is a pound, and a pound a ton. New story, on the other hand, is chosen. It is the story you choose to create and constantly tell yourself. It is the way you choose to describe your life and the meaning you choose to impart to it. It contains little drama and can be full of trauma, which it embraces without producing symptoms.

On the Court/Off the Court

This is a sports metaphor conveying the idea of whether one is actively involved and participating in life and its many relationships, or whether one is in denial, is being irresponsible, or is being unaccountable. One is either on the court of life, or one is in the stands, watching life fly by. The former is an active, mindful, responsive process, while the latter is a passive, mindless, and reactive process.

The Pain/My Pain

Common in the literature on healing from physical illnesses, this is a distinction often used by Stephen Levine, who has worked extensively with the terminally ill. "The" pain is a state of consciousness connected to the universality of all experience. It is an acknowledgment of the fundamental reality of pain. In this acknowledgement is acceptance and in this acceptance is freedom from suffering. It is a state of connection to self, others, and something beyond the limited self or ego. "My" pain, on the other hand, is a very personalized and victimized state of consciousness in which the sufferer feels alone, isolated, alienated, and often punished. "The" pain is always bearable, while even small doses of "my" pain are experienced as intolerable.

Pain/Suffering

This is one of the most important distinctions for those under the influence of any illness, addiction, or trauma. My best friend, Peter, masterfully illustrated the difference when he shared the first time he bungee jumped, which he was determined to do. Suffering occurred every time he thought about whether to jump or not. Suffering was voting in the middle of his commitment to jump. It had no beginning, middle, or end, offering scant opportunity for learning. Pain, on the other hand, occurred when his second foot left the platform. Pain offers the possibility of a beginning, middle, and end. It begins with the end of denial. It flourishes in an atmosphere of acceptance.

Put somewhat differently, suffering is a state of obsessive wondering about the outcome of something without taking any action. Pain begins with action and ends in resolution. Pain is inevitable; suffering is optional. Suffering occurs when something must be something it is not (that is, it is in essence a state of nonacceptance of the situation), while pain is dealing with what is. Thus, suffering is full of resistance. Suffering is redirected pain. When you don't grieve, for example, the pain simply redirects itself into destructive tendencies and behaviors.

For example, a family member wonders what would happen if she or he expressed a concern to another member. The person is so concerned that she or he says nothing. Instead, the person just stews. This is suffering. There is always a certain amount of psychological "leakage" when one is in suffering. Thus, there may be resentment or passive aggression (that is, aggression that is denied) on the one hand and depression and anxiety on the other. When the person actually does say something, the suffering is over and the pain begins. One of the most important jobs of the counselor is to move the client from suffering to pain.

Psychic Stunt Double/Person in Front of You

A psychic stunt double, as the name implies, is someone who represents or stands in for ("doubles for") someone else who is important in the person's past or present, as opposed to the real person in front of him or her. It is as if that important person in one's history is now perching on the shoulders of the "double." What is seen, then, is someone else entirely, an amalgam of unresolved fragments of the past. Consequently, the person is not responding to the primary person sitting in front of him or her. Instead, reacting to the "double" now obscures the real traits of the person across from him or her. It is surprisingly common for family members under the influence to find members of their family of origin in their other relationships. Thus, one's wife can be perceived to be like one's mother, or even one's father. Neither gender nor age is an important factor when dealing with psychic stunt doubles.

Reactive Power/Proactive Power, or React/Respond

Reactive power is based on fear, defense, and survival. It is usually aggressive and violating of others. It always stems from judgment. Proactive power, on the other hand, is based on growth and development. Its essence is creative action. It is assertive expression, that is, it is a nonviolating expression. It always stems from acceptance and surrender to exactly "what is" and exactly "what is not."

A useful analogy comes from the work of Stephen R. Covey, an internationally respected leadership authority, organization consultant, and family expert, who has been recognized by *Time* magazine as one of American's twenty-five most influential people. He writes that between the onset of a stimulus and its response, there is a space. He continues: "In that space lies our freedom and power to choose our response. In our response lies our growth and our freedom."

The essence of a proactive response lies in making use of the space by pausing between the stimulus and response. This pause leads to an insightful response. In a reactive style, there is no pause, and the response (reaction) is elicited automatically, rather than emerging as a thoughtful, proactive style. Reactions are "knee jerk" and are all about us and our agendas, while responses are mindful and are inclusive of others.

Relating to/Relating from

This is a very useful distinction in learning how to separate *or* become more a part of a situation. When one is "relating to" something or someone, that person has a certain emotional distance from it. It is a state of witnessing, and like all states of witnessing, it is a state of mastery and empowerment. The person is able to separate his or her essence from the experience. This state of controlled dissociation or distance can create more objectivity and often more safety in the process. On the other hand, "relating from" something implies a state of association, fusion, or merging. When relating from something, it is as if the person is that which he or she is relating from.

For example, if a family member is upset and angry with a loved one, the person can "relate to" his or her anger and express it in a constructive way, as opposed to becoming the anger and spewing all over the loved one. One can "relate to" being under the influence and thereby not be under its spell to the same degree or intensity. While this latter example requires a great deal of skill and practice, learning to "relate to" a situation is both possible and empowering.

Simple/Easy

This distinction causes more frustration than any other does. So many things in life appear simple *and* easy, especially when performed by someone who is skilled in that particular behavior. When one watches a talented dancer perform her or his act, for example, it looks almost effortless. Actually performing that behavior is anything but easy. It has taken years to develop. Reading about triumph, reading about becoming heroic, or reading about compassion all can seem so easy to accomplish. But when one actually steps forth on the playing court of life, the difficulty of the task quickly becomes apparent. Simple is one thing; easy is quite another. Give yourself the time and attention and allow the effort that many of the new skills and concepts in this book will require.

Small Story/Great Story

Small story is all the personal, idiosyncratic, linear, frag-mented, dissociated, isolated, and cut-off events in a life strewn together to make an often meaningless and almost always ba-nal life. It is cut-off from the whole. Great Story, on the other hand, represents the universality of the situation in which you find yourself. It is integrative rather than separating. It connects you to the whole instead of keeping you apart. Small story is a breeding ground for profane wounding, and Great Story is where sacred wounds lie.

Stand/Position

A stand is a direct expression of the self; it requires no proof, no data, and no explanation. It simply "is." On the other hand, a position is a changeable and argumentative sentiment. Evidence is marshaled to prove one is right or wrong in a position. In a stand there is a belief of "rightness" (whether right thought, right action, right speech, right relationship). For example, Martin Luther King, Jr. had a stand for integration and Gandhi had a stand for nonviolence. Neither needed any outside evidence for their belief. Stands anchor the person to the unshakable; positions anchor the person in sand. Stands stem from integrity; positions stem from opinion. Stands offer strength; positions offer excuses.

Teflon/Velcro

These are terms reflecting the ability to hold on or let go of issues. Both are necessary, but in different situations. It is helpful to let go of some issues, or some conversations, and stop thinking or obsessing about them. This ability to let an issue fall off your back as easily as water falling off a duck's back is what is meant by the term "Teflon." On the other hand, some people just cannot let go of an issue. When one is unable to move away from an issue, or is stuck in it, then that person is "Velcro."

Vision/Pipe Dream

Simply put, a vision is a bold statement of intent about your purpose that is possible, while a pipe dream is a statement of intent that has no chance of actually occurring.

What (Actually) Happened/What (You Think) Happened

Many people confuse what occurs with what they think occurs. When one is under the influence of any strong emotion, it is especially easy to confuse what actually happened (a factual presentation) with what one thinks happened (an interpretation). This is the source of more family arguments than probably any other single thing. What happened, as defined in this context, is to be found in the facts of a situation devoid of interpretation or story. For example, hydrogen plus oxygen yields water.

There are very few facts in interpersonal relationships, however. In intimacy, facts are a hindrance. Facts ore often more a part of the problem than the solution. When family members are locked in a debate, I often say, "Would you rather be right or happy?" as a way to alert them to distinguish fact from opinion. Even the apparent fact that all family members are here today, while a literal fact, may be figuratively an interpretation. For example, John's body is here, but he hasn't been present all session. He is not even present now. It is easier—usually—to get agreement on what happened and is generally consensual. What you think happened is always an opinion.

Your Issue Speaking You/You're Speaking Your Issue

This is a key distinction in terms of who is in control—you or your problem. When one speaks "from" his or her issue, the issue is speaking them. The message is typically accusatory and completely self-referential. It is all about you and takes little consideration of the other person. When your issue speaks you, you are more apt to be domineering and controlling and out of control. The intent is to get what you want rather than to have a conversation. On the other hand, when you speak your issue, you are in control, and your issue is not. This is generally an "I" statement and is about your experience—not about the other.

APPENDIX C

Core Issues
for Family Members

—⚉—

The following "core issues" point to where your foot may be nailed to the proverbial floor. The more of these that apply to you or your loved one, the more difficulties you or he or she may experience. Many are described more fully in *Obsessive Compulsive Disorder: New Help for the Family.*

All or None Thinking

Chronic Low Self-Esteem

Compassion Fatigue

Confusion

Control

Demoralization

Denial

Depression

Disenfranchised Loss and Grief

Dissociation or Psychic Numbing

Doubt

Emotional Symptoms

Enabling

Excessive Judgmentalism

Fatigue and Exhaustion

Frozen Feelings

Grandiosity

Grief

Guilt

High Tolerance for Inappropriate Behavior

Hypervigilance

Indirect Communication

Learned Helplessness

Loss

Loss of Self

No Personal Needs

Physical Symptoms

Preoccupation with the Primary Sufferer

Spontaneous Age Regression

Super Responsible or Super Irresponsible

APPENDIX *D*

Seven Journeys of Healing for Family Members

—ᴍᴍ—

There are seven key journeys or transitions that you will undergo in order to heal, recover, and triumph over any circumstance. They are described in great detail in *The Crucible for Triumph: Trauma and Adversity.*

1. The Journey from Addiction to Spaciousness
2. The Journey from Shame to Self-Esteem
3. The Journey from Unconscious to Conscious Living
4. The Journey from Victim to Hero
5. The Journey from Personalization to Universalization— My pain vs. The pain
6. The Journey from a Newtonian to a Quantum Physics Perspective
7. The Journey from Trauma to Triumph

—ᴍᴍ—

APPENDIX *E*

Seven Stages of Healing for Family Members

—ᴍᴍ—

The following are the seven stages of healing described in depth in *Obsessive Compulsive Disorder: New Help for the Family.*

1. Chaos
2. Diagnosis
3. Core Issues
4. Moving Beyond
5. Getting It Together
6. Refamilying
7. Transcendence

The following are the six stages of healing described in depth in *Recovery: A Guide for Adult Children of Alcoholics.*

1. Survival
2. Emergent Awareness

3. Core Issues

4. Transformations

5. Integration

6. Genesis

APPENDIX *F*

Eight Stages of Sacred Wounding for Family Members

—ꟷ—

These stages of sacred wounding are described in great detail in my upcoming publication *The Crucible for Triumph: Trauma and Adversity.*

1. The wound

2. Distinguishing the suffering from the pain

3. Creating a healing distance

4. Going through the anger

5. Embracing a spiritual path

6. Going through the stages of healing

7. Finding a great story to live out of—distinguishing "small" vs. "large" story and "old" vs. "new" story

8. Opening to grace and accepting the miracles

—ꟷ—

APPENDIX *G*

Ten Steps to Creating Meaning for Family Members

—⟋⟍—

1. Take responsibility.

2. Empty yourself of defeating attitudes and behaviors.

3. Employ your curiosity and imagination.

4. Get informed.

5. Find models to emulate.

6. Be open to synchronicity.

7. Have courage.

8. Persevere and persevere most in the most difficult times.

9. Expect miracles.

10. Create living metaphors (my current favorite is Life is like the stock market: one day it's up and great and next it is down and crashes) to guide your life.

—⟋⟍—

APPENDIX *H*

Twelve Steps to Becoming a Triumphant Family

—ɰ—

These are described more fully in *Obsessive Compulsive Disorder: New Help for the Family.*

1. Get the right diagnosis.

2. Reach out and end the isolation.

3. Get informed.

4. Get training in areas like communication, assertion, or problem solving as well as strength identification.

5. Get connected to self, others, and something beyond.

6. Get a plan, or a personal *and* family vision, and follow it.

7. Create family rituals.

8. Learn compassionate detachment.

9. Accept the illness and its effects and its gifts.

10. Embrace the hero's journey.

11. Ask for help when necessary.

12. Remember, success is getting up one more time than you fall down.

APPENDIX *I*

Roles of the
Helping Professional

—⟋⟍—

Professionals have a positive impact on the family when they:

1. **Establish** rapport with the family, that is, connect with the family.

2. **Communicate** effectively with the family in a language that they can understand.

3. **Acknowledge** strengths, resources, and expertise of each member of the family.

4. **Normalize** the horror of the family experience.

5. **Validate** the stress, trauma, loss, and exhaustion of the family.

6. **Diagnose** secondary traumatization as well as compassion fatigue.

7. **Treat** secondary traumatization and compassion fatigue.

8. **Train** the family in skills such as effective communication, problem solving, assertion, and dealing with the mental health system.

9. **Address** the expressed needs of the family themselves.

10. **Adapt** their style to a particular family.

11. **Emphasize** the value of family involvement.

12. **Initiate** a family service plan.

13. **Provide** family care that has a loving dimension.

Professionals have a negative impact on the family when they:

1. **Fail or are unwilling to listen** to what caregivers have to say.

2. **Disregard the knowledge** and need of caregivers.

3. **Make snap judgments** without much background information.

4. **Behave callously** in a way that increases the caregivers' pain.

5. **Blame** caregivers for their family member's problem.

6. **Ignore** the needs of the "neglected affected," or the loved ones.

Glossary
of Helpful Terms

—ᴍ—

Every field of information has its own vocabulary. The following terms and their definitions can help you better understand not only this book but the field of mental illness as well. Many of these expressions relate directly to the field of mental illness. However, there are a number of important concepts that come from other disciplines. The mental illnesses are such complex phenomena, and their effects and impacts so potentially devastating and extensive, that it is necessary to venture beyond the traditional boundaries of this field, and tap the rich, valuable resources inherent in other arenas of knowledge. The language unique to each field of study exposes new facets, each adding to the depth of our understanding and transmitting a vivid light that illuminates the path to the triumphant life.

Thus, the study of traumatic stress is essential for understanding the full nature of wounding, especially secondary traumatization, to *all* members of the family. The study of addiction provides useful alternatives, as it brings the knowledge of family systems, spirituality, and the value of peer-led support groups to bear on family healing, underscoring the effects of secrecy, shame, and stigma. Knowledge from the field of altered states of consciousness allows us to better understand the depth and intensity of the family experience, supplying a non-judgmental vocabulary to describe important problems and issues (e.g., codependency as a deep, negative trance). Mythology deepens our understanding of the wound, points to its recovery, highlights the stages of recovery, fosters the creation of new meanings, and provides time-tested models of coping. The fields of personal excellence, success, and joyology bring to the family a new awareness of resilience, strength, and mastery, all of which are ingredients of our natural wisdom and heritage. More importantly, these fields of personal excellence emphasize health and well-being as opposed to abnormality and pathology. Last, but not least, the modern sciences teach the family the value of chaos as a creative life force necessary for healing. Quantum physics points to the interconnectivity of all things, and neuroscience verifies the power of words and our own languaging to change the neural pathways in our brain. Modern science interweaves a vast and swiftly growing body of fact to the art of healing the family.

abuse   to treat someone as an object; a wound that does not injure the core of the self except when it occurs repeatedly in childhood

addiction   its strictest definition: a substance that creates tolerance and whose removal creates withdrawal symptoms; more broadly defined as (1) existing whenever we are internally compelled to give energy to a substance, person, thing, or activity that does not reflect our true desire or (2) any pathological relationship with life-damaging consequences to a substance, person, thing, or activity that carries the possibility of life-damaging consequences; its common denominator is the narrowing and fixating of attention

addict while in the strict sense of the word, an addict is someone who is addicted to a substance, person, or thing, I much prefer psychologist Dr. William James' definition; namely, an addict is a frustrated mystic

age progression (also called "pseudo-orientation in time") a way of time travel in which the person projects himself or herself into the future; it occurs spontaneously and automatically whenever the person's mind goes into the future; the chronically anxious person who imagines a negative outcome occurring in the future and who experiences the event as if it were happening now is demonstrating the natural occurrences of age progression

age regression a state in which a past experience is interpolated over present reality wherein the person cannot fully experience present time; it occurs whenever the mind is going back to the past

anchor a stimulus that automatically triggers, activates, or catalyzes a predictable response, like the heart automatically fluttering after seeing a police officer in your rearview mirror after going though a stop sign

baby God's opinion that the world should go on (said by the poet Carl Sandberg); in recovery, it is a term that refers to a newly sober person

betrayal a wound to the soul, which marks the end of non-reflective, unconscious, and automatic trust; it is one of the greatest agents of the sacred

the Big Lie   in the perfect life there are no problem behaviors, sad events, or failed effects

biphasic personality traits   psychologist Al Siebert's term describing the equivalent in personality of counterbalanced nervous systems and muscle systems that enable an individual to respond in both one way and another; the traits of what he calls "the survivor personality"

burnout   a feeling of being overwhelmed and not rewarded

caregiving   a mutual, rewarding, loved-based, positive, and enriching experience of helping a loved one or another person

caretaking   a one-way, sacrificial, fear-based, negative, and depleting experience with a loved one or another person

coach   someone who tells you what you don't want to hear in order that you can be who you want to be—Tom Landry of the Dallas Cowboys

codependence   driving yourself crazy trying to calm down some fool; when we get caught up in the drama and chaos of someone else's situation

compassion fatigue   the parallel disorder that family members can get—it is the ultimate fatigue of intimate relationships and is caused by close contact with a loved one in which you feel you are of no help and cannot separate yourself from that person and cannot get a rest

core beliefs   beliefs about personal safety, the meaningfulness and comprehensibility of the world, and one's essential goodness; the foundation of selfhood

courage   to proceed in a positive, meaningful, and productive way in the presence of your fear

crisis   the juncture of danger and opportunity

crucible   a place or occasion of severe test or trial; a container able to withstand the intensity of a situation in which different elements interact to provide something new

dark side (shadow)   that part of the psyche that is not exposed; the underside; when the shadow operates independently and the person is unconscious, it is the source of negative, destructive emotions, and when the person is aware, or conscious, when one takes responsibility for it, one gains access to the riches of the underworld and it becomes the source of great strength and resource

dissociation   the natural process by which undesirable or threatening experiences are attenuated by splitting the self into unconnected parts; as a result, chunks of experience are isolated or separated from each other; it is more commonly called "feeling spacey," "spaced out," "zoned out," "going somewhere else," "not present," or "floating to the top of the ceiling"; unlike repression, which excludes single memories and feelings from awareness without seriously changing the way we consciously represent our world, dissociation leads to a more global disruption of consciousness; the greater the dissociation, the greater the devastation to the personality and loss of self

DNA   the genetic material contained within the nucleus of the cells that defines who the person is

drama   the life created by people who put their problems on a pedestal instead of solving them

DSM-IV   often referred to as the Bible of psychiatric diagnoses, this 886-page book is the *Diagnostic and Statistical Manual of Mental Disorders,* Fourth Edition, published in 1994 by the American Psychiatric Association, which contains every official diagnosis of any mental disorder

dysfunctional family   a broadly defined term describing a family in which the primary caregivers consistently ignore the needs of the children; it includes families in which there is sexual, physical, emotional, or spiritual abuse

empowerment   the ability to identify, access, and utilize a variety of trance states to achieve a desired outcome; the distinction between being empowered and being victimized lies in our absolute refusal to give up on ourselves regardless of what happens

excellence   a term that is harder to define than to observe; easily recognized, it is called by many names: success, happiness, serenity, optimal experience, peak performance, mastery, recovered; it is ultimately a learned habit in which our fears may be more apparent than ever, but drive us less; it's not that we get what we want in excellence, but that we truly appreciate what we get

exceptional survivors   those who have come through great medical and emotional crises; researched by Bernie Siegel, the Simontons, and psychologist Al Siebert

exposure and response prevention   the psychological treatment of choice for OCD, which involves systematically exposing the person to the things they fear the most and then preventing the person from engaging in his or her compulsion

extraordinary person   one for whom the present is guided by the future; who believes thoughts, feelings, and behaviors cause desired outcomes; and who is guided by commitments, pledges, and promises rather than feelings

family   the homes we return to for nourishment and from which we leave more refreshed and ready to deal with the world; an umbrella term that takes into account a person's network of intimate relationships

family trance the invisible but tangible spell the family casts over its members, especially the children, who are most susceptible; it is maintained by limited rules and injunctions as well as constricted roles that can persist throughout adulthood until a healing process breaks its hold; because its induction is not limited in time or place, it is a much more powerful trance and has a much deeper impact than the trance states helping professionals utilize; in family trances one is conditioned to identify with values that may have little to do with developing one's own essence

"family under the influence" hidden victims and hidden healers

FEAR before recovery: **f**alse **e**vidence **a**ppearing **r**eal; during recovery: **f**ace **e**verything **a**nd **r**ecover

freedom "What you do with what has been done to you," states the philosopher John Paul Sartre; "Feeling comfortable in harness," writes the poet Robert Frost

hallucination any created situation that has no representation in external reality

negative hallucination not seeing, hearing, or feeling something that is there; denial is an example of a negative hallucination; when someone does not see, hear, or acknowledge abuse, that person is negatively hallucinating

positive hallucination seeing, hearing, or feeling something that is not there; if a person sees love, kindness, or caring when none is present, the person is experiencing a positive hallucination

HALT an acronym standing for **h**ungry, **a**ngry, **l**onely, and **t**ired—the four main states of mind that cause us the most trouble on our way to hope and healing

hardiness   a term first introduced by psychologist Suzanne Cobassa to describe a trait in those who stayed healthy in the midst of major stress; it enables them to be healthier, less depressed, and perform more effectively than those who do not have this personality trait

healing   from Stephen Levine, who defines it as bringing peace where there has been war, as harmonizing disquieting and dissenting conflict, as letting go of personal separation, and as sending love and mercy into the wound

healing edge   knowing when to take care of yourself first and knowing when to leave your family member to his or her own fate—that shifting slope between what is loving and responsible toward your relative and what is loving and responsible toward yourself

Healing Visions Press   where you can order all of Dr. Gravitz' materials—1-800-718-7080

hero's journey   the path of the family under the influence—the hero's journey is not a courageous act but a life lived in self-discovery, for "the ultimate aim of the quest must be neither release nor ecstasy for oneself, but the wisdom and the power to serve others—a hero is someone who has given his or her life to something bigger than oneself—the usual hero adventure begins with someone from whom something has been taken. . . . This person then takes off on a series of adventures beyond the ordinary, either to recover what has been lost or to discover some life-giving elixir—there is no reward without renunciation, without paying the price—the man or woman who has been able to battle past his personal and local historical limitations to the generally valid, normally human forms" (Joseph Campbell)

high influence communication   all messages, ideas, concepts, or feelings that penetrate deeply into the psyche and impact a person's thoughts, feelings, or behaviors

hypnosis   one type of trance state characterized by a narrowing focus of attention and heightened receptivity; it can be traced as far back as 3000 B.C., when references to "temple sleep" and to enchantment by the "evil eye" can be found in early writings

illness   an opportunity to be healed

initiation   the process by which we move from one developmental level to another; by restructuring our perceptions of the world, it enables us to experience the deeper wisdom inherent in the event it symbolizes

insanity   trying to manage and control what you cannot—also, doing the same thing again and again and expecting different results

integrity   the alignment among our professed values, convictions, beliefs, thoughts, feeling, and behaviors as well as commitments and pledges with the highest parts of ourselves; it is a much more inclusive concept than congruence; the result is the experience of wholeness; without it, there is bankruptcy on many levels

interdependence   the highest level of functioning and integration wherein everything is connected; each part is interlinked and interrelated to every other part; we are one great ecosystem living a nested reality of connectiveness

joyology   the study of happiness

larger story   universal, deeply meaningful way of mythologizing one's life; dominated by sense of self as hero, and crisis as the opportunity for excellence; it moves us beyond the focus of the our limited circumstances; it reveals levels of

4

the psyche and opens us to the awareness that everything is connected; as the domain of the real self, it moves us from "my" pain to "the" pain

learned helplessness   the feelings of utter impotence stemming from the belief that you are unable to effect any change

loss of self   a life-threatening and progressive process that underlies the "Problem" statement of many twelve-step groups; loss of self to a substance is commonly called addiction or compulsion, while loss of self to others can result in codependence

luck   what occurs when opportunity meets preparation

master communicator   anyone, who either consciously or unconsciously, is versed in high influence communication, whether that person is a therapist, politician, advertiser, or car salesperson; parents are often master communicators

mastery   the ability to dis-identify from our many states of consciousness, particularly from our problems; those who can relate "to" as well as "from" their problems; the ability to identify self as the observer or witness of the comings and goings of different deep trance states

mental disorder   health condition marked by alteration in thinking, mood, or behavior that causes distress or impairment in the person's ability to function—it is not a character flaw

miracle   a coincidence in which God chooses to remain anonymous

mourning   a process of communicating the many feelings one has over a loss

mystery school   ancient schools where special students went in order to learn the secrets of the inner mind

myths   clues our deepest spiritual potential, which can teach us the value of our wounds, sorrow, and grief and can lead us to delight, illumination, and even rapture—stories of or search through the ages for truth, for meaning, for significance—clues to the spiritual potentialities of the human life

NAMI National Alliance for the Mentally Ill, the national mental health advocacy organization

negative trance/hypnosis a trance in which the direction and focus is on life-detracting and life-depleting messages; blame, judgment, censure, and ridicule flourish

neurolinguistic programming (NLP) a system of therapy created by Richard Bandler and John Grinder, both students of the greatest medical hypnotist of all time, Milton E. H. Erickson; they studied and described the dynamics of "master communicators"

neurotheology the emerging new science that explores the links between spirituality and the brain; it bridges faith and reason, mysticism and empirical data

normal as used by Dr. Abraham Maslow: "a psychopathology of the average, so undramatic and so widespread that we don't even notice it"

OCD obsessive-compulsive disorder; the biological illness characterized by clinical obsessions, or thoughts of harming oneself or another, accompanied by compulsions, or compelling behaviors designed to reduce the anxiety generated by the obsessions

ordinary person one for whom the present is determined by the past, who believes thoughts, feelings, and behaviors are the effect of outer, historical causes, and who is guided by feelings rather than commitments

parts fragments or aspects of the psyche

PartsWork the process by which various aspects or "parts" of the psyche are identified, accessed, and utilized in order for the person to function maximally; it is based on the assumption that a host of different characters reside within everyone

perennial philosophy   the nearly universal consensus about reality held by humanity for most of its time on this earth

perspective   the ability to hold on to memories of good times during bad ones and the wisdom to know they will return

positive trance/hypnosis   a trance in which the direction and focus is on life-enhancing messages and where creativity, possibility, being, love, acceptance, and support flourish

posthypnotic suggestion   a suggestion given in an altered state of hypnosis that is later acted upon outside the hypnotic state; in its broadest sense, it occurs whenever we introduce an idea during a moment of heightened receptivity that is later carried through in behavior

power   the ability to move from failure to failure with enthusiasm (Winston Churchill)

proactive   a position in which the person takes active responsibility for the direction and meaning of his or her life; when knocked down by the wave of life, the proactive person learns to get out of the way of the next wave

pseudo-excellence   the avoidance or escape from trauma through compulsive overachievement and overperformance and development of compensatory supercompetence in areas not necessarily aligned with true talents and drives; in short, outer success is at the service of incomplete childhood fantasies and achievement based on the false self

psyche   an all-embracing term that refers to the totality of our psychological capacities and functioning; it contains the ego, soul, and spirit

psychic stunt doubles   a hologram of someone from the past projected onto someone in the present; whenever we turn someone in the present into someone from the past in order to recreate or enact an old pattern, that current person becomes a psychic stunt double for the past person; psychic stunt doubles always represent someone in the past with whom we are incomplete; the result is that the current person carries a psychic charge that has little to do with him or her and a lot to do with the person who is projecting

psychological defenses   our emotional protective wrappers

psychopathology   the study of the disordered or diseased mind

psychosis   a term indicating that a person no longer is in contact with reality because he or she is experiencing delusions, or false beliefs held despite evidence to the contrary, and hallucinations, or false sensory experiences; other telltale signs of a psychotic disorder include gross disorganization, confusion, incoherence, tangential speech, and disorientation

psychosomatic disorder   one in which there are clinically significant physical symptoms, but the cause (or etiology) is emotional or psychological

PTSD (post-traumatic stress disorder)   a behavioral and biological description of trauma and its consequences; the most current term for the kinds of symptoms and problems for which Freud used the word "hysteria" at the turn of the century; the *DSM-IV* formal diagnosis for syndrome occurring if a person is exposed to profound stress above and beyond the range of ordinary human experience

quantum physics   the study of nonphysical forces whose movements create our physical world; it is showing that emotions and feelings have a direct and indirect effect on the physical world

reactive   a position in which the person is influenced, directed, or controlled by automatic, unconscious, unmindful legacies of his or her history; when knocked down by the wave of life, the reactive person gets up the same way each time

real excellence   a state of consciousness in which thoughts, acts, and feelings are aligned with the true or authentic self; the fullest expression of the capacities of the true self; it is characterized by spaciousness, self-esteem, conscious living, heroic living, Great Story (or Larger Story), and universalization

recovery   the process of healing representing the ideal training ground for personal and psychospiritual excellence; it is a nonlinear, cyclical healing process occurring in stages

complete recovery   the state of well-being marked by the transition from survival to excellence that occurs as the destructive influences of the past no longer predetermine or condition the present; in this state a created, compelling future pulls the person forward; it is possibility and vision based; it is the awakening of the whole person; its goal is excellence not normalcy; and it unfolds in six stages and is manifested in five main journeys; as a result, we can comfortably move among life's major realms in this state: the historical or psychological, the mythical, and the unitive realm

early stage recovery   the beginning part of recovery where we discover that what happened to us is not our fault

late stage recovery   the part of recovery that begins when we realize that although we didn't cause what happened, we are responsible for doing something about it; it begins when we accept that everything is our responsibility

reframing   a communication process that takes a situation and lifts it out of its old context (frame) and places it in a new, more useful one

resiliency   the ability to bounce back from life's blows

sacred psychology   psychologist Jean Houston's term to describe soul-making, or the development of the soul; rooted in many traditions, it emphasizes union and transformation; its goal is coming home and requires us to die to one story to be born to a Larger Story by the recovery and deepening of our personal story

sacred wound   a wound that opens the soul to its greatest depths; as our entrance into Larger Story, it initiates soul-making by calling forth the deeper questions that, when answered, will reveal who we really are

Self   the end point of our individuation, for when the Self is manifested, we know who we are and we experience wholeness and integrity

self-esteem   the opposite of shame; according to Nathaniel Branden, the father of the self-esteem movement, it is the "integrated sum of self-confidence and self-respect"; "the disposition to experience oneself as competent to cope with the challenges of life and as deserving of happiness"; also the inner experience of our own preciousness

self-help programs (twelve-step programs)   the 200-plus different types of groups offering experience, strength, and hope to those similarly afflicted; they are generally patterned after the Twelve Steps of Alcoholics Anonymous (in mythic terms, AA provides crucial rites of passage, initiation, and revisioning complete with rituals, elders, and sacred space); at best, a path to psycho-spiritual excellence; at worst, semi-religious, cult-oriented groups that indoctrinate their members into a dependent state of powerlessness and helplessness

Serenity Prayer   the prayer repeated at twelve-step programs: "God grant me the serenity to accept the things I cannot change, the courage to change the things I can, and the wisdom to know the difference"

serious mental illness   those debilitating mental illnesses that include schizophrenia, bipolar disorder, major depression, obsessive-compulsive disorder, and other severe and persistent disorders

severe to catastrophic stressor   living under the influence of a major mental illness, addiction, or trauma

shame   the feeling resulting from the belief that at a fundamental level there is something wrong with us—that we are bad, sick, crazy, or dumb; as Hawthorne wrote in *The Scarlet Letter*, shame is the feeling of one thousand unrelenting eyes piercing our soul

signature strengths   those skills we have honed and developed

small story   personalized, narrow, limited historical way of mythologizing one's life; dominated by the perception of self as victim; it is the domain of the false self, seat of the reactive mind, and creator of psychic stunt doubles; like the lid on the proverbial jar that limits how high the flies inside will jump, small story is the lid we keep on ourselves that limits the full expression of our real self

Soul   the deepest part of us that knows what is real; unlike the mind, which can fool us and play tricks on us, the soul is the source of our deepest feelings; in religious thought, it is immortal, and in Jungian terms, it is often synonymous with the psyche

soul's high adventure   the quest to grasp the reality of God

spaciousness   a quality of mind that is the antithesis of addiction; it is the ability of the mind to allow the energies of the universe to pour through; it is awareness of possibility and openness created by surrender and letting go of addiction and denial; with spaciousness, there is a Teflon-like quality to experience in which it can pass through the person without the person getting stuck in it

spell   the chronic negative state (also called a trance) induced by trauma

spirituality   a broad term with many meanings and misunderstandings; it is the belief in the sacred whole of life; the feeling of awe, profound and personal appreciation that comes from embracing the mystery and magic of life, and responding and behaving daily in ways that develop and further enhance the person

SSRIs   selective serotonin reuptake inhibitors, or a type of antidepressant medication that is the medical treatment of choice for OCD—they include Prozac, Luvox, Paxil, Celexa, Luvox, and Anafranil

states of consciousness   the panoply of different alterations in which the mind functions at a given moment; waking, dreaming, and sleeping are common examples; they function to create internal representations of our external world; each state of consciousness has its own special and unique resources, attitudes, liabilities, and assets; we can do some things in one state that we cannot do in another; for example, in the dream state, we can fly; states of consciousness can either interconnect positively and be life-enhancing or negatively and be life-detracting

stress   the state of the body wherein more energy is expended than taken in; the nonspecific reaction of the body to a stimulus

stressor   events or circumstances whose effects actually or potentially interfere with life; a term from the physical sciences noting the pressure, tension, or strain in a body resulting from external force; following stress, prior equilibrium can be retrieved, unlike the situation that follows trauma

subpersonality   term used to account for the observation that we all possess multiple natures or multiple parts depending on the context; a subpersonality is one such part; "parent," "adult," and "child" are to be viewed as subpersonalities made famous by Transactional psychotherapist Dr. Eric Berne; while there are an infinite number of subpersonalities, they tend to form clusters of commonalties

suffering   an optional state of illegitimate distress characterized by little communication (few requests, few promises) and isolation from others; it is the domain of all addiction; it has no beginning, middle, or end; as such, it is unending; as used in this book, it is contrasted with *pain*, a state of legitimate distress that one can get through by communicating and sharing

systems theory   a way of understanding the psyche as an ecosystem of its own, where the fundamental principle is "the whole is greater than the sum of its parts"; causality becomes a reciprocal concept as all parts mutually influence each other

temperament   biological predisposition

thanatology   the study of death, loss, and grief

therapist   someone who needs forty hours of therapy a week

trance   a state of consciousness in which one is removed or detached from one's physical surroundings; commonly either a hypnotic, cataleptic, or ecstatic state; trance states can be used to evoke resources and change or they can be used to create the very symptoms with which we struggle

consensus trance   a term psychologist Charles Tart uses to describe "the sleep of everyday life," or normal consciousness in which we are unaware, unconscious, and caught in a state of suspended animation, illusion, and denial; it involves a loss of much of our essential vitality; in consensus trance there is limited access to the full range of human capabilities

family trance   the invisible but tangible spell the family casts over its members, especially the children, who are most susceptible; it is maintained by limited rules and injunctions as well as constricted roles that can persist throughout adulthood until a healing process breaks its hold; because its induction is not limited in time or place, a family trance is a much more powerful trance and has a much deeper impact than the clinical trance states helping professionals utilize; in family trances one is conditioned to identify with values that may have little to do with developing one's own essence

transcenders   psychologist Donna LaMar's term for "individuals who grow up in difficult, painful, destructive families and emerge with a meaningful, productive way of life"

trauma   a word derived from the Greek *traumaticos* meaning wound; thus, a wound or injury to the core of the self that usually results in the person's belief that life is meaningless, he or she is bad, and there is no safety; an indigestible experience that occurs because one is exposed to profound dilemmas; an event that induces stress beyond limits of normal human endurance and capacity

triumph   to rise above and proceed in a positive, meaningful, and productive way in the midst of adversity, usually against the odds; to grasp victory from the hands of defeat

triumphant survivors   the term used by Ann Kaiser Sterns for those who turn their problems into victories; those who come back from tragedy and trauma; those who have moved beyond their crises

true compassion   accepting the mentally ill person without suffering; approaching another with love rather than fear

victim cycle sacrifice; resentment; explosion; guilt; and then sacrifice, resentment, explosion, and guilt

victims those who use their history to explain why they aren't able to do what they need to; those whose lives are limited by their circumstances

weller-than-well a phrase often used in twelve-step groups to connote a state of health beyond the mere absence of addictions or symptoms

witness trauma a very serious form of trauma that one can incur as a result of seeing another's—especially a loved one's—horrific experiences

wound the breaking, breaching, or penetrating into the human flesh or soul by a force or power from beyond the ordinary; the holes in our soul; the wound becomes sacred when we give up our small story to embrace Great Story

wounded healer an age-old archetype of the person who has gone through great sorrow and tragedy, emerging on the other side using her or his gifts to heal others

Bibliography

—⟋w—

1. Adamec. C. *How to Live with a Mentally Ill Person: A Handbook of Day-to-Day Strategies.* New York: John Wiley and Sons, Inc., 1996.

2. Amador, X. *I Am Not Sick I Don't Need Help!* New York: VidaPress, 2000.

3. *American Heritage Dictionary of the English Language.* Second Edition. Boston, MA: Houghton Mifflin Company, 1982.

4. Andreasen, N. C. *Brave New Brain: Conquering Mental Illness in the Era of the Genome.* New York: Oxford University Press, 2001.

5. Andrews, L. M. *To Thine Own Self Be True: The Relationship between Spiritual Values and Emotional Health.* New York: Doubleday, 1989.

6. Armstrong, L. *It's Not About the Bike: My Journey Back to Life.* New York: Berkley, 2001.

7. Bateson, G. *Steps to Ecology of the Mind.* New York: Ballantine Books, 1972.

8. Berkus, R., *To Heal Again.* Encino, CA: Red Rose Press, 1986.

9. Bernheim, K., Lewine, R., and Beale, C. *The Caring Family: Living with Chronic Mental Illness.* New York: Random House, 1982.

10. Black, C. *It Will Never Happen to Me.* Denver, CO: Medical Administration Company, 1981.

11. Bolen, J. *The Gods in Everyman: A New Psychology of Men's Lives and Loves.* New York: Harper and Row, 1989.

12. Bowden, J., and Gravitz, H. *Genesis: Spirituality in Childhood Trauma.* Pompano Beach, FL: Health Communications, Inc., 1988.

13. Branden, N. *Honoring the Self: Personal Integrity and the Heroic Potentials of Human Nature.* Los Angeles: Jeremy P. Tarcher, Inc., 1983.

14. Bridges, W. *The Way of Transition: Embracing Life's Most Difficult Moments.* Cambridge, MA: Persus Publishing, 2001.

15. Bulfinch, T. *Bulfinch's Mythology.* New York: Dell Publishing Company, Inc., 1959.

16. Burr, H. S. *Blueprints for Immortality: The Electric Patterns of Life.* Essex, England: Saffron Walden, 1972.

17. Campbell, J. *Power of Myth* (with Bill Moyers). New York: Doubleday, 1988.

18. Campbell, J. *The Hero with a Thousand Faces.* Princeton, NJ: Princeton University Press, 1968.

19. Carlson, R., and Shield, B. *Healers on Healing.* Los Angeles, CA: Jeremy P. Tarcher, Inc., 1989.

20. Catherall, D. R. *Back from the Brink: A Family Guide to Overcoming Traumatic Stress.* New York: Bantam Books, 1992.

21. Cousins, N. *Head First: The Biology of Hope.* New York: E. P. Dutton, 1989.

22. Cousins, N. *Anatomy of an Illness as Perceived by the Patient.* New York: W. W. Norton and Co., 1979.

23. Covey, S. *The Seven Habits of Highly Effective Families.* New York: Golden Books, 1997.

24. Covey, S. *The Seven Habits of Highly Effective People: Powerful Lessons in Personal Change.* New York: Simon and Schuster, Inc., 1989.

25. Cozolino, L. *The Neuroscience of Psychotherapy: Building and Rebuilding the Human Brain.* New York: W. W. Norton and Co., 2002.

26. Curran, D. *Traits of a Healthy Family.* Minneapolis, MN: Winston Press, Inc., 1983.

27. Curran, D. *Stress and the Healthy Family.* Minneapolis, MN: Winston Press, Inc., 1985.

28. *Desk Reference to the Diagnostic Criteria from DSM-III-R.* Washington, DC: American Psychiatric Association, 1987.

29. *Diagnostic and Statistical Manual of Mental Disorders.* Fourth Edition. Washington, DC: American Psychiatric Association, 1994.

30. Dickens, R. M. Personal Communication. Santa Barbara, California, 2002.

31. Dickens, R. M., and Marsh, D. T. (Eds.) *Anguished Voices: Personal Accounts of Siblings and Children.* Boston: Boston University Center for Psychiatric Rehabilitation, 1994.

32. Dyer, W. W. *There's a Spiritual Solution to Every Problem.* New York: HarperCollins Publishers, 2001.

33. Edelstein, G. *Trauma, Trance, and Transformation: A Clinical Guide to Hypnotherapy.* New York: Brunner/Mazel, 1981.

34. Efran, J. S., Lukins, M. D., and Lukens, R. J. *Language Structure and Change: Frameworks of Meaning in Psychotherapy.* New York: W. W. Norton and Company, 1990.

35. Eliade, M. *The Sacred and the Profane.* New York: Harcourt Brace Jovanovich Publishers, 1959.

36. Eliot, T. S. "Four Quartets." In T. S. Eliot, *Collected Poems: 1909-1962.* London: Faber and Faber, 1963.

37. Erickson, M., and Rossi, S. *Experiencing Hypnosis: Therapeutic Approaches to Altered States.* New York: Irvington, 1981.

38. Erickson, M. H., Rossi, E. L., and Rossi, S. I. *Hypnotherapy: An Exploratory Casebook.* New York: Irvington, 1979.

39. Figley, C. R. (Ed.). *Burnout in Families: The Systemic Costs of Caring.* Boca Raton, FL: CRC Press, 1998.

40. Figley, C. R. (Ed.). *Compassion Fatigue: Coping with Secondary Traumatic Stress Disorder in Those Who Treat the Traumatized.* New York: Brunner/Mazel, 1995.

41. Figley, C. R. (Ed.). *Helping Traumatized Families.* San Francisco: Jossey-Bass, 1989.

42. Frank. A. W. *The Wounded Storyteller: Body, Illness, and Ethics.* Chicago: The University of Chicago Press, 1995.

43. Frank, A. W. *At the Will of the Body: Reflections on Illness.* New York: Houghton Mifflin, 1991.

44. Frankl, V. *The Doctor and the Soul: From Psychotherapy to Logotherapy.* New York: Vantage Books, 1986.

45. Frankl, V. *Man's Search for Meaning.* New York: Washington Square Press, 1963.

46. Freedman, J., and Combs, J. *Narrative Therapy: The Social Construction of Preferred Realities.* New York: W. W. Norton and Company, 1996.

47. Gallo, F. *Energy Diagnostic and Treatment Methods.* New York: W. W. Norton and Company, 2000.

48. Gallo, F. *Energy Psychology: Explorations at the Interface of Energy, Cognition, Behavior and Health.* New York: CRC Press, 1998.

49. Gallo, F., and Vincenzi, H. *Energy Tapping*. Oakland, CA: New Harbinger Publications, Inc., 2000.

50. Garfield, C. *Peak Performers: The New Heroes of American Business*. New York: Avon Books, 1986.

51. Gleick, J. *Chaos: Making a New Science*. New York: Penguin Books, 1987.

52. Gold, L. *The Sacred Wound: Healing from the Death of a Child*. Portland, OR: FireWord Publishing, Inc., 2000.

53. Gore, A., and Gore, T. *Joined at the Heart: The Transformation of the American Family*. New York: Henry Holt and Company, 2002.

54. Grabhorn, L. *Excuse Me, Your Life Is Waiting*. Charlottesville, VA: Hampton Roads Publishing Company, 2000.

55. Gravitz, H. L. *The Crucible for Triumph: Trauma and Adversity*. Santa Barbara, CA: Healing Visions Press (Forthcoming Publication Date, Spring, 2004).

56. Gravitz, H. L. "A Passionate Plea to Open the Doors to Other Fields of Healing." *Obsessive-Compulsive Foundation of Jacksonville*. October, 2002.

57. Gravitz, H. L. *Words That Heal: More Help for the Family*. Santa Barbara, CA: Healing Visions Press, 2004.

58. Gravitz, H. L. "The Family Experience of Mental Illness." *Psychology Today*, March/April, 2001.

59. Gravitz, H. L. "The Binds That Tie: Families under the Influence of Mental Illness." *The Journal of NAMI California*, 2 (2), 2000.

60. Gravitz, H. L. "Obsessive-Compulsive Disorder: New Help for the Family." *OCD Newsletter*, Aug/Oct., 1998.

61. Gravitz, H. L. *Obsessive Compulsive Disorder: New Help for the Family*. Santa Barbara, CA: Healing Visions Press, 1998.

62. Gravitz, H. L. "The Family as a Neglected Resource: Intergenerational Healing for Adult Children." *Trauma Response,* Fall, 1996a.

63. Gravitz, H. L. "The Neglected Affected: Counseling the Codependents of OCD Sufferers." *Professional Counselor, 11* (5), 1996b.

64. Gravitz, H. L. "Intimates and Loved Ones: The Neglected Affected." *OCD Newsletter.* February, 1996c.

65. Gravitz, H. L., and Bowden, J. *Recovery: A Guide for Adult Children of Alcoholics.* New York: Simon and Schuster, Inc., 1986.

66. Gravitz, L. A. *Choosing Life.* Santa Barbara, CA: Healing Visions Press, 1998.

67. Grinder, J., and Bandler, R. *Trance-Formations: Neuro-Linguistic Programming and the Structure of Hypnosis.* Moab, UT: Real People Press, 1981.

68. Hatfield, A. B., and Lefley, H. P. *Families of the Mentally Ill.* New York: Guilford Press, 1987.

69. Hill, N. *Think and Grow Rich.* New York: Hawthorne Books, 1972.

70. Hora, T. "Transcendence and Healing." *Journal of Existential Psychiatry, 1,* 501-511, 1961.

71. Houston, J. *The Search for the Beloved: Journeys in Sacred Psychology.* Los Angeles, CA: Jeremy P. Tarcher, Inc., 1987.

72. James, W. *Principles of Psychology* (2 Volumes). New York: Holt, 1890.

73. Jamison, K. R. *An Unquiet Mind: A Memoir of Mood and Madness.* New York: Alfred Knopf, Inc., 1995.

74. Janoff-Bulman, R. *Shattered Assumptions.* New York: The Free Press, 1992.

75. Jenike, M, Baer, L., and Minichello, W. *Obsessive-Compulsive Disorders: Practical Management.* Third Edition. St. Louis, MO: Mosley Press, 1998.

76. Karp, D. A. *The Burden of Sympathy: How Families Cope with Mental Illness.* New York: Oxford University Press, 2001.

77. *Kit for Early Childhood Professionals.* National Association for Children of Alcoholics (NACoA). Rockville, Maryland, 2002.

78. Kushner, H. S. *When Bad Things Happen to Good People.* New York: Avon Books, 1983.

79. Lafond, V. *Grieving Mental Illness: A Guide for Patients and Their Caregivers.* Toronto, Canada: University of Toronto Press, 1994.

80. Lambrow, P., and Pratt, G. *Instant Emotional Healing: Acupressure for the Emotions.* New York: Broadway Books, 2000.

81. Lebell, S. *Epictetus: The Art of Living.* San Francisco: HarperCollins, 1995.

82. Lebow, J. "Family Therapy Scorecard: Research Shows the Family Approach Is Often the Treatment of Choice." *Psychotherapy Networker,* January/February, 2003.

83. LeShan, L. *Cancer as a Turning Point: A Handbook for People with Cancer, Their Families, and Health Professionals.* Revised Edition. New York: A Plume Book, 1994.

84. LeShan, L. *The Medium, the Mystic, and the Physicist: Toward a General Theory of the Paranormal.* New York: Ballantine Books, 1974.

85. Levine, S. *Healing Into Life and Death.* New York: Anchor Press/ Doubleday, 1987.

86. Levoy, G. *Callings: Finding and Following an Authentic Life.* New York: Three Rivers Press, 1997.

87. Lopez, B. *Crow and Weasel.* San Francisco: North Point Press, 1990.

88. Lynch, M., and Harrison, D. *Consegrity: A Wellness Model.* Wichita, KS. Authors, 2002.

89. Marsh, D. T. *A Family-Focused Approach to Serious Mental Illness: Empirically Supported Interventions.* Morgansota, FL: Professional Resources Press, 2001.

90. Marsh, D. T. *Serious Mental Illness and the Family.* New York: John Wiley and Sons, Inc., 1998.

91. Marsh, D. T., and Dickens, R. M. *Troubled Journey: Coming to Terms with the Mental Illness of a Sibling or Parent.* New York: Jeremy P. Tarcher/Putnam, 1997.

92. May, R. *Love and Will.* New York: W. W. Norton and Company, 1969.

93. McFarlane, W. R. *Multifamily Groups in the Treatment of Severe Psychiatric Disorders.* New York: Guilford Press, 2002.

94. Miklowitz, D. J. *The Bipolar Disorder Survival Guide: What You and Your Family Need to Know.* New York: Guilford Press, 2002.

95. Miklowitz, D. J., and Goldstein, M. J. *Bipolar Disorder: A Family-Focused Treatment Approach.* New York: Guilford Press, 1997.

96. Miller, A. *Banished Knowledge.* New York: Bantam Doubleday Dell Publishing Group, Inc., 1990.

97. Miller, W. R., and Martin, J. E. (Eds.). *Behavior Therapy and Religion: Integrating Spiritual and Behavioral Approaches to Change.* Newbury Park, CA: Sage Publications, Inc., 1988.

98. Myers, D. G. *The Pursuit of Happiness.* New York: Avon Books, 1992.

99. National Advisory Mental Health Council. "Health Care Reform for Americans with Severe Mental Illnesses." *American Journal of Psychiatry, 150,* 1447-1465, 1993.

100. National Association for Children of Alcoholics. *Kit for Early Childhood Professionals.* Rockville, MD: Author, 2002.

101. Newberg, A., d'Aquili, E., and Rause, V. *Why God Won't Go Away: Brain Science and the Biology of Belief.* New York: Ballantine Books, 2002.

102. Nightingale, E. *The Essence of Success: 163 Life Lessons from the Dean of Self-Development.* Niles, IL: Nightingale-Conant Corporation, 1993.

103. Olshevsk, J. L., Katz, A. D., and Knight, B G. *Stress Reduction for Caregivers*. New York: Francis and Bacon, 1999.

104. Papolos, D. F. and Papolos, J. *Overcoming Depression*. Third Edition. New York: HarperCollins, 1997.

105. Parry, A., and Doan, R. E. *Story Re-Visions: Narrative Therapy in the Postmodern World*. New York: Guilford Press, 1994.

106. Pearsall, P. *Making Miracles*. New York: Prentice Hall Press, 1991.

107. Peck, M. S. *People of the Lie*. New York: Simon and Schuster, Inc., 1983.

108. Peck, M. S. *The Road Less Traveled: A New Psychology of Love, Traditional Values, and Spiritual Growth*. New York: Simon and Schuster, Inc., 1978.

109. Peters, T., and Watterman, R., Jr. *In Search of Excellence*. New York: Warner Books, 1984.

110. Phillips, N. Taken from a letter distributed nationwide from MADD in a fund-raising and education effort, December 6, 1985.

111. Ram Dass, B. *Still Here: Embracing Aging, Changing, and Dying*. New York: Riverhead Books, 2000.

112. Rately, J. J. *A User's Guide to the Brain: Perception, Attention, and the Four Theaters of the Brain*. New York: First Vintage Books Edition, 2002.

113. Reeve, C. *Nothing is Impossible: Reflections on a New Life*. New York: Random House, 2002.

114. Reeve, C. *Still Me*. New York: Ballantine Books, 1998.

115. Saldana, T. *Beyond Survival*. New York: Bantam Books, 1986.

116. Schwartz, J. M., Stossel, P. W., Baxter, L. R., and Phelps, M. E. "Systematic Changes in Cerebral Glucose Metabolic Rate after Successful Behavior Modification Treatment of Obsessive-Compulsive Disorder." *Archives of General Psychiatry, 53*, 109-113, 1996.

117. Schwartz, M. *Morrie: In His Own Words.* New York: Dell Books, 1998.

118. Secunda, V. *When Madness Comes Home: Help and Hope for the Children, Siblings, and Partners of the Mentally Ill.* New York: Hyperion, 1997.

119. Seligman, M. E. P. *Authentic Happiness: Using the New Positive Psychology to Realize Your Potential for Lasting Fulfillment.* New York: The Free Press, 2002.

120. Seligman, M. E. P. *Learned Optimism.* New York: Knopf, 1991.

121. Seligman, M. E. P. *Helplessness: On Depression, Development and Death.* San Francisco: Freeman, 1975.

122. Siebert, A. *The Survivor Personality.* Portland, OR: Practical Psychology Press, 1993.

123. Siegel, B. S. *Love, Medicine, and Miracles.* New York: Harper and Row, 1986.

124. Siegel, B. S. *Peace, Love, and Healing.* New York: Harper and Row, 1989.

125. Siegel, D. *The Developing Mind.* New York: Guilford Press, 1999.

126. Sommer, R., Clifford, J. S., and Norcross, J. C. "A Bibliography of Mental Patients' Autobiographies: An Update and Classification System." *American Journal of Psychiatry, 155,* 1261-1264, 1998.

127. Sprenkle, D. *Effectiveness Research in Marriage and Family Therapy.* Alexandria, VA: AAMFT, 2000.

128. Stearns, A. K. *Coming Back: Rebuilding Lives After Crisis and Loss.* New York: Random House, 1988.

129. Stinnett, N., and DeFrain, J. *Secrets of Strong Families.* Boston: Little, Brown and Company, 1985.

130. Styron, W. *Darkness Visible: A Memoir of Madness.* London: Jonathan Cape, 1991.

131. Tart, C. *Waking Up: Overcoming the Obstacles to Human Potential.* Boston: Shambhala, 1986.

132. *The Bhagavad Gita.* Berkeley, CA: Nilgiri Press, 1985.

133. Thomsen, R. *Bill W.* New York: Popular Library, 1975.

134. Torrey, E. F. *Surviving Schizophrenia: A Manual for Families, Consumers, and Providers.* Fourth Edition. New York: HarperCollins, 2001.

135. U.S. Department of Health and Human Service. *Mental Health: A Report of the Surgeon General.* Rockville, MD: 1999. (Author: David Satcher.)

136. van der Kolk, B. A. *Psychological Trauma.* Washington, DC: American Psychiatric Press, 1987.

137. Van Noppen, B., Pato, M., and Rasmussen, S. *Learning to Live with OCD.* Third Edition. Milford, CT: OC Foundation, 1993.

138. Walsch, D. N. *The Little Soul and the Sun: A Children's Parable Adapted from Conversations with God.* Charlottesville, VA: Hampton Roads Publishing Company, Inc., 1998.

139. Wattles, W., and Powell, J. *The Science of Becoming Excellent.* Largo, FL: Top of the Mountain Publishing, 1993.

140. Wegscheider, S. *Another Chance: Hope and Health for the Alcoholic Family.* Palo Alto, CA: Science and Behavior Books, 1981.

141. Wheatley, M. *Leadership and the New Science: Learning about Organization from an Orderly Universe.* San Francisco: Berrett-Koehler Publishers, Inc., 1992.

142. White, M., and Epston, D. *Narrative Means to Therapeutic Ends.* New York: W. W. Norton and Company, 1990.

143. Wright, R. *Nonzero: The Logic of Human Destiny.* New York: Vintage Books, 2000.

144. Wolin, S. J., and Wolin, S. *The Resilient Self: How Survivors of Troubled Families Rise Above Adversity.* New York: Villard Books, 1993.

145. Woolis, R. *When Someone You Love Has a Mental Illness: A Handbook for Family, Friends, and Caregivers.* New York: Jeremy P. Tarcher, Inc., 1992.

146. Wright, L. M., Watson, W. L., and Bell, J. M. *Beliefs: The Heart of Healing in Families and Illness.* New York: Basic Books, 1996.

147. Wylie, M. S., and Simon, R. "Discoveries from the Black Box: How the Neuroscience Revolution Can Change Your Practice." *Psychotherapy Networker,* September/October, 2002.

148. Yapko, M. D. *Hand-Me-Down Blues: How to Stop Depression from Spreading in Families.* New York: St. Martin's Griffin, 1999.

149. Yapko, M. D. *Trancework: An Introduction to the Practice of Clinical Hypnosis.* New York: Brunner/Mazel Publishers 1990.

—ɯ—

About the Author

—⁓—

Herbert L. Gravitz, Ph.D., received his Master's Degree and Doctor of Philosophy in psychology from the University of Tennessee in 1969. A licensed psychologist, his private practice in clinical psychology is located in Santa Barbara, California. He specializes in the diagnosis and treatment of the effects of illness, addiction, and other trauma on the individual and the family. He is known for his innovative work in systemic traumatology, specifically the impact of alcoholism, post-traumatic stress disorder (PTSD), obsessive-compulsive disorder (OCD), bipolar disorder, major depression, and schizophrenia on the individual and the whole family.

Dr. Gravitz has authored or coauthored books and articles on trauma, healing, and recovery, and he has led workshops and seminars throughout the United States on the traumatic impact of alcoholism, as well as major mental illness, on the family. He is the coauthor of *Recovery: A Guide for Adult Children of Alcoholics,* a classic in the field of children of alcoholics, and he is coauthor of *Genesis: Spirituality in Recovery from Early Childhood Trauma.* He authored *Obsessive Compulsive Disorder: New Help for the Family,* which has received overwhelming endorsement from professionals and organizations, as well as individuals and their families. He recently finished *Words That Heal: More Help for the Family,* the companion book for *Unlocking the Doors to Triumph,* and is currently completing a new book, titled *The Crucible for Triumph: Trauma and Adversity,* in which he shares in depth his pioneering synthesis of the fields of trauma, addiction, loss and grief, altered states of consciousness, physical healing, mythology, personal excellence, the new sciences, the energy therapies, and spirituality, all of which lead to a powerful healing transformation. His Web site is www.HealTheFamily.com and his e-mail address is mail@HealTheFamily.com.

Dr. Gravitz' message of hope and optimism regarding the impact of illness, addiction, and trauma on both the individual and the family make him a frequent guest on radio and television. In addition to his busy private practice in Santa Barbara, he is a Founding Board of Director of the National Association of Children of Alcoholics (NACoA) and served on its Advisory Board. He is currently a Founding Board of Director of The Memory to Action Project, a not-for-profit organization whose mission is to commemorate genocide, encourage tolerance, and promote commitment to social action. He holds Diplomates in Psychotherapy, Traumatic Stress, and Forensic Psychology. In addition, he is Board Certified in Illness Trauma by the American Academy of Experts in Traumatic Stress.

Dr. Gravitz' first experience with people suffering from mental illness occurred following his first year of graduate school, when he worked as a psychiatric aide at Chestnut Lodge, an internationally known residential treatment center in Rockville, Maryland. He did his clinical internship at Larue D. Carter Memorial Hospital in Indianapolis, Indiana, in 1968, where he worked with the seriously mentally ill in an in-patient setting. From 1972 to 1980, while first Assistant Director and later Program Director of the University of California at Santa Barbara Counseling Center, he worked extensively with students who experienced serious mental illness. When he entered private practice in 1980, he counseled the seriously mentally ill and their families in his role as Psychological Consultant to Sanctuary House. Sanctuary House was started as an alternative residential treatment program for the seriously mentally ill, and it became a nationally respected treatment facility that continues to serve the needs of the mentally ill and their families. While at Sanctuary House, he formed the first group psychotherapy program for its residents and frequently consulted with family members. In 1983, he served as a consultant to the Santa Barbara Psychiatric Emergency Team where he provided staff development.

It was not until the early 1990s that Dr. Gravitz became aware of how many clients in his outpatient private practice also were the family members of those who suffered from serious mental illnesses, such as schizophrenia, bipolar disorder, major depression, obsessive-compulsive disorder, or some other severe illness. By the middle of the 1990s, he began to describe the plight of the family that was living under the influence of mental illness.

Because illness, addiction, and trauma often occur together in the family, Dr. Gravitz has learned to address all three in unique ways that go beyond traditional family approaches. In this process, he has discovered ways to speak simultaneously to the sufferer and to the sufferer's loved ones. Dr. Gravitz routinely began to treat the family as a whole in the late 1990s, regardless of how many family members were actually present in a session. He continues to forge new frontiers in his intensive and creative consultations. In this regard, he is known for his innovative intergenerational treatment protocols and his pioneering work in "untimed" consultation sessions, in which the family works on an issue until everyone present agrees it is time to stop.

—∿—

INDEX

Dopamine, 252
Dossey, Larry, 160
Dowling, Ed, xlvi, 155–156
Drama, profane wounds and, 11
Dual diagnoses, 87–88
Durante, Jimmy, 157
Dyer, Wayne, 262–263
Dysfunctional roles in family, 72

E

Easy/simple distinction, 299
Edison, Thomas, 250
EEG (electroencephalogram), 253
Effective families, 146–147
Effort and triumph, 191–192
Einstein, Albert, 67, 208
Emergencies, family plan for, 167
Emerson, Ralph Waldo, 107
Emotions, 289–290
Empowerment, 184
Endorphins, 252
Energy therapies, 208, 259–261
Enlightened witnesses, 122
Enmeshment, 271
Enrolling/selling distinction, 292
Entanglement, 116, 271
Epics, 201
Epictetis, 159
Ethics, compassion fatigue and, 101–102
Evil, presence of, 268–269
Expectations, realistic, 124
Experience
    brain and, 252
    gene expression and, 253–254
Expressed emotions, 37
Extended family, effects on, 83

Externalizing problems, 179, 211–212

F

Fairy tales, 159–160
Faith of practitioner, 230
Family. *See also* Roles
    burden of care, 35–38
    case scenarios, 40–46
    children, effects on, 81–82
    definition of, 39
    dysfunctional roles in, 72
    effective families, 146–147
    extended family, effects on, 83
    fatigue in, 75
    grandparents, effects on, 82–83
    guilt and, 74–75
    healing journeys, 305
    importance of, 40
    individual members, impact on, 77–84
    limitations of, 268
    negative reactions of, 37
    paradoxes in, 220–223
    parents, effects on, 89
    resources of, 227–228
    responses of, 271–272
    sacred wounds and, 19–20
    sadness of, 73–74
    segregation of care in, 51
    siblings, effects on, 80–81
    spouses, effects on, 79–80
    stress in, 73
    trauma and, 71–76
    triumphant families, 145, 313–314
Family mission, 175
Family systems approach, 47–53
    larger society and, 50–52

HEALING VISIONS PRESS

Quick Order Form

Online orders:	www.HealTheFamily.com
Fax orders:	805-543-5160
Telephone orders:	800-718-7080 or 805-545-8398
E-mail orders:	orders@HealTheFamily.com
Postal orders:	Healing Visions Press
	P.O. Box 4035
	San Luis Obispo, CA 93403

I would like to order additional copies of *Mental Illness and the Family: Unlocking the Doors to Triumph* at $24.95 each. (See below.)

For quantity discounts and special sales please go to orders@HealTheFamily.com or call 800-718-7080.

If you found this book helpful, you might be interested in the following from Healing Visions Press

Quantity	Item	Total Price
_____	*Mental Illness and the Family: Unlocking the Doors to Triumph* @$24.95	_____
_____	*Words That Heal: More Help for the Family* @$21.95	_____
_____	*Obsessive Compulsive Disorder: New Help for the Family* @$21.95	_____
	Sales tax:	_____
	(Please add 7.75% for books shipped to CA addresses)	
	Shipping & handling:	_____
	($5.00 for the first book and $3.00 for each additional book)	
	Total Due:	_____

Name:_____

Address: _____

City: _____

State:_____ Zip: _____

Telephone: _____ E-Mail address: _____

Payment: ____Check *(Make checks payable to Healing Visions Press)*

   ____Visa ____MasterCard

Card number: _____

Name on card:_____ Exp. Date:_____

Thank you for your order!
Please visit our website at www.HealTheFamily.com